RC424
Comp

C0-AVX-488

3 3073 0026l6l2 4

A COMPENDIUM OF RESEARCH
AND THEORY ON STUTTERING

Publication Number 344

AMERICAN LECTURE SERIES®

A Monograph in

The BANNERSTONE DIVISION *of*
AMERICAN LECTURES IN OTOLARYNGOLOGY

Edited by

NORTON CANFIELD, M.D.
Yale University
School of Medicine
New Haven, Connecticut

A Compendium Of
Research And
Theory On Stuttering

By

CHARLES F. DIEHL, Ph.D.

Professor of Psychology
Director, Speech Center
University of Kentucky
Lexington, Kentucky

SETON HALL UNIVERSITY
McLAUGHLIN LIBRARY
SO. ORANGE, N. J.

CHARLES C THOMAS • PUBLISHER
Springfield • Illinois • U.S.A.

CHARLES C THOMAS • PUBLISHER

BANNERSTONE HOUSE

301-327 East Lawrence Avenue, Springfield, Illinois, U.S.A.

Published simultaneously in the British Commonwealth of Nations by

BLACKWELL SCIENTIFIC PUBLICATIONS, LTD., OXFORD, ENGLAND

Published simultaneously in Canada by

THE RYERSON PRESS, TORONTO

This book is protected by copyright. No
part of it may be reproduced in any manner
without written permission from the publisher.

© *1958, by* CHARLES C THOMAS • PUBLISHER

Library of Congress Catalog Card Number: 58-12152

With THOMAS BOOKS careful attention is given to all details of
manufacturing and design. It is the Publisher's desire to present books
that are satisfactory as to their physical qualities and artistic possibilities
and appropriate for their particular use. THOMAS BOOKS will be true
to those laws of quality that assure a good name and good will.

R C
424
D 56

Printed in the United States of America

This book is dedicated to all the workers in the field who have contributed so much to our understanding of the phenomena we call stuttering.

PREFACE

It has been estimated that there are at least one million stutterers in the United States. In an effort to help them, at least two thousand articles published in English can be found in the literature on the subject—so much literature, in fact, to the average reader it probably seems overwhelming.

The *Compendium* does not add more; it merely brings together a great deal of what already exists. It reports as objectively as possible leaving final conclusions entirely to each reader.

In all there are 193 abstracts of published articles in the *Compendium*. And it should be made clear here that those publications abstracted were not necessarily selected on the basis of an evaluation of their excellence, but rather as being representative of certain areas of research and theory. Unquestionably many papers published in English and other languages have been unavoidably omitted, as have unpublished studies and materials from texts. However, additional reading references relating to each of the four major units have been placed at the end of each section. A general reference list and some limited foreign language references also appear at the end of the final unit.

A great many people have shared in the preparation of the *Compendium*. Students, colleagues, and friends have all assisted in the enormous task of sifting from the complex literature the kinds of material we felt were most appropriate. For their help and encouragement I am very grateful. To the original authors of the articles represented I am indebted. Without their initial contributions there would be no *Compendium*.

The following journals also deserve a great deal of credit—for having published the articles in the first place and for having given me permission to abstract material from them.

American Journal of Orthopsychiatry
American Journal of Physiology
American Journal of Psychology
American Psychologist
Archives of Internal Medicine
Archives of Neurology and Psychiatry
Atlantic Monthly
Bureau of Publications, Teachers College, Columbia University
Elementary School Journal
Human Biology
Journal of the American Medical Association
Journal of Abnormal and Social Psychology
Journal of Clinical and Experimental Psychology
Journal of Comparative Psychology
Journal of the International Council for Exceptional Children

Journal of Experimental Education
Journal of Experimental Psychology
Journal of Psychology
Journal of Social Psychology
Journal of Speech and Hearing Disorders
Nervous Child
Pedagogical Seminary and Journal of Genetic Psychology
Pennsylvania State Review of Educational Research
Psychoanalytic Review
Psychological Monographs
Quarterly Journal of Speech
Science
Scientific Monthly
Speech Monographs
University of Iowa Studies: Studies in Child Welfare

Special thanks are also due Marian Coates, Marlene Long, Rose Shrimpton and Kenneth Burk for their valuable help in preparing and editing the manuscript.

As a basic reference text, the Compendium has already proven valuable. Specialists should find it useful as a reading guide and as a reference to research methods in the area of stuttering.

CHARLES F. DIEHL

Lexington, Ky.

HOW TO USE THE COMPENDIUM

THE phenomena called stuttering have been a challenge to both laymen and specialists for many decades. The fact that stuttering has remained an enigma in spite of the enormous amount of published theory and research has not led to a diminishing interest—the experts continue to search; the laymen to conjecture.

One of the problems related to the total problem of understanding stuttering lies in the mass of literature about it. Only limited attempts have been made to organize references into related units of study. Consequently the physician, therapist, teacher, or student has in the past had little guidance toward a comprehensive understanding of all that has been reported about stuttering.

An average college student, for example, may select the general topic of "Stuttering" for a research paper. After several weeks of reading he begins to feel as if he is traversing an endless maze. He may read one report which seems to present impressive evidence for regarding stutterers as neurotics. Several journals later —there are at least fifty different magazines and journals carrying articles on stuttering—he reads another publication which seems to refute the neurotic theory with equal impressiveness.

As days go by, on the basis of what he reads, he finds himself trying to decide whether stuttering is a neurological or a psychological deviation; whether it is a learned or an unconscious response. He reads about stutterers who have poor motor coordination and some who do not; about stutterers with different blood chemistry and some with no difference. He discovers that some stutterers have apparently learned to talk better after hypnosis; after psychoanalysis; after taking drugs; after learning to chew or visualize words; after their parents were counseled; or after an understanding physician or teacher talked with them.

He finally gives up the project, probably more fascinated than when he began, but certain that he will not have sufficient time to read and organize all that has been written about stuttering.

In addition to the enormous number of publications on stuttering there is also a second problem—the problem of evaluating them. How have the published theories and conclusions about stuttering been formulated? Are they purely theoretical or were they experimentally tested? If experimentally tested, what was the design of the experiment? How many subjects were used? Were the data statistically analyzed? Almost no attention has been given to examining in an organized way the methodology of published articles concerning stuttering.

The two problems we have been discussing—(1) the abundance of publications and (2) the evaluation of them—are the major concern of this *Compendium*. *The Compendium* has been organized and written, first, to bring together in an orderly way the information we have about stuttering and, second, to provide for an adequate evaluation by the reader of the kind of article he is reading—theoretical or experimental.

The first problem—that of quantity—has been handled in the following way. All materials has been organized into five study units: *Unit I*, History; *Unit II*, Symptomatology; *Unit III*, Etiology-Physiological; *Unit IV*, Etiology-Psychological; and *Unit V*, Therapy. Each unit in turn contains abstracts of published articles which relate directly to that unit. Each article can thus be evaluated as part of a related body of information. For example, if the reader is interested in personality and stuttering he will find in *Unit IV*, Etiology-Psychological, a representative selection of abstracts of articles which have reported theories or research having to do with the psychology of stutterers. He may find in this unit that one article may refute its neighbor. However, he will be reading these reports in sequence. At the conclusion of the unit he should have a general idea of the major areas of agreement or disagreement, and he should have at least a fair idea after studying the methodology of the paper—and we shall have more to say about this shortly—why certain disagreements do exist.

Anyone using the *Compendium* will, of course, have his own objectives. We do not recommend, however, that the beginning student start with *Unit IV* of the *Compendium* as in the example mentioned above. We would suggest he begin with Unit I. The organization of the units has been directed toward guiding the reader logically through the literature.

Unit I: History, the reader is introduced to background information relative to stuttering theories from the first recorded history. It may surprise some, for example, to discover that stuttering has been recognized as a problem since the fifth century B. C.

Unit II: Symptomatology, familiarizes the reader with terminology he will meet time and time again in later sections. In this unit he becomes acquainted with the kinds of things a stutterer does that have given him his label. He can read how stuttering symptoms develop and how they relate to situations, parts of speech, speech sounds, etc.

Unit III: Etiology-Physiological, is concerned with the cause of the symptoms of stuttering. Much time and energy have been spent attempting to determine the cause of stuttering. Two major schools of thought have evolved: stuttering as a physiological deviation and stuttering as a psychological deviation. *Unit III* sets forth the arguments for and against stuttering as a physiological deviation.

Unit IV: Etiology-Psychological, is a continuation of *Unit III* in that it also relates to the cause of stuttering. However, in this Unit, stuttering is examined as a psychological deviation.

Unit V: Therapy, presents the various theories for treating the symptoms of stuttering.

At the end of each unit, an additional list of related reading references will be found. These are provided for anyone who cares to probe further into any one unit of study. At the very end of the Compendium there is a general reading list in which will be found articles which discuss stuttering in a general way. Along with the general reference list will be found a list of some representative foreign publications.

In all, the *Compendium* contains 193 abstracts and 364 additional reading references—all organized, we believe, to minimize confusion and facilitate understanding.

The second problem—the evaluation of a publication—has been considered in the following way. The content of each publication has been abstracted into four major divisions: Purpose, Experimental Design, Summary, and Conclusions. These divisions have been made to enable the reader to evaluate easily the items explained in the discussion which follows.

We have mentioned previously the difference between pure theory and theory experimentally tested. What do we mean by this? We do not mean that one exists without the other. Quite the contrary. All research roots in theory. It is theory that the experimental method tests. But a theory in and of itself is just a theory—correct or incorrect depending on the evidence.

How does one go about evaluating the methodology and support of a theory? The first step we suggest is to evaluate the purpose of the publication. This information has been summarized under the Purpose division of each abstract. After reading the Purpose division the reader should be able to have a clear idea of the questions the publication was attempting to answer.

Step two is to examine the experimental design. The design is explained in the Experimental Design division of the abstract. Occasionally the single word "None" will be listed under this division. This means merely that the article is reporting pure theory and has no experimental design.

As a part of evaluating the experimental design it is important to examine the *sample,* that is, the number and kinds of individuals (subjects) used in the research. The value of experimental data depends on adequate sampling. We want to know whether what has been proposed—no matter what—holds up, not merely for a few, but for all—all stutterers, for example. To know this the sample must be adequate. If, to illustrate one kind of sampling, we were interested in knowing the favorite foods of adult property owners in the United States we would have to gather information from all the states in the United States and from a proportionate number of the property owners in each state—all randomly selected; that is, not every home owner would be interviewed, but perhaps every tenth or twelfth as selected randomly from an alphabetized list of all property owners in each state, and the larger the sample the better. The reasons for this highly involved process should be obvious. To predict for any population —large or small—we must be sure that all members of that population have had an equal chance at being represented. The mathematical formulas for testing our findings are based on the premise that the sampling has been both representative and random.

It is true that there would probably be little research completed if we were forced to adhere strictly to the procedure just mentioned. The task would become too enormous. Consequently all samples have limitations. However, these limitations must be recognized. Sweeping conclusions based on a limited number of subjects selected from a restricted portion of the population should be viewed cautiously by the reader. It should be made clear here that the individual reporting results of his research is usually fully aware of the limitations of his sample. It is the reader skimming quickly over the published article who is more likely to make sweeping generalizations, disregarding the limitations of the sample.

There are additional details to be checked as a part of sampling under the Experimental Design division. If, for example, the purpose of a paper is to determine whether a group of stutterers differs from a group of non-stutterers in, say, blood chemistry, it is important to see if both groups were matched on as many variables as possible—for age, sex, disease history, etc. Then one might also check to see whether all blood samples were taken in the same way, at the same time, after the same feedings, etc. And finally, one should determine whether all samples were analyzed by the same technique by the same technician or technicians.

Step three is to check the *reliability* and *validity* of certain items mentioned in the experimental design. Reliability refers to consistency; validity to the soundness of arguments or conclusions. This information usually will be found under the Experimental Design division: however, occasionally it will be reported under the Summary division.

To explain one kind of reliability let us suppose that in a study three judges have described the kinds of stuttering symptoms a group of stutterers evidenced. All judges may have agreed perfectly. Perfect agreement is rare, but in this case it would be written as r (correlation coefficient) $= \pm 1.00$. The poorer the agreement the farther from ± 1.00 is the reliability. Thus $r = .20$ would mean very poor judge agreement. Conclusions drawn on judgements with an $r = .20$ would therefore mean little. An $r = .85$ or higher is usually considered good enough to substantiate conclusions.

Sometimes a measuring instrument is used to evaluate two groups. In such cases, both reliability and validity of the instrument might be important to know. Let us suppose, for example, a group of stutterers and non-stutterers are being studied to determine personality differences. If the Rorschach Personality Test was used, it might be worth-while to know the reliability and validity of the Rorschach Test. Reliability in this sense refers to whether the test is so structured that with repeated performances on it by the same person it will yield similar results. Validity refers to whether the test truly measures what it purports to measure—in this case, personality. Frequently such information is not reported in a published article and if it seems critical it might be important enough to consult test manuals to obtain it.

Step four is to determine whether the data reported have been statistically analyzed. In other words, were mathematical formulas used to determine whether a difference found was merely a chance difference? This information will be found usually under the Summary division. Statistically, a difference is usually considered to be a true difference if the probability of its happening by chance is no greater than five times in 100 trials. This is written as ".05 level of significance." A significance level of .01 means that the probability is only one in 100 that the difference found could have happened by chance. A level of .001 would indicate a highly significant difference with the probability of its happening by chance being only one in 1000.

Finally, step five is to examine the conclusions drawn by the author or authors. Conclusions will, of course, be listed under the Conclusions division of the abstract.

After the reader has worked through the five units of the *Compendium* evaluating each article in the manner just described, he may feel that he still has no definite answers—only a great many questions. This is probably as it should be. Remember we began by saying that stuttering was an enigma, a challenge.

On the positive side, the reader may have found certain clues, certain parts of the total puzzle which he may be able to fit together. He may become absorbed in the search. And in the final analysis he may come up with a new theory—one which he may ultimately be able to prove and thus supply an additional clue to the unsolved mystery of stuttering.

CONTENTS

A COMPENDIUM OF RESEARCH
AND THEORY ON STUTTERING

UNIT I
HISTORY

TITLE

Klingbell, G.: The Historical Background of the Modern Speech Clinic, *Journal of Speech Disorders*, 4 (1939), 115-131.

Purpose: To describe the evolution of etiological concepts and therapies.

Experimental Design: None.

Summary: The highlights of the history are as follows.

Herodotus (484-424 B.C.) the Greek historian, records the treatment of stuttering by a Phythian priestess who recommended emigration south to Libya.

Hippocrates (450-375 B.C.) "Father of Medicine," remarked that there existed among stutterers a chronic diarrhoea—not of words —and described its cure by means of varices which resulted in suppurating ulcers.

Aristotle (334-322 B.C.) described a number of speech defects, and attributed the cause of stuttering to the tongue.

Demosthenes (383-322 B.C.) is said by Plutarch to have been cured by Satyrus, a Greek actor, who prescribed talking with pebbles in the mouth while watching oneself in a mirror. He also advised declaiming while walking uphill.

Celsius (42 B.C.-37 A.D.) compiled treatises on medicine and presumably rendered medical treatment gratis. Though ignored by the Roman practitioners of his time, his book, *De Re Medica*, was printed and came into its own in 1478. The sixth volume deals with diseases of eye, ear, nose, throat and mouth. He advocated the use of gargles for the faulty articulation rising from disease of the tongue, massages of the tongue and throat, eating of pungent substances, performing physical and respiratory exercises, and the economizing of breath during speech.

Galen (131-201 A.D.) ascribed the cause to various abnormalities of the tongue, for which he suggested cauterization and the cutting of the nerves to the afflicted part.

AEtius of Amida (sixth century) a royal physician to Justinian, left writings published in Venice in 1534. His work is said to contain the best account of diseases of the eye, ear, nose and throat in the literature of antiquity. He blamed stuttering on the tongue and recommended division of the frenum.

Avicenna (930-1037) a philosopher and physician of Arabia, compiled the *Karum fi'l tebb* a system of medicine based on an Arabic translation of Greek medical works, which became the textbook of both the West and East for many years. Stuttering, he believed, was due largely to the tongue, brain lesions, and sometimes spasm of the epiglottis, which he advised, should be treated by taking a deep inspiration before speaking.

De Chauliac (1300-1380) a French surgeon, ascribed stuttering to convulsions, ulcers, or other affections of the tongue; to paralysis or to moisture of the nerves or muscles. His treatment consisted of embrocations to desiccate the brain, cauteries for the vertebrae, blisters, frictions and gargles for the tongue.

Mercurialis (1530-1606) attributed the cause of stuttering to abnormal dryness or moisture of either the brain or the tongue. He followed the treatment of De Chauliac adding systematic exercises for the voice and body.

Bacon, Francis (1560-1626) attributed stuttering to coldness, dryness, and moisture of the tongue.

Amman (1667-1724) a Swiss physician, was one of the earliest writers on the instruction of the deaf and dumb. He believed "hesitantia" was caused by vicious habit. He directed his treatment for it chiefly to the tongue.

Santorini (1681-1737) the Italian anatomist who discovered the corniculate cartilages of the larynx, believed that abnormal size of "two holes in the middle region of the palate" were the cause of stuttering.

Morgagni (1682-1771) is considered the founder of pathological anatomy. He rejected Santorini's theory and blamed the hyoid bone.

Hahn (1694-1745) court physician to King Frederick, blamed stuttering on the hyoid bone.

Haen (1704-1776) an Austrian doctor who established the clinical method in Germany, believed pulmonary vomicae were the cause of stuttering.

Hartley (1705-1757) in his *Observations on Man* postulated that all conscious processes had physical correlations in the brain, and considered stuttering a nervous derangement and occasionally the result of imitation.

Mendelssohn (1729-1786) insisted that stuttering was psychical, due to a collision among many ideas flowing from the brain simultaneously. He recommended slow reading aloud, with succeeding words covered and not seen until they were enunciated.

Darwin (1731-1802) believed that emotions like awe or bashfulness cause interrupted association of the movements of the organs of speech. He advocated constant practice of difficult sounds with softening of the initial consonants.

Thelwall (1764-1834) considered the cause to be in the lips, tongue, pharynx or bronchi, and differentiated four different types, all of which he treated through rhythm.

Itard (1765-1838) maintained stuttering was caused by muscular debility. He used a golden or ivory fork placed in the cavity of the alveolar arch of the lower jaw to support the tongue. He reported two cures, neither of which was permanent.

Combe (1788-1858) helped to found the Phrenological Society. The cause of stuttering to him lay in irregular nervous action. He recommended exercises for the vocal muscles, care of diet and hygiene, combined with cheerful society and encouragement.

Bertrand (1795-1831) a French doctor of psychology, believed stuttering was caused by a spasmodic nervous affection, curable by any method which would distract the patient from his speech.

For the following contributors the single date given represents the approximate years in which their theories were published or became known.

Yates (early 1800) a New York doctor, and apparently the inventor of the system called the "American method." His treatment was carried out in an institute under the direction of the "widow Leigh," governess of Yates' daughter, to avoid professional disrepute. Yates ascribed stuttering to a spasm of the glottis and treated it by advocating the raising of the tip of the tongue to the palate, and holding it there while speaking. The secret was bought by Malebouche (1841) who traded on it, selling it to the Prussian and Belgian governments. It was reported to the French Academy in 1828 and died a natural death after receiving a phenomenal amount of attention.

McCormac (1828) set forth a curative method consisting of deep inspiration and forcible expirations. He believed stuttering was caused by an attempt to speak with nearly emptied lungs.

Deleau (1829) was a specialist in maladies of the ear. The general cause of stuttering he held to be an infirm will, incomplete cerebral action, or deficient innervation. His treatment consisted in educating the vocal and articulating organs, not by ears, but by sight, in order to secure their being placed in the correct position for each sound.

Colombat de l'Isere (1831) believed stuttering was caused by disharmony between nervous excitation which follows thought, and the muscular actions related to its expression. His treatment consisted in using rhythmic vocal gymnastics to develop regularity of the muscles of respiration, phonation, and articulation. By a system of opposing movements of the muscles of articulation he aimed at preventing the repetition of sounds. He used many mechanical devices for the teeth and mouth—the most famous of which was his "Muthonome." The French Academy awarded him a prize for his work on stuttering.

Bell (1832), an anatomist, believed stuttering was due to a type of chorea.

Magendie (1833), a physiologist, attributed speech to an organic intelligence (instinct) and stuttering to a lack of this intelligence. He believed that will power could replenish this sufficiently to bring about a cure in those with enough moral force.

Muller (1833) investigated the anatomy of the larynx. He related stuttering to a spasm of the glottis and advised the entire omission of the explosive sounds in reading exercises to keep the glottis open.

Hall (1841), an English physiologist, related stuttering to an imperfect act of volition due to the involuntary action of the reflex spinal center regulating articulation. He refuted the theory that it was caused by a spasm of the glottis. He recommended using a continuous flowing manner of speech.

Blume (1841) was a "stutter-doctor" who believed stuttering was caused by disharmony between thought and speech. He believed those who stuttered while singing or climbing a steep ascent were incurable. His treatment consisted of mechanical contrivances with exercise of the speech organs.

Dieffenbach (1841), a German surgeon, began the surgical treatment for speech defects fashionable in Europe for several years. His operation involved making a horizontal section at the root of the tongue, excising a triangular wedge completely across and nearly through it. The object was to divide the lingual muscles and thereby interrupt their innervation in order to modify or cure the muscular spasm.

Velpeau (1841), a French surgeon, believed that stuttering was caused by an unusual depth of the palate. He divided the hypoglossi, geniohyoglossi, and styloglossi muscles for different types of the affection.

Braid (1842), an English physician, attempted to cure stuttering by excising the tonsils or uvula.

Parker (1845), an American surgeon, was one of those who introduced the operative treatment for stuttering into America.

This fashion for treating stuttering surgically, rampant in the
early forties of the eighteenth century, varied considerably in
its details. The German school in the main followed the practice
of Dieffenbach, the French school, Velpeau, and the English
school, Braid. The results, at first encouraging, soon proved to
be merely of temporary duration. When it was shown that not
five per cent had received any permanent benefit, the method was
abandoned.

Graves (1848), an Irish physician, favored a spasm-of-the-glottis
theory. He directed the attention of the patient away from his
speech by having him strike some object synchronously with the
words spoken, keeping strict time. Treatment afforded temporary
relief.

Wutzer (1850), a professor, invented a tongue lever for the purpose of keeping the tongue out of the fossa behind the inferior
incisors.

Eich (1858) believed that the primary causes of stuttering were
psychical rather than physical, and that abnormal respiration was
the result, not the cause of stuttering. He recommended treatment in an institution where each case could be treated separately
according to individual needs.

Kingsley (1859), orator and writer, believed stuttering was caused
by either conscious or unconscious imitation. He prescribed rules
for the treatment: open mouth widely and speak from a full lung;
breathe inwards at every stop and keep the tongue down; use
dumbbell exercises to help breathing; place a bit of cork between
the back of teeth when speaking; keep the upper lip drawn down
tightly. He considered childhood an unsuitable time for treating the defect, and considered boxing "over and above a healing
art" for the stutterer.

Rosenthal (1861) placed the pathogenic cause of stuttering in an
hereditary morbid excitability. He described it as a disorder of
co-ordination, increased by anxiety and embarrassment, during
the emission of sounds. He advocated treatment based on rhythm.

Wolff (1861) placed the cause of stuttering either in the nerves or in the organs themselves, each case requiring careful examination in order to differentiate. His treatment consisted of trying all methods and almost all drugs, and finally of dividing the hypoglossal nerve.

Chervin (1867), a teacher in Lyons, wrote about brain-irradiations, their comparative rapidity, continuity, energy and precision, and concluded that the "higher" brain was chiefly to blame for stuttering. He used many systems successfully, but believed that education of the will was most important.

Marshall (1867), an English surgeon, blamed the irregular action of the nervous centers for stuttering.

Thome (1867) held that stuttering was caused by abnormal functioning of the central nervous system, induced by certain emotions which lead to respiratory disturbances.

Lehwess (1868) placed the cause of stuttering on either abnormal action of the respiratory organs, anomalies of individual muscles, abnormal physical condition, or conflict between the will and movements concerned in the production of speech. He recommended rhythm as a radical cure.

Wyneken (1868) believed stuttering was a neurosis, and that the larynx was the chief seat of the disturbance. The physical cause he held to be the defective influence of the will, produced by doubt. His treatment was based largely on imbuing the patient with faith in his preceptor and in himself. He also used exercises for respiration, and speech accompanied by rhythmical beating of time.

Guillaume (1868) defined stuttering as an affection of irregularly intermittent type, having two characteristic symptoms, the convulsive repetition of the same syllable and a convulsive stoppage at a syllable. He believed it was caused by incoordination of the speech muscles. The foundations of his treatment lay in whispering exercises. He believed there was no essential difference between speech and whispering other than the number and amplitude of the vibrations of the vocal cords. He used lip gymnastics, stressed the necessity for keeping the tongue up to the palate, and for taking deep inspirations before every sentence.

Hunt (1870) successfully treated stuttering in England for many years. His treatment was "naturally and without dodge or trick, to teach the patient to speak consciously, as other men spoke unconsciously." By comparing the normal with the abnormal, he reduced the phenomena to action of the lip, tongue, jaw, and breath, either singly or combined. His treatment hinged upon disciplinary exercise of the organs of voice.

Helmore (1874) claimed that stuttering was caused by neglect of muscular activity, and inability to regulate the action of the lips because of weakness of the facial muscles.

Coen (1879), of Vienna, probably the first physician to specialize in speech disorders, believed stuttering was the result of a deficient atmospheric pressure in the lungs caused by disturbances of innervation. Later he thought it was due to pathological changes in the respiratory system which caused a breath spasm. His treatment, along elocutionary lines, was combined with Swedish exercises and electric therapy.

Bates (1884), an American, treated stuttering with a variety of appliances: (1) a narrow flattened tube of silver applied to the median line of the roof of the mouth (to aid the formulation of the linguo-palatal letters); (2) a hollow biconvex disk with a projecting silver tube placed between the lips to help the labials and dental-labials; and (3) a belt and spring adjusted on the neck over the thyroid cartilage to help the gutterals.

Ruff (1885) believed that the center of speech in stutterers has become accidentally exposed to some injurious influence; e.g., suffusion or insufficiency of blood due to sudden or spastic expansion of the blood vessels. The center of speech is consequently disposed to respond to any inducement however slight—a lesion, shock, or some extraordinary emotion—to renew an attack of stuttering.

Hammond (1897), an American professor, called stuttering a chorea of the muscles. He considered it a functional disorder of that part of the brain presiding over the faculty of speech. He had a system of "consentaneous" muscular action for each troublesome word (tapping with the foot or finger) to attract the attention away from the effort of speaking—thus rendering speech more automatic.

Sandow (1898) believed stuttering was a psychoneurosis on the debility of the nerves involved in speech. Each paroxysm of stuttering was induced by psychic stimuli, caused by dread of speaking, intense eagerness, or by too violent innervation while talking. He recommended rest and relaxation.

Rouna (1907) advocated the use of arm gestures to cure stuttering believing that cerebral activity overflows from the arm centers to the speech centers.

Steckel (1908) described stuttering as one of the worst forms of fear hysteria—as much a psychological betrayal as are slips of the tongue and pen. The neurosis (generally a pure anxiety) begins always in childhood. He used psychoanalysis in treatment.

TITLE

Sortini, A. J.: Twenty Years of Stuttering Research, *Journal of the International Council for Exceptional Children,* **21 (1955), 181-183.**

Purpose: To analyze the type of research in the field of stuttering during the past twenty years.

Experimental Design: *Psychological Abstracts* was used as a basic reference. A twenty-year span, 1932 through 1951, was studied. The author, interested only in experimental research, established a criteria to determine which abstracts could be classified as experiments. Those falling in the following classifications were termed experiments: (a) experimental laboratory investigation, (b) questionnaire or rating scale studies, and (c) case history studies where personal opinion was not involved. Criteria to determine the type of experimentation, were as follows: (a) laterality, (b) physiological, (c) neuro-physiological, (d) behavioral or psychological, (e) genetic, (f) personality, and (g) miscellaneous (studies of other speech defects including stuttering).

Summary: In the twenty year span studied, 551 articles were investigated, yielding the following results: (a) 225, 40.8 per cent, were of an experimental nature and (b) 326, 59.2 per cent, were of a non-experimental nature and were, therefore, not used. Of 225 experiments, the psychological or behavioral classification, constituted 64, or 28.5 per cent; the physological 43 or 19.1 per cent; the miscellaneous 37 or 16.4 per cent; the combined laterality and neuro-physiological 46 (23 each) or 20.5 per cent; and personality 21 or 9.3 per cent. Genetic studies provided the fewest experiments with 14 or 6.2 per cent. The greatest number of experiments (28) during a single year occurred in 1937; the lowest (5), during the years 1948 and 1949. There was a concentration of research during the years 1936, 1937, 1938 and 1939. Research during the first ten-year span was concerned generally with changing handedness, conducting laterality and "sidedness" tests, and improving the breathing of stutterers. There was a steady interest in the neuro-physiological research for the first fifteen of the twenty-year span studied but only one experiment was reported over the last five years. In only one five-year span (1937-1941) was there any significant interest in genetic studies. Psychological studies had their peak in the 1937-1941 period and showed steady rise over all other types of experiments since. One reason for the interest in personality studies, it was suggested, was an increased awareness of personality inventories as research tools.

Conclusions: It was concluded that experimental research should be integrated in order to explore systematically various etiologies and uncover new therapeutic techniques for stutterers.

TABLE I
NUMBERS AND TYPES OF EXPERIMENTS (1932-1951)

Year	Types of Experiments*							Totals
	a	b	c	d	e	f	g	
1932	3	3	1	0	1	1	0	9
1933	2	3	1	0	1	1	1	9
1934	0	3	1	3	0	0	0	7
1935	3	4	1	1	0	1	1	11
1936	2	4	3	5	0	0	2	16
1937	3	3	5	11	1	0	5	28
1938	1	3	0	7	1	0	4	16
1939	2	2	2	4	4	1	6	21
1940	2	4	2	4	1	0	1	14
1941	1	4	0	1	0	0	0	6
1942	1	2	3	3	0	2	4	15
1943	1	4	3	2	0	0	1	11
1944	0	1	0	3	0	6	1	11
1945	0	0	0	3	2	0	1	6
1946	0	1	0	2	2	1	1	7
1947	1	1	1	2	1	1	3	10
1948	0	1	0	2	0	1	1	5
1949	1	0	0	1	0	3	0	5
1950	0	0	0	5	0	1	1	7
1951	0	0	0	5	0	2	4	11
Totals	23	43	23	64	14	21	37	225

*Key—a. Laterality
b. Physiological
c. Neuro-Physiological
d. Psychological or Behavioral
e. Genetic
f. Personality
g. Miscellaneous

TABLE II
TRENDS IN TYPE AND AMOUNT OF RESEARCH FOR FIVE YEAR PERIODS (1932-1951)

Year	Types of Experiments*							Totals
	a	b	c	d	e	f	g	
1932-1936	10	17	7	9	2	3	4	52
1937-1941	9	16	9	27	7	1	16	85
1942-1946	2	8	6	13	4	9	8	50
1947-1951	2	2	1	15	1	8	9	38
Total	23	43	23	64	14	21	37	225

*Key—see Table I.

UNIT II

SYMPTOMATOLOGY

TITLE

Métraux, R. W.: Speech Profiles of the Pre-School Child 18 to 54 Months, *Journal of Speech and Hearing Disorders*, 15 (1950), 37-53.

Purpose: To determine the patterns of speech from ages 18 months to 54 months.

Experimental Design: Observations were made of 207 children at the following pre-school ages: 18 months, 24 months, 30 months, 36 months, 42 months, 48 months and 54 months. Recordings during activities were taken as well as a phonetic transcription of all speech. Notes concerning the children's total behavior were also taken. These records were supplemented by interviews with the parents regarding their child's speech at home. All of the children were average or above average in intelligence.

Summary: *18* months (23 children) Much inconsistency and uncertainty in the production of words. A given vowel sound changes within the same word. Initial and final consonants are usually omitted. The child repeats syllables or words more frequently than not. *"Repetition is easy and unforced and can be terminated by himself or by the responses of others."*

24 months: (37 children) Inconsistency in the production of words still present. Initial consonants and occasionally the final are in appearance. *A kind of compulsive repetition on a word or phrase is present.*

30 months: (42 children) At this age, the tendency to shorten words or phrases results in the slighting of the medial consonants while the initial and final consonants become more specific. *Compulsive repetition is more marked. "Developmental stuttering is usually experienced for the first time . . ." It gives the child little concern.*

19

36 months: (38 children) The sounds [θ] and [ð] are noticeable because of the frequent substitution or omission of them. A word may be pronounced correctly only to be mispronounced a few seconds later. Voice seems well controlled. *Easy repetition replaces compulsive repetition.*

42 months: (20 children) Substitution for [ð] is still made. Pronunciation of any one word changes little. *Repetitions are frequent with a compulsive quality again.* This can be broken up by repeating the phrase back to him. *"Developmental stuttering is again prominent . . ."*

48 months: (26 children) Medial sounds in phrases are omitted because of haste. Any change in pronunciation is with words containing [θ] and [ð]. *Little repetition is present in comparison with preceding ages.*

54 months: (16 children) ". . . minimal difficulty in word and phrase production . . ." Appears to meditate a good deal as he talks. *Seldom repeats except for emphasis but may begin a phrase with [ʌm].* Speech is now a tool.

Conclusions: No conclusions were drawn as a result of this study.

TITLE

Voelker, C. H.: A Preliminary Investigation for a Normative Study of Fluency: A Clinical Index to the Severity of Stuttering, *American Journal of Orthopsychiatry,* 14 (1944), 285-294.

Purpose: To determine fluency norms which might help in the diagnosis of stuttering, indicate the severity of stuttering, and provide an index for the possibility of cure. ("A fluent speaker is one who is ready in the use of words. His speech is voluble and facile.")

Experimental Design: Sixty-two non-stuttering orphans ranging in age from 12 to 19 years (31 boys and 31 girls), were given a test of ability to talk for five minutes about a topic of their own choice. They were informed that they were being tested on their ability to talk without stopping. A group of seven stutterers (two boys and five girls), ages 12-26, were then given the same test with identical instruction. The fluency patterns of the two groups were then compared.

Summary: The number of words spoken in the five minutes ranged from 53 to 912. It was found that the more words spoken the less fluent was the speaker.

The normal speaker had no syllable repetitions in every 100 words, had less than one word repetition, less than one phrase repetition, about ten hesitations, one vocalized pause, changed his mind about which word to use far less than once, never revamped phrases, never mentioned how hard it was to keep thinking of things to say, had no prolongations and was never unintelligible.

Statistically, stutterers were found to be defective only in prolongations, syllable and word repetitions. Girls talked slower and more smoothly. Fluency and verbal output were found to be unique psychological abilities, unrelated to each other or to chronological age, mental age, intelligence, ability in silent reading, vocabulary, arithmetic, English, effectiveness in public speaking, fundamental speech habits, hearing acuity, grade in school or to school achievement.

It was also found that stutterers did not talk faster than the normals. The normals had a break in fluency every five to five and a half words while the stutterer had approximately two and a half words of fluent speech before he had a break in fluency.

Conclusions: The author concluded that there can be no doubt about the variations between stutterers and non-stutterers in fluency, but, that fluency is a broader term than stuttering. "Lowness in fluency, *per se*, does not necessarily mean stuttering." The diagnosis of stuttering, he suggested, should include counts of number of prolongations, syllable and word repetitions which will indicate quantitatively the severity of the defect.

TITLE

Steer, M. D.: Symptomatologies of Young Stutterers, *Journal of Speech Disorders*, 2 (1937), 3-13.

Purpose: "To test the validity of the common assumption that symptoms are applicable regardless of the age or developmental level represented by the stutterer."

Experimental Design: Subjects were 67 stuttering children between the ages of three and thirteen years and 20 normal-speaking children between the ages of three and five years.

All subjects were utilized in the study of breathing symptoms obtained by use of a kymographic technique. Seven major breathing symptoms were observed: (1) long duration of inspiration-expiration, (2) strikingly different patterns for abdomen and thorax, (3) interruption of expiration by inspiration, (4) speaking during inspiration, (5) opposition in breathing between wave forms, (6) general inequality in successive wave forms, and (7) obvious lack of movement of thorax and abdomen.

Eight stuttering and ten normal-speaking children, all of approximately the same age, were used to study vocal symptoms. A qualitative rather than a quantitative evaluation of the vocal symptoms was used.

Ten children from each of the two groups, all of approximately the same age, were used to study functional dissociation of the two masseter muscles. These data were obtained by standard action-current methods.

Summary: Symptoms of breathing disturbances, of vocal anomalies and of dissociation between masseter muscles were found for both stutterers and non-stutterers. There were no statistically significant differences between the two groups. A comparison of these records with those already recorded for adult stutterers revealed no significant observable breathing or vocal differences.

Conclusions: The author interpreted the results as suggesting that one or all of the following might be valid:

1. Children do not stutter, but some emphasize deviations possessed by all.

2. Most children stutter; adults who stutter merely indicate a condition of arrested maturation in the speech mechanism.

3. The symptoms accepted as characteristic of stuttering do not discriminate the stutterer from the non-stutterer at the pre-school level.

TITLE

Davis, D. M.: The Relation of Repetitions in the Speech of Young Children to Certain Measures of Language Maturity and Situational Factors: Part I, *Journal of Speech Disorders*, 4 (1939), 303-318.

Purpose: To determine if the speech of young children is affected by the factor of age and certain situational factors such as labeling.

Experimental Design: Sixty-two children (36 boys and 26 girls) ranging in age from 24 to 62 months and in IQ's from 105 to 162 were used as subjects. One hour of extemporaneous speech was recorded by a speed writing method during the free-play period in the pre-school routine to minimize teacher dominations. The recording was done in two and one-half hour periods within one week of each other. The experimenter was interested in the following data: number of repetitions of words, groups of words, syllables and unintelligible sounds. If the repetitions had a chanting quality or a definite recurrence of pitch pattern, they were not included as repetitions. For the purpose of deriving some type of "norms," the group was divided into three age levels: 24 to 35, 36 to 49, and 50 to 62 months. The data for the boys were considered separately from the girls.

Summary: Although there was considerable variability in the amount of repetition from child to child, when all kinds of repetitions were combined a fairly normal distribution resulted indicating that repetition was probably a part of the speech pattern of all the children in the population studied. In the rank order of frequency of occurrence, phrase was first, then word and syllable. Those children who deviated markedly from the group were found to be high in the number of syllable repetitions. It was found that with respect to word repetition alone that the child who repeats one word in four is "normal."

Those children who had a marked tendency to be thought of as stutterers had a higher number of repetitions than the others. Those labeled as stutterers and who believed they had a speech defect had the highest number of repetitions in the entire group.

In the inter-group comparisons there were more syllable repetitions among boys than among girls. No other statistically significant differences between the sex groups were found. In the three age groupings there appeared to be a decrease with age in amounts of repetition. Syllable repetition appeared to be unaffected by age within the limits of the population examined.

Conclusions: It was found that the three types of repetitions combined showed a fairly normal distribution with all the group. Syllable repetition was found to be the best measure for those who varied markedly from the group. Prediction from one type of repetition to another is limited. No clear cut sex differences were noted with the exception of syllable repetition.

TITLE

Davis, D. M.: The Relations in the Speech of Young Children to Certain Measures of Language Maturity and Situational Factors: Part II, *Journal of Speech Disorders*, 5 (1940), 235-241.

Purpose: To relate syllable, word and phrase repetitions to various measures of language maturity.

Experimental Design: Data were obtained by recording verbatim the speech of 62 pre-school children during two one-half hour periods chosen from the free-play portion of the pre-school day. The repetitions found in this sample of speech were related by correlation technique to measures of language complexity derived from the same speech sample. Five measures of repetition which were correlated with the various measures of language maturity and general development were: (1) composite measure, (2) syllable repetition/verbal output, (3) word repetition/verbal output, (4) phrase repetition/verbal output, (5) all repetitions/ verbal output.

Summary:

1. None of the obtained correlations were sufficiently large to be considered the key to an explanation of repetitions.

2. Chronological age showed correlations of approximately the same magnitude with each of these five measures of repetition except # 2.

3. Mental age showed a slight negative correlation with all measures of repetition.

4. IQ showed low correlations with all measures of repetition.

5. Verbal output showed no particular relationship except with # 3 and instances of # 5 where there was only slight negative correlation.

6. Vocabulary showed a low negative correlation with all measures of repetition except # 2 with which no relation was shown.

7. Correct articulation and the degree of intelligibility each showed a low negative correlation with the measures of repetition except # 2.

8. The percentage of incomplete responses had a slight positive correlation with measures of repetition execept # 2.

9. The percentage of functionally complete but structurally incomplete responses had a slight positive correlation with all measures of repetition.

10. The correlations with the percentage of simple responses were all low and negative with exception of # 2 which was practically zero.

11. Complex responses correlated low negatively with measures of repetition except with # 2 which was practically zero.

12. It would appear that the incidence of syllable repetition was not significantly related to any of these measures.

Conclusions: It was concluded that language maturity as measured in this study could not be considered an important factor in relation to the large number of repetitions found in the speech of pre-school children.

TITLE

Davis, D. M.: The Relation of Repetition in the Speech of Young Children to Certain Measures of Language Maturity and Situational Factors: Part III, *Journal of Speech Disorders*, 5 (1940), 242-246.

Purpose: To study how extreme magnitudes of repetition relate to situational factors.

Experimental Design: Data were obtained by observing 62 pre-school children. One recorder wrote verbatim all that was said by a child during two one-half hour periods of observation during the free-play period in the pre-school routine. Another observer was present who recorded as much as was possible of all that was said to the child and also the activity of the child and his companions. The second observer was asked not to interpret the situations, but to record them descriptively.

Summary:
1. There seemed to be such a superfluity of situations surrounding the repetitions that no selective situations seemed to be present. This was true either because there was no systematic situational tie-up for all repetitions or because the data or situations were too meager to reveal it. It was observed, though, that in relation to extremes of repetition, those instances when a child uttered the same syllable, word, or phrase three or more times, that certain situational factors could be recognized. A classification of these was attempted.

2. The rank order of situations (32 situations were used) was as follows: (1) excitement over own activity; (2) wants to divert activity of another child according to his own plan; (3) attempts to attract attention of child; (4) coercion by teacher resulting in changed activity: (5.5) attempts to attract attention of teacher; (5.5) upholds status in spite of another child; (7) offers information to another child; (8) wants an object possessed by another child; (9) criticizes another child; (10) offers information to teacher.

Conclusions: The results of this study, the author feels, give a small amount of weight in favor of maintaining a child's environment as a possible preventative measure. Further research, however, is recommended before any additional generalizations are attempted.

TITLE

Bluemel, C. S.: **Primary and Secondary Stammering,** *Quarterly Journal of Speech*, 18 (1932), 187-200.

Purpose: To differentiate between "primary" and "secondary" stuttering, to discuss the adequacy of several of the recent theories which attempt to account for stuttering and to present the author's own theory in this respect.

Experimental Design: None.

Summary: The author defines *"primary" stuttering* as ". . . a simple disturbance of speech in which a delay ensues between the commencement and completion of a word." *"Secondary" stuttering* is defined as ". . . . consciousness of the defect and attempts to control and conceal it, employing starters, synonyms, etc." Fear is considered the dominant symptom of stuttering, a result of stuttering rather than a cause. That is to say, anyone may know fear in a speech situation but that fear does not necessarily produce the impediment of speech known as stuttering.

With regard to the theories, "renewal of handedness," the author feels, appears inadequate since it is based on the conception of cerebral dominance which in itself is somewhat confused. Also, there is the evidence that English children who are taught to use the dinner fork in the left hand do not exhibit wholesale stuttering. "Visual lack," or the lack of mental pictures, would seem to be ruled out as a cause since congenital blindness has no effect on speech development. Lastly, the theory of "subconscious emotional conflict" appears to be inadequate because of the many different arguments among its own exponents. At this time, it is felt, there is no valid research that has shown that repressions and conflicts precede the onset of "primary" stuttering.

It is the author's opinion that stuttering is an impediment of thought and not primarily a speech defect and that the support for this view might be found in Pavlov's experiments in "internal inhibition." It was found in these experiments that a negative stimulus presented close in time with a positive stimulus would inhibit the response normally elicited by the positive stimulus. The negative stimulus is unable in and of itself to produce a conditioned reflex. Using the former principle it was concluded that stuttering is due to a negative stimulus being present during the conditioned type of reflex that is speech, leading hence to internal inhibition. The internal inhibition appears to be in the form of weak or dim auditory memory which causes a delay in the flow of mental speech and then to a delay between the commencement and completion of a word. The stuttering is continued, not only because of weak auditory memory, but because hearing the words produces the conditioned reflex of stuttering the words.

Conclusions: It was concluded that the theory of temporary amnesia or internal inhibition is based on psychological considerations, but finds support in physiological research. If correct, it applies to basic or primary stuttering. Thus, speech disturbances and emotional reactions of the confirmed stutterer are symptoms far removed from the basic speech disorder with which the impediment begins.

TITLE

Glasner, P. J., and Vermilyea, F. D.: An Investigation of the Definition and Use of the Diagnosis, "Primary Stuttering," *Journal of Speech and Hearing Disorders*, 18 (1953), 161-167.

Purpose: To report and discuss the results of a questionnaire investigation of what the term "primary stuttering" means to workers in the field, how it is used in diagnosis, and of what the therapy for primary stuttering consists.

Experimental Design: A questionnaire was sent to 425 members of the A.S.H.A. The members fell into nine major classifications ranging from director of a clinic, professors, speech correctionists, private practice, various affiliations, medical, public health, special schools, and an unsorted category. Three questions were asked:

1. How do you define primary stuttering?
2. Do you use the diagnosis primary stuttering?
3. How is the case handled after such a diagnosis is made?

One hundred and seventy-one or 40 per cent replied.

Summary: Question 1: The results of the first question were highly diversified. The authors divided replies into nine major classes with over 30 qualifications. (1) 19% described primary stuttering in terms of repetitions, hesitations, and prolongations with individual reservations. (2) 20% indicated they did not make a distinction between primary and secondary stuttering. (3) 11% defined it as a stage usually qualified with the term, "with or without awareness." (4) 5% defined it as developmental stage occurring between the ages two and five. (5) 12% used text book definitions with Van Riper and Bluemel as sources. (6) 17% defined it as speech that differs significantly from normal. (7) 6% defined it as normal non-fluency. (8) 2% defined it as excessive non-fluency reflecting emotional disturbance. (9) The remaining 7% did not define it, giving various reasons: the term is worthless; the term is not used; the term is used only for students as an index to reference books, etc.

There appeared to be a wide range for the definition of primary stuttering. While many used the term *awareness*, it was pointed out that no criteria to measure awareness or unawareness, or fluency norms were presented.

Question 2: A definition was given by 93%, but only 61% indicated they used the diagnosis.

Question 3: 14% indicated they would determine and eliminate the underlying emotional causes, although only 2% used emotional causes in their definition. 7% would inform the parent the child was normal in every respect. 16% indicated group therapy. Another 5% indicated individual psychotherapy. 8% indicated individual speech therapy—rhythmical games, etc.: 8% indicated psychotherapy for both parent and child; and 34% indicated parent-teacher education. The last 5% used Van Riper or Bluemel as outlined in their literature to prescribe therapy. It appeared that the therapy was directly related to whether primary stuttering was regarded as normal or abnormal speech behavior.

Conclusions: No one who replied, the authors concluded, could give a satisfactory technique for making a differentiation between primary and secondary stuttering. The results showed that 87% felt that there is definitely something in the speech of young children that the parent and therapist should work on.

TITLE

Barr, H.: A Quantitative Study of the Specific Phenomena Observed in Stuttering, *Journal of Speech Disorders,* **5 (1940), 277-280.**

Purpose: To answer the following questions: (1) What types of specific phenomena occur during the moment of stuttering? (2) To what degree are individual differences to be observed in this respect? (3) To what degree is it true that a given stutterer presents a consistent pattern of stuttering? (4) To what degree are individual differences among stutterers to be observed in this respect, and (5) To what degree do the observations made without apparatus agree with the observations made with apparatus?

Experimental Design: Ten subjects with a Mdn age of 18 years and an age range of 7-32 years were utilized. The subjects were required to read passages from various types of materials (e.g., magazine and newspaper) which were different for each stutterer. Data were recorded in two ways: (1) two observers recorded their direct observations on a 34 item checklist, and (2) complicated mechanical apparatus designed to measure breathing (polygraph), phonation (voice key) and various facial movements were used.

Summary: It was found that there were 25 specific phenomena to be observed at least once during the 500 moments of stuttering. These were those having to do: (1) specifically with the form of sound production (repetition, prolongation, etc.), (2) with respiration, (3) with the action of the muscles of the articulators and/or voice, (4) with general body position or change of position, and (5) with extraneous movements of the facial muscles not used in the production of speech.

Nine specific phenomena occurred in more than 25% of the total moments of stuttering. These were: repetition, prolongation, silent interval, lip tremor-pucker, etc., audible sound, eye-blink-close-etc., holding breath, jaw tremor-movement, movement of the forehead and eyebrows. It was also found that for each stutterer there was a most frequently occurring phenomenon, e.g., for one subject, the holding of breath and emission of audible sounds each occurred 98% of the time.

For each subject there was also a most frequently occurring combination of specific phenomena recorded by direct observation. Considered individually, two subjects had five specific phenomena, two others had seven phenomena, three more had eight phenomena and the last three subjects had 10 phenomena (all of these phenomena occurred in more than 25% of the moments). Prolongations, silent intervals and breath holding were the most recurring phenomena in combination.

Conclusions: It was found that although direct observations appeared to be more inclusive, they compared favorably (87% agreement) with mechanical observations when studying the act of stuttering. It was tentatively concluded that while stuttering is comprised of many observably distinct phenomena, there is a tendency for relatively consistent combinations of phenomena to occur for each individual.

TITLE ✓

Froeschels, E.: Differences in the Symptomatology of Stuttering in the U.S. and in Europe, *Journal of Speech Disorders*, 6 (1941), 45-46.

Purpose: The author offers his theory regarding the nature of the stuttering phenomena and the differences in symptoms observed on the two continents.

Experimental Design: None. The author bases his theory on the observation of 15,000 stutterers in Europe, and an unknown number in the speech centers of St. Louis and Ann Arbor.

Summary: The European stutterer, about 15 years of age at the time of puberty, does *not* show obvious secondary symptoms. Seldom are there ugly grimaces, wide-opening of the mouth, protrusion of the tongue, etc. Instead he avoids looking into the eyes of those to whom he is speaking, and hides his clinched hand in his pocket. The author calls this stage, "Hidden Stuttering."

In speech clinics in the U.S. the author observed that stutterers either do not experience this stage at all or enter into it much later than puberty.

The author believes that the explanation lies in the difference of opinion concerning the cause and cure of stuttering that prevails in the two countries. In the U.S. the layman believes its cause is organic and that it is incurable. This opinion does not prevail in Europe.

Conclusions: The author suggests that therapists should avoid putting the theories with organic basis for stuttering into the hands of the layman. He feels that confidence in the curability of stuttering is important in its treatment.

TITLE

Douglas, E., and Quarrington, B.: The Differentiation of Interiorized and Exteriorized Secondary Stuttering, *Journal of Speech and Hearing Disorders,* **17 (1952), 377-385.**

Purpose: To differentiate between those secondary stutterers who "mask" their stuttering and those secondary stutterers who exhibit overt secondary symptoms.

Experimental Design: Subjects were 20 masked stutterers seeking treatment. Case history covering speech development, previous treatment, family, self and others attitudes toward stuttering was obtained. When possible, relatives were interviewed. Psychological history was obtained, and autobiographies were acquired. Observations and conclusions were based on these materials.

Summary: Interiorization is referred to as hidden or masked stuttering exemplified in anti-social behavior, inferiority, ill health, and anxiety. Interiorized and exteriorized stuttering differ in the following:

1. Behavior and Use of Devices: Both fear entering the speech situation but for different reasons. The interiorized stutterer's main concern is to avoid stuttering even to the point of sacrificing expression. Devices are used with dexterity and diversity and are appropriate to the circumstance; spasm is of catastrophic nature, short in duration, intense in severity, rapidly clonic and usually confined to the sound uttered. The exteriorized stutterer's main goal is oral expression and avoidance of stuttering is secondary to that.

2. Personality: Interiorized—characterized by sensitivity to social world. They need to belong, especially to those with authority and prestige. They are submissive and retiring. Exteriorized are more heterogeneous and seem to assume acceptance in society. Relationship with peers is better than with authorities who are regarded as threatening. They are aggressive, concerned with personal needs and desire to make an impact on the world. They do not feel compelled to conform if the social demands are contrary to their personal ambition.

3. Social Mobility and Child-rearing Practices: Interiorized—all proved to be socially mobile. Child rearing was upwardly oriented. Discipline and moral training accomplished by anxiety producing threats to withhold affection. Parents expect high level of achievement. Exteriorized—do not have strong mobility aspirations. Child rearing lacked strong pressure toward conformity and high levels of achievement. Threats of emotional deprivation were seldom used.

4. Development: Interiorized—parents tried to conceal stuttering of child. The secondary stage was not as severe as that of the exteriorized stutterer. Exteriorized—development of secondary stuttering is due to effort to facilitate verbal self-expression, and to maintain attention so that ideas, etc., will be heard.

5. Self-Concept: The interiorized reacted to the smallest stuttering spasm with great concern. When confronted with the recording and pictures of himself, the exteriorized stutterer found it difficult to believe he looked and sounded as abnormal as shown.

Conclusions: It was concluded that interiorized and exteriorized stuttering behavior differ in a number of ways. Conclusions concerning this behavior, it was suggested, might be used as tentative clinical hypotheses for future investigations.

TITLE

Van Riper, C.: The Growth of the Stuttering Spasm, *Quarterly Journal of Speech,* **23 (1937), 70-73.**

Purpose: To explain the variety of stuttering symptoms and to describe the way primary devices of release originate and develop.

Experimental Design: None. The author believes that the variety of symptoms must be explained if stuttering is to be considered a discrete disorder.

Summary: Bluemel called primary those first stuttering symptoms characterized by rapid, effortless repetitions of comparatively short and unforced prolongations of some part of the movements involved in speech. These are found in both children and adults but are usually overlooked in the latter as they are hidden by secondary symptoms. In the little child these primary symptoms exist without reactions of expectancy or awareness and are accepted by the child as his way of speech.

At some time this state of non-reacting acceptance is disturbed and the child becomes aware of an unpleasant element in his speech. Awareness is indicated by: repetitions, pauses, alteration of pitch, rate, and intensity of speech, giving up of the speech attempt, compensating behavior, and increased tension of chest and oral musculature. Fears of stuttering begin to develop. "The essence of fear is expectation of unpleasantness." The fears attach themselves to words or situations. The first "Jonah" words or situations are: (1) those most frequently associated with past stuttering experiences; and (2) those whose association with past stuttering were made vivid by the social penalties inflicted. Generalization then occurs to other words and situations.

Various devices or tricks are developed to ward off the expected abnormality. They have been found in either voluntary or automatic form in children as young as four years and in nearly every adult stutterer. There are four major categories of expectancy devices: (1) *avoidance;* (2) *postponement;* (3) *starters;* and (4) *anti-expectancy.* These release devices become habitual and a part of the abnormality. There are two main classes, those involving cessation and those involving prolongations. The child who reacts to the primary symptoms by stopping can stop and try again; stop and finish the rest of the word; or stop and recourse to an expectancy device. If he prolongs it he can do it with or without increased tension. These "release" devices become habitual and cease to release.

Conclusions: The grotesque symptoms, the author concludes, result from turning expectancy or release devices into habits. This is the major part of the individual's handicap. Treatment must involve reconditioning and eradication of the secondary symptoms as well as removal of the causes of the primary symptoms, whatever they might be.

TITLE

Van Riper, C.: Effect of Devices for Minimizing Stuttering on the Creation of Symptoms, *Journal of Abnormal and Social Psychology*, 32 (1937), 185-192.

Purpose: To attempt a more complete delineation of the symptoms of stuttering.

Experimental Design: In a preliminary study, 30 adult stutterers were carefully evaluated to determine what symptoms related directly to overt speech, and what the stutterers did to make communication abnormal.

A multiple-choice questionnaire using questions concerning the more common symptom devices found in the preliminary study was then constructed. It was administered to 50 adult stutterers with a retest a month later to check the instrument's reliability. The validity was checked by subsequent interviews with the stutterers.

Summary: It was found in the preliminary study that the only symptoms common to all the stutterers were clonic or tonic blocks. Utilizing a symptom classification proposed by Bluemel, these common symptoms were termed primary symptoms. Those remaining symptoms which met the criterion of being habitual and involuntary responses were in turn termed secondary symptoms. Concerning these secondary symptoms, the following results were gleaned from the questionnaire:

Purpose of Device	% Reported Using	% Reporting these devices to become habitual-involuntary
Using any device	100	90
To avoid speech attempt	96	7
To postpone speech attempt	98	80
As a starter	84	83
To minimize fear and expectancy of stuttering	76	60
To release blocks	92	48
To disguise stuttering	96	—

Conclusions: According to the author, primary symptoms originate from lack of cerebral dominance assumed to be due to the bad emotional habits associated with the experience and expectation of stuttering. The general progression for the initiation of symptoms was conceptualized: cerebral imbalance = primary symptoms = attempts to minimize speech difficulties by devices (need to avoid, postpone or start the feared word, need to destroy the expectancy of stuttering, need to release the mechanism from experiencing blocks, need to disguise those symptoms)—thse devices then become habitual and involuntary. In this sense the author believes that primary symptoms can be considered the cause of secondary symptoms. The implications of therapy would be the unconditioning of these secondary symptoms.

Lastly, a conception of the behavior pattern of stutterers was formulated. In this pattern, two types of expectancies were theorized: (1) Generalized Expectancy—present when the stutterer confronts a speech situation similar to those in which he has previously stuttered, (2) Specific Expectancy—represents a narrowing down of the generalized expectancy to specific characteristics of the speaking situation.

TITLE

Knott, J. R., Johnson, W., and Webster, M. G.: Studies in the Psychology of Stuttering: II. A Quantitative Evaluation of Expectation of Stuttering in Relation to the Occurrence of Stuttering, *Journal of Speech Disorders,* **(1937), 20-22.**

Purpose: To determine if there is any relation between expectation of stuttering and the occurrence of stuttering, and if there is a relationship, to what degree is it present.

Experimental Design: Twenty-two adult stutterers were required to read aloud a standard passage of 500 words, each word being considered a unit. The subjects were required to express judgments on each word concerning their expectation of stuttering on that word, thus: (1) tap on the table with a pencil three times if sure of stuttering, (2) tap two times if not sure but thought he might, and (3) tap once if he did not expect to stutter. "Following the signal, and not coincident with it, the subject spoke the word."

The data were divided into two sections: (1) data from 12 persons who had undergone considerable clinical treatment and were more or less informed as to the nature of their disorder, and (2) data from 10 persons who had had little or no clinical treatment and were relatively naive as to the nature of the disorder. Chance percentage was defined as the per cent of words stuttered by each group respectively.

Summary: The percentage of words stuttered under the three degrees of expectancy was tabulated. The significance of differences in per cent of expected and unexpected stuttering was shown, and the significance of differences between the anticipation percentages and chance percentage of stuttering following prediction was tabulated. These percentages were computed for both the experienced and inexperiencd group.

Analysis of the data showed that in both groups (1) either definite or doubtful expectation followed by stuttering was significantly more frequent than definite expectation of no stuttering; (2) significantly more of certain expectancies were followed by stuttering than not followed; (3) expectation of stuttering followed by stuttering was greater than can be accounted for by chance, while expectation of not stuttering followed by stuttering was less frequent than can be accounted for by chance.

Conclusions: It was concluded that a positive statistically significant relationship exists between the expectation of stuttering and the occurrence of stuttering.

TITLE

Van Riper, C., and Milisen, R.: **A Study of the Predicted Duration of the Stutterer's Blocks as Related to Their Actual Duration,** *Journal of Speech Disorders,* 4 (1939), 339-345.

Purpose: To answer the question: Can the stutterer, in the period prior to speech attempt, predict the duration of the overt spasm?

Experimental Design: I. *Milisen:* Forty-three adult stutterers served as subjects. The stimulus consisted of 50 or more cards per stutterer bearing one word each. These words included the 25 most difficult or "Jonah" words provided by the subject, together with words chosen from the lists of other stutterers. Words were presented one at a time by means of the exposure box and the stutterer was asked to estimate the spasm duration of each word as: (1) no stuttering; (2) short spasm; (3) medium spasm; or (4) long spasm. Actual duration of the spasms when the word was attempted was measured on a polygraph.

II. *Van Riper:* The design was identical with Milisen's except that only 13 cases were used. Also, breathing records for six of these cases were obtained as an additional check of the spasm duration.

Summary:

1. The average time taken to speak words on which a slight spasm was anticipated was .62 of a second longer than the time taken to speak non-anticipated words.

2. The time taken to speak words on which a spasm of medium length was anticipated was 1.42 seconds longer than the time taken to speak non-anticipated words.

3. The time taken to speak words on which a long spasm was anticipated was 3.9 seconds longer than the time taken to speak non-anticipated words.

4. In general, the results indicated that not only do the averages of overt spasm durations increase with the increase in the length of the predicted duration, but that there is no great overlapping between the various classes. Stutterers, therefore, can predict in a general way the duration of their overt spasms.

Conclusions: It was concluded that:

1. Devices which provide distraction for the stutterer to help him avoid spasms are of little value for therapy since the stutterer soon becomes adapted to the device.

2. The handicap of stuttering is fundamentally due to two features of the overt spasm: The interruption to communication, and the abnormality of speech as expressed through repetition, prolongation, and contortion.

3. Certain factors exist in the period just prior to speech attempt which determine the duration of blocks. Hence, a therapy which is focused on those factors might be valuable by shortening the duration of the spasms. This type of therapy would entail the alteration of preparatory sets prior to speech attempt.

TITLE

Johnson, W., and Solomon, A.: Studies in the Psychology of Stuttering: IV. A Quantitative Study of Expectation of Stuttering as a Process Involving a Low Degree of Consciousness, *Journal of Speech Disorders*, 2 (1937), 95-97.

Purpose: To investigate the expectation of stuttering as a factor related to stuttering when experimental conditions are such that expectation cannot readily occur as a highly conscious process.

Experimental Design: Thirteen adult stutterers were given four different 100 word readings. In reading I, the subject was told to go over the passage carefully and underline every word on which he expected to stutter when reading it aloud. He read it aloud from a duplicate copy 15 minutes later and the experimenter marked the stuttered words. In reading II the same procedure was repeated. In reading III the oral reading was repeated one day after marking. In reading IV, the stutterer marked possible stuttering words and immediately afterward recorded the selection. Reliability: the reading situations were highly constant for all stutterers. The experimenter and another trained observer agreed on 92.5% spasms.

Summary: It was considered important to determine whether and to what extent expectation is associated with stuttering when the stutterer does not have a reasonable opportunity to decide on a highly conscious level whether or not he expects to stutter. This is essentially the condition that prevails during ordinary speech or oral reading when the stutterer seldom has adequate time between words to formulate a thoroughly deliberated judgment as to expectation of stuttering. The following table illustrates the relationship between per cent of anticipatory and non-anticipatory words stuttered in the four readings plus CR between percentages.

	No. subjects	No. Words read	No. Words stuttered	No. Words antic.	% antic. stut.	Cr.	% non-antic. words stut.
Reading I	13	12,948	2,553	1,942	53.2	35.8	13.8
Reading II	13	13,000	2,342	2,314	64.2	56.2	8.0
Reading III	12	12,000	2,084	2,556	51.1	42.9	8.2
Reading IV	10	9,360	1,060	905	42.7	26.7	8.0

In this study stuttering occurred on approximately 53% of the words on which stuttering was expected and on 10% of the words on which stuttering was not expected. The size of the CR's indicated that expectation of stuttering was associated in some way with precipitation of moments of stuttering. The following indicated that expectation of stuttering not only functions in relation to the precipitation of moments of stuttering but also that it need not operate on a highly conscious level.

Conclusions: It was concluded that even though a stutterer does not have time to formulate a deliberate judgment as to expectation of stuttering, he may still stutter.

TITLE

Johnson, W., and Brown, S.: Stuttering in Relation to Various Speech Sounds, *Quarterly Journal of Speech,* **21 (1935), 481-496.**

Purpose: To determine if stutterers experience more stuttering in relation to one speech sound than to another, and to account for differences in the difficulty of certain sounds (not innately more complex phonetically or physiologically) on psychological grounds.

Experimental Design: Seventy stutterers were tested. Adequate data were obtained on 32 (26 males and 6 females) ranging from 18 to 30 years of age. Each subject read aloud an especially prepared selection in the presence of one experimenter who recorded on a copy of the script all blocks that the reader experienced. There were five different tests of 1,000 words, each of which included as many speech sounds as possible in the initial position. In preparing the tests an effort was made to use simple syntax and vocabulary and to keep them free from any emotional coloring to avoid eliciting any excessive blocks. The tests were given once each week and each subject took each test twice. While the experimenter—whose efficiency had been previously established—recorded all blocks, only those that involved a sound in the initial position were tabulated. Due to sickness, etc. the interval between tests varied somewhat. That this had no significant bearing on the results was statistically determined. The per cent of stuttering on each sound, the average blocking on each reading, and the consistency of blocks were computed.

Summary: All stutterers were found to experience more difficulty with some sounds than with others. The more severe stutterers seemed more consistent in their differencs. Ninety-two per cent of the stuttering spasms observed occurred in relation to the initial sounds of words. In terms of rank of difficulty based on the median per cent of difficulty in relation to each sound, the [z] sound was most difficult with [l], [j], [g], and [d] close followers. In general, there was found to be more blocking in relation to consonants than vowels. However, in detail this was not consistent. The stutterers differed markedly in the distribution of their greatest difficulties. The differences showed *no* consistency in relation to phonetic difficulty. However, for almost all, some sounds were more difficult than others; no sound was the most difficult for all.

Conclusions: It was concluded that since there seems to be a definite pattern of difficulty, some general factor—psychological, phonetic or physiological—must be exerting influence. Since no sound is most difficult for all subjects, the individual differences seem to be psychologically caused.

TITLE

Brown, S.: **The Influence of Grammatical Function on the Incidence of Stuttering,** *Journal of Speech Disorders,* 2 (1937), 207-215.

Purpose: To test the hypothesis that different functions performed by various parts of speech of contextual material might effect the occurrence of spasms.

Experimental Design: Data were taken from the records of the oral reading performance of 32 stutterers who read five 1,000 word reading selections twice, or approximately 10,000 words each. A grammatical analysis of the selection was made using the eight conventional parts of speech. For finer differentiation, 23 classifications of speech were set up of which 18 occurred in sufficient numbers to be used for statistical treatment. A rank of difficulty was determined for the eight conventional and the finer 18 parts for each case, using the percentage of stuttering as a measure of difficulty. All stuttering spasms were recorded by the experimenter whose rating reliability was found to be .99.

Summary: Although the results showed there was a definite rank of difficulty for the various parts of speech with adjectives and nouns at the top and prepositions and articles at the bottom, the differences were not great enough to be statistically significant. This carried over to the finer differentiation with participial adjectives and proper nouns at the top and articles and prepositions at the bottom. Correlations were done with each individual case compared with the composite results. Correlations ran from .36 to .97, with a Mdn of .85.

In comparing the phonetic factor of difficulty with the grammatical factor, there seemed to be an obvious relationship between the two. The question whether a grammatical factor exists or whether all differences can be accounted for by the phonetic factor arose. Three facts seemed to indicate that it was not possible to account for the grammatical rank of difficulty entirely on a phonetic basis: (1) A considerable majority of the cases found less difficulty with articles than with all other words beginning with the same sounds. (2) Even more found proper nouns more difficult than all other words beginning with the same sounds. (3) There was agreement among the cases as to the relative difficulty of various parts of speech as opposed to difficulty of various sounds.

A fact of psychological significance, it was felt, was that those parts of speech which were stuttered on least are those which contribute least to the meaning the speaker wishes to convey. These parts of speech constituted the lower half of the grammatical rank of difficulty.

Conclusions: It was concluded that (1) There exists for stutterers a rank of difficulty for parts of speech, whether a conventional or finer differentiation of speech is made. (2) This rank of difficulty is not statistically significant, but does indicate a psychological significance of rank. (3) The grammatical factor is related to the phonetic, but operates independently of it. (4) Stutterers are more consistent with regard to relative difficulty of parts of speech from one time to another than with regard to difficulty of sounds. (5) The words which are less important for conveying meaning of a sentence are stuttered less. (6) Individual cases of difficulty do not appear to be important by comparison with group tendencies.

TITLE

Brown, S.: A Further Study of Stuttering in Relations to Various Speech Sounds, *The Quarterly Journal of Speech,* **24 (1938), 390-397.**

Purpose: To study the role that speech sounds play in influencing the occurrence of spasms.

Experimental Design: This study investigated words arranged in random order with no context. The test consisted of 700 words arranged in haphazard order with two precautions: (1) to keep words beginning with the same initial sound or blend separated by a considerable number of words in an attempt to minimize the effect of memory of spasms upon the same sound: (2) to keep the whole test as free as possible from arrangement of words which might carry meaning.

Each stutterer read to the experimenter who recorded on mimeographed copies of the test all stuttering spasms, word omissions, substitutions or insertions, reversals, mispronunciations, or other variations. Printed instructions were: "Please read each word carefully and distinctly." The test was given to 32 stutterers (26 males) ranging in age from 18 to 30 years with average age of 22. In only 14 of the 32 cases did the test elicit sufficient stuttering to make collection of data worthwhile. These 14 were given the test six times, with intervals of several days. Correlations were obtained between the first and second three readings and between the total data of this test and the test of contextual material. The experimenter's rating reliability was found to be .99.

Summary:

1. The 18 stutterers who had experienced difficulty with contextual material but were eliminated had fewer than seven, and most had fewer than three stuttering spasms on the 700 word list.

2. Of the 14 subjects used, 13 had statistically significantly more stuttering on same sounds than on others; only two stuttered on all sounds. Group correlations between rank of difficulty of sounds in contextual vs non-contextual material was .91.

3. Ten had a higher percentage of stuttering on one sound or blend than on another. One stuttered in relation to every sound and blend. The degree of relationship between the ranks of difficulty is reduced when the various blends are separated from their initial component. There were 63 differences of this type: 38 occurred when blends were associated with significantly less stuttering than its initial component, and 25 when the reverse was true. Individual differences were also found in this case.

Conclusions: It was concluded that (1) Reading of non-contextual material appears to be an easier situation for most stutterers than contextual material. (2) Existence of a general phonetic factor of difficulty seems to be indicated by statistically significant results when other factors were apparently eliminated. (3) Individual patterns of difficulty for sounds appear stronger than the group tendency. (4) The individual patterns vary more from the contextual to the non-contextual material than does the general phonetic factor of difficulty.

TITLE

Brown, S.: Stuttering with Relation to Word Accent and Word Position, *Journal of Abnormal and Social Psychology*, **33 (1938), 112-120.**

Purpose: To determine whether stuttering is more likely to occur on the accented or on the unaccented syllables of words, and whether words in certain positions in the sentence are more likely to be stuttered than other words.

Experimental Design: Thirty-two stutterers served as subjects, each reading approximately 10,000 words consisting of two readings of each of five 1,000 word reading selections. The experimenter marked on mimeographed copies of the selections all stuttering spasms and reading errors. The experimenter's reliability was found to be .99.

Summary:

Stuttering with relation to word accent:

1. About 87.5% of stutterers had significantly greater percentages of stuttering on accented than on unaccented syllables.

2. On words accented on the first syllable, 31 cases had significantly greater percentages of stuttering on the first syllable than on the unaccented following syllable or syllables.

3. In criticism of results No. 1 and No. 2, the beginning of a word had a far greater importance for the stutterer than the rest of the word (92.2% of spasms were in relation to the initial sounds of words). Also, introspections of stutterers revealed a "psychological primacy" of the initial part of a word (many fearing s-sounds in the initial position but not in medial or final positions). Hence, since 78% of the words read were accented on the first syllable, it might appear that a greater percentage of stuttering occurs on accented syllables. However, when spasms were studied which occurred only on other syllables than the first, 75% of the cases stuttered a significantly greater number of times on the accented than on the unaccented first syllables.

Stuttering with relation to word position:

1. The study was limited to the study of first, second and third words of sentences and paragraphs.

2. First words of sentences and paragraphs elicited more stuttering than words in all other positions. The percentage of stuttering was generally of decreasing magnitude from the first to the third word position.

Conclusions: The author suggested that:

1. These findings may be accounted for in terms of the relatively greater demands placed upon the speech mechanism at

accented syllables and at the beginning of sentences and paragraphs.

2. Accented syllables are characterized by longer duration, greater intensity and higher pitch than unaccented syllables creating greater tension and increased activity of the speech mechanism.

3. There may be a "psychological primacy" associated with greater demands.

4. Because of the prominence of accented syllables and initial words, the stutterer may place a greater premium on fluency in relation to them and thus feel a greater difficulty in "getting started."

TITLE

Brown, S., and Moren, A.: The Frequency of Stuttering in Relation to Word Length During Oral Reading, *Journal of Speech Disorders,* **7 (1942), 153-159.**

Purpose: To determine whether word length as such is one of the factors of importance in locating spasms at various points in the speech sequence.

Experimental Design: Thirty-two stutterers read five 1,000 word reading selections twice or approximately 10,000 words each to the experimenter. The experimenter recorded on a mimeographed copy of the selection being read all stuttering spasms, reading errors, mispronunciations, and variant pronunciations. The reliability of the experimenter was found to be .99. Two measures of word length were used—the number of syllables and the number of letters. The study was limited to adjectives and prepositions.

Summary:

1. For adjectives, there was a general trend for the mean per cent of stuttering to vary directly with the word length.

2. If the one-syllable adjectives which are least difficult are compared with the two-syllable adjectives which were stuttered

least, the two-syllable group showed a higher per cent of stuttering.

3. The comparison between the lowest means within the two and three-syllable groups showed similar results.

4. Within any one syllable group there was not a regular increase in the per cent of stuttering with an increase in the number of letters in the group.

5. There was a great deal of variation from one individual to another.

6. Comparable results were found with prepositions, i.e., a general rise in mean per cent of stuttering accompanied increase in syllable length.

7. Within each syllable group of prepositions, the per cent of stuttering varied systematically with the number of letters in the word.

8. When data were grouped to show the difficulty for all words of each syllable and each letter length, a steady increase in the mean per cent of stuttering was found to accompany an increase in syllable length. A similar but irregular increase was noticed in letter length categories.

Conclusions: The following conclusions were drawn:

1. Longer adjectives and prepositions are more difficult for stutterers than shorter ones, whether syllable-letter, syllable, or letter categories are used as a basis for measuring word length.

2. The factor of phonetic difficulty explains some of the above relationships, but not all of the variations can be explained in this way.

3. The amount of stuttering tends to vary directly with word length.

4. A possible explanation of this is found in terms of the greater prominence of longer words and the stutterer's consequent desire to avoid stuttering at those points.

TITLE

Brown, S.: The Loci of Stutterings in the Speech Sequence, *Journal of Speech Disorders*, 10 (1945), 181-192.

Purpose: In earlier experimental investigations it was shown that: (1) some sounds occasion greater difficulty for stutterers than others considering initial position only; (2) stutterers experience greater difficulty in relation to certain parts of speech than others; (3) the position of a word in a sentence affects the degree of difficulty that stutterers experience; (4) longer words are stuttered more often than short ones (not to be explained in terms of phonetic or grammatical factors). It was concluded that words containing these characteristics are more likely to produce stuttering. The purpose of this experiment was to determine if these four characteristics are the only significant ones or whether there are other more subtle influences at work.

Experimental Design: A passage containing 1000 words which had been read once by 31 of an original sample of 32 stutterers was analyzed with each word being evaluated in terms of the presence $(+)$ or absence $(-)$ of each of the four characteristics mentioned above. Having accomplished this, each of the 31 stutterers was required to read the entire passage one more time. Also, for purposes of the analysis, the group was subdivided into: mild, moderate, severe, in terms of the number of stuttered words in the initial reading of the passage.

Summary: In each of the subgroups as well as in the composite, the per cent of stuttering varied directly with the increase of $+$ value of the words. The rank-order correlation for the severe group was .98; for the composite, .99. Also of significance was the fact that of the 206 words never stuttered, 55% had a zero $+$ value. In terms of relative difficulty it was also found that:

$$+1 \text{ words } 2.5 \times \text{ as difficult as } \quad 0$$
$$+2 \text{ words } 5 \ \ \times \text{ as difficult as } +1$$
$$+3 \text{ words } 9 \ \ \times \text{ as difficult as } +2$$
$$+4 \text{ words } 10 \ \ \times \text{ as difficult as } +3$$

Conclusions: It was concluded "that the loci of stutterings in the speech sequence are not determined by chance." This conclusion, it was felt, was given strong support by the high order rank-order correlation (.99) between increasing + values and the per cent increase in stuttering.

For both stutterers and non-stutterers, these characteristics appear to be the chief factors for the evaluation of the prominence and conspicuousness of the words in context. Of 5,136 words stuttered only 5.3% could not be accounted for by one of the four factors. The author suggests that the evaluation of words as being prominent and conspicuous has more bearing on the loci of stutterings than on the sheer presence or absence of any factor or factors, e.g., the stutterer having so evaluated the word or words, tries to avoid stuttering and reacts with caution, hesitancy, effort, conflict—these reactions being termed stuttering.

TITLE

Trotter, W.: Relationship Between Severity of Stuttering and Word Conspicuousness, *Journal of Speech and Hearing Disorders,* 21 (1956), 198-201.

Purpose: To determine whether there is a relationship between severity of stuttering and the "weight" or conspicuousness of the word stuttered, as defined by Brown in previous studies.

Experimental Design: Previously recorded reading passages (500 words) of 20 stutterers, which had been played back twice to two judges and rated as to which words were stuttered, were utilized in this study. These recordings were played to a group of 11 speech pathology students who judged the stuttered words for severity on a nine point continuous scales, one representing least severe and nine most severe. A mean severity rating was calculated from all these ratings, providing the basic data for the present study.

The stuttered words in the recordings were categorized, according to Brown's criteria, as words of weight zero through four (Brown's four points of consideration were (1) noun, adjective, verb, or adverb; (2) one of first three words in sentence; (3) begins with consonant other than ð, h, w, m, and t; (4) contained five or more letters. Word weight is the sum of the criteria the word meets). Data on one stutterer were omitted, since he stuttered on no zero weight words, leaving 19 in the experimental group for purposes of tabulating results.

Summaries: Mean severity for the zero through four weight words were, respectively, 2.93, 3.09, 3.27, 3.40, 3.44. The differences between the zero weight category and the one, two, three, and four weight categories were significant, as were the differences between the one weight category and the three and four weight categories. The results indicate a functional relationship between word-weight and the severity of stuttering on the word.

Conclusions: The present findings are in agreement with Brown's hypothesis that the higher weight words are deemed, by the stutterer, to be more important or conspicuous; thus his greater desire for fluency on these words precipitates more stuttering on them.

TITLE

Moore, W. E., Soderberg, G., and Powell, D.: Relations of Stuttering in Spontaneous Speech to Speech Content and Verbal Output, *Journal of Speech and Hearing Disorders,* **17 (1952), 371-376.**

Purpose: To determine whether there is any difference in the duration of stuttering spasms which occur in spontaneous speech on six different topics.

Experimental Design: Sixteen male stutterers, 13 to 21 years of age, with I.Q.'s ranging from 90 to 133 were used as subjects. Each subject first took a sentence-completion test which covered six topics (parents, hopes, fears, good times, misdeeds, and associates). He was then thoroughly familiarized with the recorder and the testing situation. Then he was interviewed on the same six topics mentioned above. Immediately following the first interview, two repetitions of the interview on the same topics were carried out in which the subject was asked to tell more and even more about the topics. Recordings were transcribed and checked for accuracy. From the recordings the duration of each spasm was measured.

Summary: By analysis of covariance technique it was determined that there were no significant differences between the means of stuttering duration for the six different topics. Although not statistically significant, the topic *Parents* shows the greatest relationship to the severity of stuttering. It was noted that the number of words spoken on *Parents* was equal to that of the other five topics, even though the duration of stuttering was greater.

Conclusions: Further study of the relationship between the topic *Parents* and stuttering severity is suggested by the authors. The possibility that conceptual system or constellations of ideas and values are related to stuttering severity is presented. A possible method for more precise investigation of relationships between personality traits, etc. and stuttering severity by a combination of projective tests and controlled interviews is suggested.

TITLE

Bloodstein, O.: A Rating Scale Study of Conditions Under Which Stuttering Is Reduced or Absent, *Journal of Speech and Hearing Disorders,* **15 (1950), 29-36.**

Purpose: To determine conditions under which stutterers report their stuttering to be reduced or absent.

Experimental Design: The major portion of the study was personal interviews with 50 stutterers. They were also given a questionnaire of 115 conditions under which stuttering would be expected to be reduced. They were asked to rate their stuttering in these situations on a one to four point scale: (1) as much or more than usual; (2) definitely less than usual; (3) hardly any at all; and (4) no stuttering, no tendency to stutter.

In a supplementary study, 154 stutterers completed a questionnaire which seemed to be of more than ordinary interest. In all, 204 stutterers ranging in age from 16 to 44 years of the age were used. 75% of the group were between 17 and 25 years of age and 16 were females.

Summary: One of the most conspicuous findings was that in very few instances were reductions in stuttering reported by the whole group. In many cases large proportions of subjects reported no reduction at all. In some situations some subjects reported more stuttering than usual while others reported marked reductions. Eight items were particularly suspicious. Of the first 50 subjects, 35 were given the interviews first and then given the questionnaire a month later. On these eight items marked disparity occurred. The ratings changed more than one to two points from the interview to the questionnaire. The variability appeared to be due either to the artifact in the wording of the test or to the subjects not understanding or ignoring the instructions. For example, one item explored ordinary conversation with mother and involved many different stimulus conditions, i.e., whether mother tends to be critical, sympathetic, indifferent, or understanding. Also in closer examination of the first fifty subjects it was found that many answered questions without previous experience in that condition. Many stated that stuttering increases in play acting although they had never been in a play.

Grouping the 115 items under six general headings, it was found that stuttering appeared to diminish under *conditions of reduced communicative responsibility, reduced need for favorable impression, absence of unfavorable listener reactions, changes in speech patterns, associated activity, and intense or unusual stimulation.* On only one item (unison reading) did 100% of the subjects report no stuttering. Talking to animals and infants showed high incidence of reduction and general group agreement.

Conclusions: The author concluded that: (1) It is possible to specify over 100 situations under which fairly large proportions of subject report reduced stuttering. (2) Very few conditions appear to result in reduced stuttering for all subjects, and in many instances the subjects vary markedly in their degree of reduction. (3) Most of the conditions can be reduced to six general categories under which stuttering appears to be reduced for all subjects.

TITLE

Pittenger, K.: **A Study of Duration of Temporal Intervals Between Successive Moments of Stuttering,** *Journal of Speech Disorders,* 5 (1940), 333-341.

Purpose: To determine the length of time intervals between successive moments of stuttering in order to discover whether there exists systematic distribution of the length of these time intervals or cyclic (consistent) pattern of a temporal nature in the occurrence of stuttering moments. Particular attention was paid to the following points: variability of time intervals between successive moments of stuttering for each individual; the existence of cyclic patterns for each individual; and variations in time interval sizes between moments of stuttering among all of the stutterers.

Experimental Design: The subjects were 20 stutterers (ages 15 to 34). Each read 1000 word passages while being observed by two concealed experimenters. Each observer recorded every stuttering moment and its duration by use of a key attached to a polygraph. Both visual and auditory cues were used in these evaluations. Correlations of .99 indicated excellent agreement between the observers.

Summary: It was found that the time intervals between successive moments of stuttering in any one individual tended to be different in length. Also, there was greater variability in the length of temporal intervals between moments of stuttering than in the measures of other physiological phenomena considered (heart beat, breathing, brain waves).

The time intervals between successive moments of stuttering did not tend to follow any consistent cyclic pattern. This was shown when graphs of these time intervals were compared with graphs of heart beat, breathing and brain wave time intervals. One general pattern noticed was that intervals tended to increase in length as the subject read more and approached the end of the reading passage.

Conclusions: It was concluded that (1) there is marked variability in the length of temporal intervals between successive moments of stuttering, both for a single individual and from one individual to another; (2) time intervals between successive moments of stuttering exhibit no consistent regularity in length. Had the reverse been true, the author felt, it might have been assumed that stuttering was an organic condition, because, such physiological phenomena as heart beat, respiration, etc. do occur with a relatively high degree of regularity. "It may be concluded that stuttering is either functional in origin or that it arises out of some organic condition which does not produce regularly occurring phenomena."

TITLE

Johnson, W., and Rosen, L.: Studies in the Psychology of Stuttering: VII Effect of Certain Changes in Speech Pattern Upon Frequency of Stuttering, *Journal of Speech Disorders*, 2 (1937), 105-109.

Purpose: To ascertain whether specific changes in the stutterers' speech pattern would affect changes in frequency of stuttering.

Experimental Design: A sample of 18 adult stutterers was used. Each subject read normally three passages of 500 words each. Twelve passages of 500 words each were then read, using prescribed speech patterns. All 15 of the passages were equated for difficulty.

Summary: The following table shows the results obtained:

Reading	Total Number	Words Stuttered Per Cent	*t	# S's Not Stuttering	# S's Showing Reductions
No. 1 (ordinary)	683	7.6		1	......
			11.5		
No. 8 (ordinary)	340	3.8		1	......
			0.8		
No. 15 (ordinary)	316	3.5		4	......
Combined 1 & 8	1023	5.7	......	0	......
Combined 8 & 15	656	3.6	......	1	......
Slow	120	1.3	21.1	5	16
Fast	697	7.7	6.3	0	3
Whispering	72	0.8	25.8	4	17
Low Intensity	189	2.1	15.7	5	14
High Intensity	229	2.5	13.3	2	17
Singing	0	0.0	......	18	18
Metronome	5	0.06	17.8	15	18
Arm-Swing	1	0.01	18.2	17	18
Sing-Song	8	0.09	17.6	15	18
High-Pitch	95	1.1	11.1	10	18
Chorus-Stutterer	1	0.01	18.2	17	18
Chorus-Normal	1	0.01	18.2	17	18

* Data from Readings 2-7 inclusive are compared with data from Readings 1 and 8 combined; data from Readings 9-14 inclusive are compared with data from Readings 8 and 15 combined. A t to be significant for 18 subjects at .05 level would have to be 2.11 or greater.)

With the exception of the "fast" condition, there was a gradual decrease in stuttering instances. In the "fast" condition there were more instances than during normal reading (instructions being to read as fast as possible and retain distinct speech), indicating that the mere intention to read fast as well as the actual increase in rate, played a part in determining stuttering.

In order of the greatest reduction, the conditions were: singing, metronome, arm-swinging, sing-song, chorus-stutterer, chorus-normal, whispering, high pitch, slow, low intensity, high intensity, fast. The greatest reduction was found in the instances where some very definite rhythm was imposed.

Conclusions: The reason offered by the authors to account for the reduction in stuttering falls within the realm of distraction and suggestion. The general thesis was that the stimulus value of words and cues is altered by the redirection of attention. That is to say, the stutterer pays more attention to the rate, pitch, and intensity of the superimposed pattern than to the avoidance reactions and fears of stuttering, and hence stutters less.

TITLE

Bloodstein, O. N.: Studies in the Psychology of Stuttering: XIX. The Relationship Between Oral Reading and Severity of Stuttering, *Journal of Speech Disorders*, 9 (1944), 161-173.

Purpose: To compare the rate of oral reading of stutterers with normal speakers and to investigate the relations between this rate and the severity of stuttering.

Experimental Design: Thirty adult stutterers (27 males, 3 females) ranging in age from 17 to 42 read three 300 word passages of factual prose. One passage was composed entirely of monosyllabic words, one of average word length, and one of polysyllabic words. Reading rate was measured in two ways: (1) the total number of words read divided by the total reading time, and (2) the reading rate exclusive of time spent in stuttering. Two independent observers recorded the data on a constant speech polygraph. The agreement of the observers in judging the duration of the blocks yielded an r of .95. Reading rate reliability yielded an average r of .82 for the three passages.

Summary: The outstanding results of this study were as follows: (1) the non-stuttering reading rates of the stutterers were significantly slower than the oral reading rates of normal speakers (Darley norms—167.3 words per minute for normals as compared with 122.7 for the stutterers); (2) The non-stuttering reading rate is inversely related to both frequency of stuttering and total duration of stuttering; (3) The over-all reading rate of stutterers is also inversely related to both frequency and total duration of stuttering; (4) Frequency of stuttering and total duration of stuttering were found to be very highly correlated. (r = .95 ± .01); (5) The reading rate of stutterers like the non-stutterers varied most widely in reading the monosyllabic passage, and least widely in reading the polysyllabic passage.

Conclusions: From these results it was concluded that: (1) The oral reading rates of stutterers are significantly slower than for normal readers. (2) Overall reading rate and reading rate during fluent intervals are negatively related to stuttering. The author also suggests that the speech of stutterers is characterized by anxious anticipation of stuttering which might reasonably be expected to retard their oral reading rates. He adds that it might reasonably be assumed that a stutterer not only tends to proceed cautiously as it were, but also and particularly, that he slows down and sometimes even stops in anticipation of difficulty on a given word.

TITLE

Johnson, W., and Ainsworth, S.: **Studies in the Psychology of Stuttering: X. Constancy of Loci of Expectancy of Stuttering,** *Journal of Speech Disorders,* 2 (1938), 101-104.

Purpose: To determine whether the stutterer anticipates stuttering relatively consistently on certain words to the exclusion of other words in repeated inspections of the same material.

Experimental Design: Sixteen male and four female adult stutterers served as subjects. Two did not complete the tests and one did not stutter at any time, so only the results of the remaining seventeen were used for statistical analysis.

Subject was given a pamphlet containing 558 words of unfamiliar material. He read the article silently, striking a tin pan for each word on which he would not expect to stutter; for each word he expected to stutter on if he read it aloud, he was to strike on wood. An observer seated opposite underlined every word the stutterer expected to stutter on a similar pamphlet. After a period of two to six weeks the subject again read the pamphlet and the observer underlined the words he expected to stutter on in red. The period of two weeks was used to offset the possibility of the subject's remembering any of the words on which he had previously anticipated stuttering. The subjects, when questioned claimed no remembrance of the predictions.

The data were treated as follows: The percentage of the words on which stuttering was anticipated in the first reading was found. Then the percentage of those words which were anticipated words on the second reading which were also anticipation words on the first reading was computed. The percentage of stuttering to be expected by chance in any random sample of words read in the first reading was also computed.

Summary: The results showed that by chance 9.3% of the words in the sample would be stuttered. 52.5% of the words on which stuttering was anticipated on the second reading were words on which stuttering was anticipated in the first reading. (1012 words were expected to be stuttered on in the second reading. Of these, 52.5% were also words expected to be stuttered on in the first reading.) The critical ratio of 27.7 indicated that this difference was highly significant.

Expectancy of stuttering is regarded as a response to words that is made more frequently (consistently) to some words than to others. It is, it was suggested, a response that is a relatively stable part of the order of events termed "stuttering."

Conclusions: "We are probably bound to conclude that any theory of 'Stuttering' which does not involve an adequate account of the 'expectancy of stuttering' does not by virtue of that fact involve an adequate account of 'stuttering.' "

TITLE

Johnson, W., and Inness, M.: Studies in the Psychology of Stuttering: XIII. A Statistical Analysis of the Adaptation and Consistency Effects in Relation to Stuttering, *Journal of Speech Disorders,* **4 (1939), 76-86.**

Purpose: To answer the following questions:

1. What is the degree of the stutterer's adaptation to word content as indicated by change in the frequency of stuttering from a short segment to a whole passage?

2. What is the degree of the stutterer's adaptation to word content as indicated by change in the frequency of stuttering from one reading to another of the same length?

3. To what degree are the loci of stuttering consistent for five successive readings of the same passage?

Experimenal Design: Data were drawn from three sources: Johnson-Brown study—31 S's, average age 22; Johnson-Knott study—16 male S's, average age 23; Maddox study—20 (18 males) average age 21.6. Procedure, methods, etc., were basically the same for all studies. (Observer and stutterer alone; duplicate copies of reading in their hands. Observer drew a line through word stuttered on.) Experimenter reliability was .97.

Summary:

A. *Adaptation Effect*

1. Total frequency of stuttering reduced 18.9% from first segment to fifth segment of whole passage mentioned above. This difference was statistically significant.

2. Total frequency of stuttering reduced 48.9% from first reading of a short passage to fifth reading of same passage.

3. In general there was significantly more adaptation in the readings in which the word content remained constant.

B. *Consistency Effect*

There was a marked tendency for the loci of the moments of stuttering to be constant for readings of the same material.

Conclusions: It was concluded that stutterers appear to adapt to the word content of a reading passage more than to the reading situation.

The tendency to stutter on the same words in succesive readings of a given passage, the authors feel, indicates some semantic reason for the reactions to these words.

TITLE

**Harris, W. E.: Studies in the Psychology of Stuttering: XVII.
A Study of the Transfer of the Adaptation Effect in Stuttering,**
Journal of Speech Disorders, 7 (1942), 209-221.

Purpose: To determine if reduction in stuttering frequency with
repeated readings of the same passage is associated with reduction in stuttering frequency (1) in the oral reading of a similar
passage and (2) in a conversational situation.

Experimental Design: Twenty stutterers (19 males, 2 females)
ranging in age from 11 to 27 read a 180-word passage, *The Rainbow,* four times, the first two and the last two readings being
separated by one-half hour—during which they were engaged
in non-reading "neutral" activity. A similar 180-word passage,
The United States, was read 15 times (or the stutterer was
stopped short of this maximum number of readings provided he
gave three consecutive readings of the passage with two, one or
no stutterings in each). Another 180-word passage, *My Grandfather,* was read four times, twice before the "repeat" readings,
and twice after. All stuttered words were marked by the experimenter on mimeographed copies of the passage. Two four minute
recordings of conversational speech were made, the first just prior
to the "repeat" readings, and the second at the end of the experiment.

Summary: Using the amount of adaptation (difference in per
cent of stuttered words between the first and last readings) involved in the control *Rainbow* readings as a base, it was found
that there was statistically significant transfer of the adaptation
effect occurring in the several successive readings of the *United
States* passage, to the reading of another similar passage, *My
Grandfather,* but that there was no transfer of the adaptation
effect to "conversational" speech. There was a positive correlation of .98 between the per cents of adaptation effect from one
passage to another to vary directly with the amount of adaptation. The more the reduction in frequency of stuttering with several successive readings of the same passage, the greater was the

consequent reduction—though the consequent reduction itself may not necessarily have been great—in reading of another passage.

The younger subjects (11-17) adapted to the *United States* passage more readily and to a greater degree than did the older stutterers.

Six stutterers showed wide fluctuation in stuttering frequency during the repetitions of the *United States* passage, and their failure to show as much or as consistent adaptation as the other subjects appeared to be due to some kind of "fatigue," complicated perhaps by "emotional" factors unknown to the experimenter.

Conclusions: It was concluded that (1) reduction in stuttering frequency with repeated readings of the same passage does tend to be associated with reductions in stuttering frequency in a similar passage, but (2) that it is not associated with a reduction in stuttering frequency in a "conversational" situation. However, none of the stutterers appeared to be perfectly at ease during the recording periods.

It was suggested that since the reduction in stuttering frequency with repeated readings tends to be transferred to the reading of a similar passage implications for therapy are suggested.

TITLE

Starbuck, H. B., and Steer, M. D.: The Adaptation Effect in Stuttering Speech Behavior and Normal Speech Behavior, *Journal of Speech and Hearing Disorders*, 18 (1953), 252-255.

Purpose: To discover whether the non-fluency of normal speakers behaves like the non-fluency of stutterers. The investigation is concerned with the adaptation effect (both psychologically and physically, i.e., respiration), in a stuttering and non-stuttering group.

Experimental Design: There were 44 male subjects of which half were stutterers. The two groups were matched as closely as possible for height, weight, age, and chest and waist circumference.

Each subject was seated in a sound-proof, air-conditioned room facing three observers, and a pneumograph was attached to his chest. (Respiratory data were not included in this report). The subject read a prepared passage five successive times with thirty second pauses between readings.

During the reading the three observers marked on a duplicate sheet each word stuttered. All non-fluencies or interruption in the continuity of the reading performance were counted as moments of stuttering. Inaudible mannerisms such as rehearsal movements of the vocal mechanism and facial grimaces when associated with an attempt to speak were also counted as moments of stuttering.

Summary: The results showed that the adaptation effect leading to a reduction of stuttering was present in both groups and also present between trials in both groups. The stutterers showed a greater number of blocks on all trials than the normals. The difference between groups was statistically significant.

There were also significant differences between trials within the stuttering group and trials within the non-stuttering group. This suggests that the adaptation phenomena are different in the two groups.

Due to the fact that stuttering is generally considered to be a progressive disorder, i.e., stuttering leads to more stuttering, the adaptation effect is all the more unusual in that the stuttering spasms do not elicit more stuttering, but a reduction in stuttering during successive oral readings of the same material.

Conclusions: It was concluded on the basis of the results that both adult non-stutterers and stutterers show an adaptation phenomenon in successive oral reading of the same passage. The adaptation phenomena, the authors feel, for stutterers and non-stutterers are not the same.

TITLE

Newman, P. W.: A Study of Adaptation and Recovery of the Stuttering Response in Self-Formulated Speech, *Journal of Speech and Hearing Disorders,* **19 (1954), 450-458.**

Purpose: To determine whether in successive speaking situations, with communicative speech formulated by the stutterer, adaptation and recovery of the stuttering response are demonstrable.

Experimental Design: Twenty adult subjects were used in two experimental conditions. One of the conditions consisted of five consecutive self-formulated descriptions of simple drawings, starting with a simple square up to a toy train. Twenty-four hours after the initial session a sixth description was obtained for the purpose of studying the recovery effect. The second condition was a reading passage describing how to draw an hour glass. An interval of one week separated the two conditions. The order of conditions was counter-balanced.

In all, 240 speech samples were taken on recordings and played back to the experimenter. Every ten seconds, he would make a rating of the severity of the ten second passage on a scale of one to nine, one representing least severe stuttering, and nine, the most severe. A mean severity rating was computed for each of the samples.

Summary: The results revealed adaptation and recovery in each condition. In the self-formulated speech conditions, there were significant differences between trials 1 and 5, 2 and 4, and 2 and 5. The adaptation effect therefore seemed to begin on the third trial. In the reading condition significant differences were found between trials 1 and each succeeding trial. Therefore, adaptation seemed to start on the second trial.

Consistency data on words stuttered were run on the first and fifth trials of self-formulated speech. Correlations between adaptation and consistent use of words stuttered were found to be .04, indicating no relationship. Correlation between consistent usage of words and adaptation were found to be —.02, indicating no relationship. There was no evidence that significant avoidance

of stuttered words took place, indicating that adaptation unin-
fluenced by avoidance of words stuttered occurred with self-
formulated speech.

As for the recovery effect, in self-formulated speech, the difference between trials 5 and 6 was significant at the .04 level.

Conclusions: On the basis of the results, it was concluded that
the adaptation and recovery phenomena are similar for self-
formulated speech and oral reading. The amount of adaptation
in a self-formulated speech condition appears *not* to be influenced
by the subject's avoidance of words stuttered in earlier trials.

TITLE

**Johnson, W., and Millsapps, L.: Studies in the Psychology of
Stuttering: VI. The Role of Cues Representative of Past Stuttering in the Distribution of Stuttering Moments During Oral Reading,** *Journal of Speech Disorders,* **2 (1937), 101-104.**

Purpose: To determine whether stuttering occurs only in relation
to certain words, or whether it occurs in relation to a specific cue
representative of past stuttering.

Experimental Design: Twenty-six adult stutterers read a standard
180-word passage to the experimenter, who marked all stuttered
words on duplicate copies. Each subject read the passage nine
times. After the first three readings, all words stuttered up to
that point were blotted out. The subject then read the remaining
words three times and the stuttered words were recorded. The
words stuttered in these three readings were then marked out,
and the remaining words were read three times, stuttered words
being recorded.

Summary: Group A (14 subjects) stuttered on all readings.
Group B (10 subjects) did not stutter after the sixth reading, and
Group C (2 subjects) did not stutter after the third reading.
Groups B and C contained relatively mild stuttering.

It was noted that significantly more stuttering occurred in the
second and third series on words adjacent to previously stuttered
words. The experimenters' reliability was .97.

Conclusions: It was concluded that:

1. Stuttering does not necessarily occur only on certain words.

2. "Stuttering does occur with marked consistency in relation to cues (blots) representative of past stutterings."

TITLE

Johnson, W., Larson, R. P., and Knott, J. R.: Studies in the Psychology of Stuttering: III. Certain Objective Cues Related to the Precipitation of the Moment of Stuttering, *Journal of Speech Disorders;* **2 (1937), 23-25.**

Purpose: To test the hypothesis that stuttering is precipitated, at least in part, by certain cues resident in the situation as perceived by the stutterer.

Experimental Design: Three experiments, utilizing 10 adult stutterers each, were designed.

1. Experiment I—a cue sheet consisting of a 100 word reading passage surrounded by a 1-inch colored border, and a control sheet, consisting of the same passage without the border, were read by each stutterer in four situations:

   (a) Pre-audience—Subjects read to experimenter alone from both cue and control sheets.
   (b) Audience—Subject read from cue sheet in front of an audience of at least 30 persons.
   (c) Post-Audience—Subject read to experimenter alone from both sheets.
   (d) 24-Hour Post-Audience—Subject read to experimenter alone 24 hours after the audience situation from both sheets.

Stuttering spasms were recorded by drawing a line through each word stuttered. Observer reliability was determined by use of recordings and comparisons with another observer. In both cases the per cent of agreement was .99.

2. Experiment II—The procedure was the same as I, except the cue was content, the control sheet contained different words from the cue sheet.

3. Experiment III—The cue was a diagonal pencil mark drawn through certain words. Subjects made two readings of a passage, not previously read, and each word stuttered was marked by the examiner. A cue sheet was prepared on which all words stuttered in both readings were marked by the diagonal line. In addition, five other words which had not been stuttered were similarly marked. Five other previously non-stuttered words were selected in essentially chance manner to serve as controls. These were not marked. The stutterer was told that each mark represented a previously stuttered word. He was required to read this cue passage two times. The frequency of stuttering on the five cue words and the five control words was then determined.

Summary:

1. Statistically significantly more stuttering occurred in the audience than pre-audience situation.

2. On the control sheet there was actually a decrease in frequency of stuttering in the post-audience situation; but, on the cue sheet there was an increase, and the significant difference (I, CR $= 5.7$ and II, CR $= 9.2$) shows that cues of color and content acted as cues in the post-audience situation.

3. The color cue of Experiment I was not effective after 24 hours, but the content cue of Experiment II remained considerably effective after that time.

4. In Experiment III spasms were recorded on 10 per cent of the control words and on 26 per cent of the cue words. A critical ratio of 3.0 indicated that these differences were statistically significant.

Conclusions: It was concluded that the results of these experiments support the hypothesis that both general cues and specific cues may be related to the precipitation of moments of stuttering.

TITLE

Hahn, E. F.: A Study of the Relationship between the Social Complexity of the Oral Reading Situation and the Severity of Stuttering, *Journal of Speech Disorders,* **5 (1940), 5-14.**

Purpose: To determine whether stuttering occurrence and frequency are associated with the social complexity of the speech situation.

Experimental Design: Fifty-two stutterers (42 males, 10 females) ranging in age from 18 to 39 read four selections containing 550 words each. The selections included exposition in telling a simple story and also fifteen lines of conversation. Every consonant and common consonant combination appeared in initial position. Each contained the same words but were placed in varying arrangements. Four situations were also used, each to correspond with a separate selection: (1) reading alone, (2) reading before an unseen listener known to be present, (3) reading directly to a single listener, and (4) reading before a small group of stutterers. The experimenter at all times recorded the amount of stuttering.

Summary:

Number of words upon which stuttering occurred in the four varied oral reading situations (all 52 Ss):

	1	2	3	4
Mean	25.3	49.0	47.6	63.1
Median	15.0	32.0	32.5	40.0
Standard Deviation	31.1	52.6	50.8	66.7

Intercorrelation between the various situations:

Test situation 1 with test situation 2 .... .74
Test situation 1 with test situation 3 .... .67
Test situation 1 with test situation 4 .... .51
Test situation 2 with test situation 3 .... .78
Test situation 2 with test situation 4 .... .69
Test situation 3 with test situation 4 .... .91

The results showed that the larger audiences are associated with increases in stuttering frequency. As the complexity of the social situation is increased the amount of stuttering tends to increase. Individual differences were extremely varied in the different situations and these differencs affected the number of stuttering spasms more than did the differences in situation. The extent of dependence of the number of spasms on the test situations was indicated by a correlation of .285. The extent of the dependence upon individual differences was expressed by the correlation of .825. Both are significant.

Conclusions: It was concluded that stutterers do experience difficulty when reading alone and that stuttering becomes more severe when the stutterer reads aloud to an unseen audience than when he reads aloud alone; stutterers have more difficulty when reading before a group than when reading alone or to an unseen listener; variation in the amount of stuttering is more affected by individual differences than by differences in the social complexity of the oral reading situation.

TITLE

Porter, H.: **Studies in the Psychology of Stuttering: XIV. Stuttering Phenomena in Relation to Size and Personnel of Audience,** *Journal of Speech Disorders,* 4 (1939), 323-333.

Purpose: To investigate certain stuttering phenomena in relation to the size and personnel of the audience.

Experimental Design: Thirteen adult stutterers (19 males, 3 females) ranging in age from 18 to 32 each read 500 words in each of eight situations, using a different but essentially equivalent passage in each one. Each stutterer read (1) while alone (a concealed microphone enabled the experimenter to hear the reading); (2) to the experimenter; (3) to two persons; (4) to four persons; (5) to eight persons; (6) to one listener previously evaluated by the subject as "easy" to read to; (7) to one listener previously evaluated as "neutral" to read to; (8) to one listener previously evaluated as "hard" to read to. In the last three situations a concealed microphone enabled the experimenter also to hear the reading. Experimenter checked the stuttered words in each reading. In each, except the first situation, both the subject and the listeners filled out a questionnaire designed to indicate how they evaluated certain aspects of a stutterer's reactions. Before each reading, the subject estimated the number of words he expected to stutter. The experiment was conducted during one evening for each S. Experimenter reliability was .96.

Summary: Main results of the study were: (1) The group as a whole showed a significant increase in stuttering frequency with increase in size of audience in situations ranging from reading aloud alone to reading to four persons. Subjects did not differentiate overtly in terms of frequency of stuttering between four and eight listeners; (2) Group showed a significant increase in per cent of words on which stuttering was expected with increase in size of audience, although between an audience of one person and one of two persons the increase in expectancy was a bit short of statistical significance; (3) Group expected to stutter more frequently than they did in seven situations (in four situations the differences were statistically significant), and they stuttered more than they expected to in one situation (audience of two listeners); (4) Subjects' rating-scale judgments of their own reactions of "emotionality," "strain," etc. agreed generally with corresponding judgments tended to rise with increase in size of audience, with the exception that there was little difference in this respect between four and eight listeners.

Conclusions: It was concluded that large variations in stuttering frequency can be accounted for essentially on psychological, or semantic, or evaluational grounds. The stutterer's assumptions regarding the "difficulty" of a situation, a particular audience, a word, a speech sound, a "type of performance," etc. appear to be significantly related to the frequency with which he stutters in a given situation.

TITLE

Van Riper, C.: The Influence of Empathic Response on Frequency of Stuttering, *Psychological Monographs*, 49 (1937), 244-246.

Purpose: To measure what effect, if any, the hearing and seeing of stuttering would have upon a stutterer's speech. For many years speech pathologists have been confronted by the popular belief that stuttering is often caused by imitation and transferred through social inheritance. In clinical examinations several mothers reported that their children's stuttering began after they had observed someone stuttering. Some groups of stutterers were observed giving empathic responses ranging from obvious breathing abnormalities to facial grimaces while hearing another stutterer address his group.

Experimental Design: Sixteen adult stutterers were introduced to two experimenters, one a normal speaker and the other a simulated severe stutterer. Each subject was briefed as to the purpose of the experiment, which was to determine if he stuttered while attempting to say words after someone else pronounced them. In *Situation A,* 50 words at a time were pronounced by the normal speaker. After each word, the stutterer attempted to pronounce the word. In *Situation B,* the second experimenter pretended to stutter badly on each word of the list and again the subject tried to pronounce the word. *Reliability:* Only those spasms upon which both experimenters and the stutterer agreed were counted. The percentage of agreement between the three ranged from 83-98, but only those with unanimous agreement were used.

Summary: Results demonstrated that stutterers had more spasms when the stuttering experimenter pronounced the words than when the normal experimenter pronounced them. The average difference between number of spasms occurring in Situations A and B was 7.1. This difference was significant at the .01 level. Some stutterers seemed to stutter in a manner very much like the pronouncer, though they claimed to have never before stuttered in such fashion.

Conclusions: Results suggest the effects of empathic response.

TITLE

Van Riper, C.: The Effect of Penalty Upon Frequency of Stuttering Spasms, *The Pedagogical Seminary and Journal of Genetic Psychology*, 50 (1937), 193-195.

Purpose: To test the hypothesis that in any given speech situation one of the factors which determines the frequency of stuttering spasms is the felt or expected penalty attached to the stuttering spasm.

Experimental Design: Sixteen stutterers were used. The stutterer was seated in a room with two experimenters and electrodes were attached to his neck. He was given a passage to read containing all the sounds of the alphabet in the initial position and asked to read the passage six consecutive times with a minute rest between each reading. Before the fourth reading he was told that for every spasm in this reading he would receive an electric shock immediately following it. Each subject was given a sample shock before the reading. To make sure the stutterer was reacting to the fear of penalty for stuttering and not the fear of the shock, at the beginning of the sixth reading (no shock was threatened or given for the fifth reading) the subject was informed he was to receive a shock for each spasm made in the first reading regardless of how he did in the sixth reading. The procedure was reversed for half of the subjects to counter-balance effects.

Summary: It was found that the threat of a shock for each spasm produced in that reading caused an average increase of 5.2 ± .8 over the preceding reading in which shock was not threatened. This difference was significant at the .01 level.

The control threat (shock from the first reading) caused an increase of only 1.5 ± .7 spasms over the preceding reading, while approximately one-third showed no increase whatsoever. No essential differences were found by reversing the trials.

Conclusions: It was concluded that in order to decrease the number of spasms, it appears necessary to decrease the penalty attached to them. Fundamentally, what society penalizes is the interruption to communication and the abnormal way communication is achieved. Since the only symptoms common to all stutterers are repetition and prolongation, and variation in symptoms from stutterer to stutterer seem largely a function of the habitual reactions he makes to these primary symptoms, it would, it was suggested therefore, seem advisable to teach the stutterer a manner of stuttering which minimizes the interruption as much as possible.

SYMPTOMATOLOGY

Additional Reading References

Adams, L. H.: A Comparison of Certain Sound Wave Characteristics of Stutterers and Nonstutterers, *Stuttering in Children and Adults,* University of Minnesota Press, Minneapolis, 1955.

Bloodstein, O. N.: Conditions Under Which Stuttering Is Reduced or Absent: A Review of the Literature, *Journal of Speech and Hearing Disorders,* 14 (1949), 295-302.

————: Hypothetical Conditions Under Which Stuttering Is Reduced or Absent, *Journal of Speech and Hearing Disorders,* 15 (1950), 142-153.

Branscom, M. E., Hughes, J., and Oxtoby, E. T.: Studies of Nonfluency in the Speech of Preschool Children, *Stuttering in Children and Adults,* University of Minnesota Press, Minneapolis, 1935.

Brown, S. F.: An Analysis of Certain Data Concerning Loci of "Stutterings" from the Viewpoint of General Semantics, *Papers from the Second American Congress of General Semantics,* 2 (1943), 194-199.

———— and Moren, A.: The Frequency of Stuttering in Relation to Word Length During Oral Reading, *Journal of Speech Disorders,* 7 (1942), 153-159.

Bryngelson, B.: A Phonophotographic Analysis of the Vocal Disturbances in Stuttering, *Psychological Monographs,* 43 (1932), 1-32.

————: A Study of the Speech Difficulties of Thirteen Stutterers, *Stuttering in Children and Adults,* University of Minnesota Press, Minneapolis, 1955.

Chotlos, J. W.: Covariation in Frequency of Types of Stuttering Reaction, *Ibid.*

Connett, M. H.: Experimentally Induced Changes in the Relative Frequency of Stuttering on a Specified Speech Sound, *Ibid.*

Donohue, I. R.: Stuttering Adaptation During Three Hours of Continuous Reading, *Ibid.*

Downton, W.: Effects of Instructions Concerning Mode of Stuttering on the Breathing of Stutterers, *Ibid.*

Egland, G. O.: Repetitions and Prolongations in the Speech of Stuttering and Nonstuttering Children, *Ibid.*

Eisenson, J.: A Note on the Persevering Tendency in Stutterers, *Pedagogical Seminary,* 50 (1937), 195-198.

————: Some Characteristics of the Written Speech of Stutterers: I, *Ibid.,* 457-458.

————, and Horowitz, E.: The Influence of Propositionality on Stuttering, *Journal of Speech Disorders,* 10 (1945), 193-197.

————, and Wells, C.: A Study of the Influence on Communicative Responsibility in a Choral Speech Situation for Stutterers, *Ibid.,* 7 (1942), 259-262.

Fagan, L. G.: Certain Reflexes During Stuttering, *Archives of Neurology and Psychiatry,* 19 (1928), 1006-1013.

————: Graphic Stuttering, *Psychological Monographs,* 43 (1932), 67-71.

Fairbanks, G.: Some Correlates of Sound Difficulty in Stuttering, *Quarterly Journal of Speech,* 23 (1937), 67-69.

Fierman, E. Y.: The Role of Cues in Stuttering Adaptation, *Stuttering in Children and Adults,* University of Minnesota Press, Minneapolis, 1955.

Frick, J. V.: Spontaneous Recovery of the Stuttering Response as a Function of the Degree of Adaptation, *Ibid.*

Golub, A.: The Cumulative Effect of Constant and Varying Reading Material on Stuttering Adaptation, *Ibid.*

Hahn, E. F.: A Study of the Relationship Between Stuttering Occurrence and Phonetic Factors in Oral Reading, *Journal of Speech Disorders,* 7 (1942), 143-151.

Heltman, H. J.: History of Recurrent Stuttering in a 25-year old Post-Graduate Student, *Journal of Speech Disorders,* 6 (1941), 49-50.

Henrikson, E. K.: A Study of Breathing and Vocal Disturbances of Stutterers, *Archives of Speech,* Studies in Speech Pathology, I, No. 2 (1936), 133-149.

Herren, R. Y.: The Effects of Stuttering on Voluntary Movement, *Journal of Experimental Psychology,* 14 (1931), 289-298.

————: The Relation of Stuttering and Alcohol to Tremor Rates, *Ibid.,* 15 (1932), 87-96.

Hill, H.: An Interbehaviorial Analysis of Several Aspects of Stuttering, *Journal of General Psychology,* 32 (1945), 289-316.

Jamison, D. J., Spontaneous Recovery of the Stuttering Response as a Function of the Time Following Adaptation, *Stuttering in Children and Adults,* University of Minnesota Press, Minneapolis, 1955.

Johnson, W.: A Statistical Evaluation of Specified Cues Related to the Moment of Stuttering (Abstract), *Psychological Bulletin,* 35 (1938), 632.

————: Stuttering in the Preschool Child, *University of Iowa Child Welfare Bulletin,* No. 37 (1934) Revised, 1941.

———— and Brown, S. F.: Stuttering in Relation to Various Speech Sounds: A Correction, *Quarterly Journal of Speech*, 25 (1939), 20-22.

————and Colly, W. H.: The Relationship between Frequency and Duration of Moments of Stuttering, *Journal of Speech Disorders*, 10 (1945), 35-38.

———— and Knott, J. R.: Studies in the Psychology of Stuttering: I. The Distribution of Moments of Stuttering in Successive Readings of the Same Material, *Ibid.*, 2 (1937), 17-19.

————: The Moment of Stuttering, *Journal of Genetic Psychology*, 48 (1936), 475-480.

Jones, E. L.: Explorations of Experimental Extinction and Spontaneous Recovery in Stuttering, *Stuttering in Children and Adults.*, University of Minnesota Press, Minneapolis, 1955.

Knott, J. R.: A Study of Stutterer's Stuttering and Non-stuttering Experiences in the Basis of Pleasantness and Unpleasantness," *Quarterly Journal of Speech*, 21 (1935), 328-330.

———— and Johnson, W.: The Factor of Attention in Relation to the Moment of Stuttering," *Journal of Genetic Psychology*, 48 (1936), 479-480.

————: An Interpretive Demonstration of Ten Observable Facts about Stuttering, *Proceedings of the American Speech Correction Association*, College Typing Co., Madison, 6 (1936), 150-154.

Mann, M. B.: Nonfluencies in the Oral Reading of Stutterers and Non-stutterers of Elementary School Age, *Stuttering in Children and Adults*, University of Minnesota Press, Minneapolis, 1955.

Maltzer, H.: Talkativeness in Stuttering and Non-Stuttering Children, *Journal of Genetic Psychology*, 46 (1935), 371-390.

Moore, W. E.: Relations of Stuttering in Spontaneous Speech to Speech Content and to Adaptation," *Journal of Speech and Hearing Disorders*, 19 (1954), 208-216.

Morley, A.: An Analysis of Associative and Predisposing Factors in the Symptomatology of Stuttering, *Psychological Monograms*, 49 (1937), 50-108.

Oxtoby, E. T.: Frequency of Stuttering in Relation to Induced Modifications Following Expectancy of Stuttering, *Stuttering in Children and Adults*, University of Minnesota Press, Minneapolis, 1955.

Reid, L. D.: Some Facts About Stuttering, *Journal of Speech Disorders*, 11 (1946), 3-12.

Robbins, S. D.: Relative Attention Paid to Vowels and Consonants by Stammerers and Normal Speakers, *Proceedings of the American Speech Correction Association*, 6 (1936), 7-23.

Rousey, C. L.: Stuttering Severity During Prolonged Spontaneous Speech, *Journal of Speech and Hearing Research*, 1 (1958), 40-47.

Schaef, R. A.: The Use of Questions to Elicit Stuttering Adaptation, *Journal of Speech and Hearing Disorders,* 20 (1955), 262-265.

Shaffer, G. L.: Measures of Jaw Movements and Phonation in Non-Stuttered and Stuttered Production of Voiced and Voiceless Plosives, *Speech Monographs,* 7 (1940), 85-92.

Shames, G. H., and Beams, H. L.: Incidence of Stuttering in Older Age Groups, *Journal of Speech and Hearing Disorders,* 21 (1956), 313-316.

Shaw, S. S.: A Study of Tonal Intensity and Duration in the Nonstuttered Speech of Stutterers and Nonstutterers, *Stuttering in Children and Adults,* University of Minnesota Press, Minneapolis, 1955.

Shulman, E.: Factors Influencing the Variability of Stuttering," *Ibid.*

Tanberg, M. D.: A Study of the Role of Inhibition in the Moment of Stuttering," *Ibid.*

Travis, L. E.: A Phonophotographic Study of the Stutterer's Voice and Speech, *Psychological Monographs,* 36 (1926), 109-141.

————: Studies in Stuttering I. Dysintegration of the Breathing Movements During Stuttering, *Archives of Neurology and Psychiatry,* 18 (1927), 672-690.

————: Studies in Stuttering II. Photographic Studies of the Voice in Stuttering, *Ibid.,* 998-1014.

————: A Study of the Horizontal Dysintegration of Breathing During Stuttering, *Archives of Speech,* Studies in Speech Pathology I, No. 3 (1956), 157-169.

Trotter, W. D. and Bergmann, M. F.: Stutterers' and Non-Stutterers' Reactions to Speech Situations, *Journal of Speech and Hearing Disorders,* 22 (1957), 40-45.

Tuthill, C.: A Quantitative Study of Extensional Meaning with Special Reference to Stuttering, *Speech Monographs,* 13 (1946), 81-98.

Van Riper, C.: A Study of the Stutterer's Ability to Interrupt Stuttering Spasm, *Journal of Speech Disorders,* 3 (1938), 117-119.

———— and Hull, C. J.: "The Quantitative Measurement of the Effect of Certain Situations on Stuttering, *Stuttering in Children and Adults,* University of Minnesota Press, Minneapolis, 1955.

UNIT III

ETIOLOGY—PHYSIOLOGICAL

SETON HALL UNIVERSITY
McLAUGHLIN LIBRARY
SO. ORANGE. N. J.

TITLE

Boland, J. L.: **Type of Birth as Related to Stuttering,** *Journal of Speech and Hearing Disorders,* 16 (1951), 40-43.

Purpose: To determine whether the number of instrumental births among a group of stutterers is significantly larger than would be expected in the general population, and whether, therefore, instrumental birth and stuttering may be related.

Experimental Design: Case histories of 300 stutterers at the University of Michigan Speech Clinic were examined for information concerning the type of birth of the stutterer. Only 209 of the 300 case histories contained information of this type although all patients were requested to fill out the case history completely.

Summary: Twenty-two per cent of the group of 209 stutterers were reported born with the aid of instruments. An Iowa state survey indicated that instrumental births accounted for 11.8% of all births. Other studies showed that in the general population the percentage of instrumental births ranged from 20-27%. These data were considered reliable, for they were obtained from hospital records. Since the information on the stutterers was obtained from the parents, usually years after the birth of the child and dependent on the memories of the parents for accuracy, a correction term was applied to the data for stutterers. The correction term of one-third had been empirically determined in a previous study. With the correction, the 22% instrument births for stutterers was raised to 33%. This figure, when compared to the average number of instrument births in the general population (24%) showed a significant difference between the occurrence of instrumental births in the stutterers and in the general population. No significant differences were shown between premature and Caesarean births in stutterers and the general population.

Conclusions:

1. A significantly larger number of instrument births, the author concluded, was found among a group of 209 stutterers than was found in a study of instrument births for the state of Iowa.

2. A significantly larger number of children delivered with instruments was found among a group of 209 stutterers than was found among other large samples of the general population born in hospitals, if it is assumed that one-third of mothers whose children were delivered with instruments will fail to report that fact 21 months or more after birth.

3. The results of this study, the author felt, indicate that instrument birth and stuttering may be positively related, to the extent expressed by the probabilities quoted above.

TITLE

Berry, M. F.: A Study of the Medical Histories of Stuttering Children, *Speech Monographs,* **5 (1932), 97-114.**

Purpose: To inquire into the chronological relationship between stuttering and disease.

Experimental Design: Medical records of stuttering and non-stuttering children were obtained from four Chicago hospitals and from various social agencies. The records of 500 of each group were examined. Of the 500 stuttering children, 430 records and of the non-stuttering children 462 records were found adequate for study. The bases of selection were: (1) a medical record beginning with infancy or very early childhood and (2) a record extending to 9-10 years of age. Since the average age for onset of stuttering was found to be 4.86 years, the author tabulated all diseases suffered by the stutterer up to five years of age and compared these with a similiar record of diseases suffered by the control group. Since certain diseases do not typically appear before five years, another set of data was obtained extending the age to nine years.

Summary: The disorders in which incidence occurred approximately two times more frequently in the stuttering than in the control group are as follows:

	Respiratory Diseases	Rheumatic Fever	Scarlet Fever	Cervical Adenitis	Encephalitis
	Stut.—Non-S.	Stut.—Non-S.	Stut.—Non-S.	Stut.—Non-S.	Stut.—Non-S.
5 years	27—15	7—3	36—20	19—2	17—2
9 years	42—26	13—3	55—40	24—7	17—5

	Epilepsy	Convulsions	Tonsillitis	Bronchitis
	Stut.—Non-S.	Stut.—Non-S.	Stut.—Non-S.	Stut.—Non-S.
5 years	12—1	24—11	70—27	27—39
9 years	13—3	25—15	90—41	69—42

Diseases suffered in parity or more in the control group were: Specific infectious diseases (chicken pox, measles, hemorrhagic); diseases peculiar to infancy (malnutrition and rickets); diseases of eye and ear (otitis media, acute and chronic); disease of intestines (indigestion); and allergy (eczema and dermatitis).

Conclusions: The author concludes that the most frequent and most immediate disorders associated with the inception of stuttering are specific infectious diseases of the respiratory tract and those of the nervous system. It is suggested that stuttering may be due to absence of a resisting gene or the stutterer may have been endowed with the predisposition for stuttering which the disease made active. For the diseases most frequently associated with stuttering, the author feels there has been demonstrated in *some* individuals a constitutional predisposition.

TITLE

Johnson, W.: A Study of the Onset and Development of Stuttering, *Journal of Speech Disorder,* **7 (1942), 251-257.**

Purpose: To yield more definite information as to the characteristics of stuttering at its onset, and to explore the problem of the changes that occur as stuttering develops through its early stages and into its more advanced phases. It is also designed to throw some light on the problems surrounding its disappearance.

Experimental Design: Two groups of Ss were investigated: 46 stuttering children (32 males, 14 females) and 46 non-stuttering children (33 males, 13 females). The age range of both groups was from two years to nine years. The groups were equated for I.Q. level. Interview and case study techniques were utilized, and special care was taken to minimize the usual shortcomings of such techniques.

Summary: Comparative data for the stutterers and non-stutterers were obtained with regard to birth conditions, general developmental conditions, speech development, diseases and injuries, stuttering and handedness in the family background, and handedness and eyedness of the children themselves.

1. Every indication of a deviation from an entirely normal birth was noted in each case with the two groups proving to be essentially similar.

2. Developmental data were essentially the same for the two groups.

3. Ages for onset of speech were the same for both groups.

4. A few more diseases and injuries were reported for the stuttering group, but they were not significantly different from the non-stuttering group.

5. There were more stutterers in the families of stutterers than in the families of non-stutterers. Any attempt to interpret this difference must involve a consideration not only of possible hereditary factors but also of family patterns of evaluation.

6. The parents and siblings of the two groups did not differ significantly as far as handedness was concerned. However, 15 stutterers and 4 non-stutterers had left-handed relatives outside the immediate family.

7. There was practically no difference between the two groups with respect to eyedness and handedness. Also, 12 stutterers and 14 non-stutterers had their handedness changed.

8. In 92% of the cases of stutterers, the first phenomena diagnosed as stuttering were clearly effortless repetitions of words, phrases or initial sounds and syllables. The secondary symptoms occurred after the diagnosis of stuttering was made.

Conclusions:

1. In summarizing all the comparative data, the author concluded that the similarities between the two groups appeared to be much more significant than the differences.

2. Highly similar varieties of speech in young children appeared to be evaluated 'differently' by different parents, and the way in which the evaluations are made, it was felt, plays a determining role in the subsequent speech development of the child.

3. An intensive investigation of the apparent probability that stuttering in its serious forms develops after the diagnosis rather than before, and is a consequence of the diagnosis is suggested.

TITLE

Kennedy, A. M., and Williams, D. A.: Association of Stammering and the Allergic Diathesis, *British Medical Journal*, **2** (1938), 1306-1309.

Purpose: To determine if there is any association between stuttering and allergic diathesis.

Experimental Design: A sample of 100 stutterers ranging in age from 5-14 years was selected at random from town, suburban and industrial areas (81 boys, 19 girls). Extensive case histories of the children were taken to reveal past family history and personal history of stuttering and allergies (asthma, eczema, hay-fever, migraine, urticaria).

Summary: Of the 100 stutterers, 52 cases were found in which there was a personal history of allergy. A comparison of these 52 cases with the remaining 48 for various characteristics indicated the following:

Characteristics	$N = 52$ Personal History	$N = 48$ Non-Personal History
Fasitidiousness with food	30 cases	15 cases
Family history of allergy	48 cases	47 cases
One/both parents suffering 2 sp. allergy manifestations	37 cases	37 cases
Family history of stuttering	33 cases	32 cases
Left-handedness	7 cases	4 cases

The table illustrates the general agreement in the varying of the presence of allergy (personal or family history) with the presence or history of stuttering. It was found, furthermore, that in all but one case, positive evidence of allergy in personal or family history was present.

Conclusions: The vasomotor system, the authors feel, with its close connection to the nervous system, may be influenced by fear, anxiety, anger, and other emotions in stuttering and in allergy. In view of the close constant association between stuttering and allergic manifestations, something more than a casual relationship between stuttering and allergic diathesis is suggested. The existence of a cerebral cortex which is hypersensitive to any transient vasomotor disturbance brought about not by a specific allergen but by the effect of speech is proposed. The authors suggest that an attempt to influence the sensitive constitution of the stutterer by special diets, ephedrine, etc., might be worthwhile.

TITLE

Card, R. E.: A Study of Allergy in Relation to Stuttering, *Journal of Speech Disorders*, 4 (1939), 223-230.

Purpose: To discern whether or not stuttering and allergies are related and whether allergy may be concluded to be an important and basic contributory cause of stuttering. Factors related, the author feels, are: studies revealing that the Vagus nerve is important to both speech and allergic reaction; other nerves involved in allergic spasms of sneezing and coughing which are also involved in stuttering spasms; and doctors' reports that the untreated allergic patient may become so irritable and depressed that he is incoherent and may stutter.

Experimental Design: A case history was taken to determine the relative number of stutterers in whom conditions symptomatic of allergic reactions were present in the stutterer or in his family. There were 104 stutterers and 104 non-stutterers who participated. Percentages within the stuttering group warranted proceeding further and intradermal tests were made on a group of 40 of the stutterers.

Summary:

1. Case Histories

One hundred and two of the 104 stutterers indicated that allergies had been noticed in themselves or their families. The two who reported negatively gave very positive reactions, after having been tested intradermally.

Of the non-stuttering group, 62% indicated an heredity of allergy. Jimenez (1938) indicated that approximately 53% of the student body of a college indicated positive allergic reactions.

2. Intradermal Tests (40 stutterers)

All 40 showed reactions to the intradermal tests. A total of 726 tests were administered. Forty-eight per cent showed positive in the following degrees:

    (1)   11.7% of total tests rated $+4$
    (2)   14.5% of total tests rated $+3$
    (3)   11.7% of total tests rated $+2$
    (4)   10.6% of total tests rated $+1$

It was quite noticeable that the severity of stuttering was usually in proportion to the percentage of reaction and/or the severity.

The blood count of those tested seemed to come within the normal range. The largest number of food protein tests showed the most severe reactions in the following order of frequency: pork, fish, nuts, spinach, tomatoes, oranges, strawberries, and cow's milk. Elimination diets have in some cases (two who stuttered over 30 years in duration) reportedly reduced definitely the nervous irritability and spasms of stutterers.

Conclusions: It was suggested that allergic conditions could be a possible cause of stuttering either because of impairment of the control mechanisms in the embryonic or later developmental stages, or because of a condition of functional unbalance in otherwise adequately developed structures.

TITLE

Dunlap, K.: **A Possible Dietary Predisposition to Stammering,** *Science,* 80 (1934), 206.

Purpose: A brief non-experimental report of a hypothesis that diet may be related to stuttering.

Experimental Design: None.

Summary: The author hypothesizes that an insufficiency of meat, especially in infancy and early childhood may be a predisposing cause to stuttering. He states that he has not tested his theory and recommends that someone do so.

He feels that children over the age of two years should have meat twice daily, and states that some "incidence of stammering has been noted" among children who had a proper meat diet in infancy but refused it after attaining several years of age.

He suggests that adult stutterers are quite different from children who stutter, and because their reaction to the ailment may have more psychological implications, the introduction of meat into their diets may not be helpful (as he conjectures it will be with children). However, he states, large numbers of adult stutterers are relative vegetarians, and an attempt probably ought to be made to treat them with a meat-rich diet.

He suggests that experimental studies should be made to test his hypothesis.

Conclusions: None.

TITLE

Anderson, J., and Whealdon, M. L.: **A Study of the Blood Group Distribution Among Stutterers,** *Journal of Speech Disorders,* 6 (1941), 23-28.

Purpose: "To determine whether or not there is any relation between stuttering, this outward manifestation of an inner disturbance, and certain protein characteristics which control the agglutination of red corpuscles"—i.e., to determine whether or not the distribution of the four blood groups, A, B, AB, and O, is the same among stuttering individuals as it is in the general population.

Experimental Design: A group of 50 stutterers served as subjects for interviews and blood grouping. The control group consisted of 38,000 individuals who had been grouped by other investigators in the United States. The fact that there is a 1:1 sex ratio of all types of blood groups, it was felt, would lead one to predict that stuttering would not classify itself as a correlate of any one blood group since stuttering has a high sex ratio, but, nevertheless, it seemed wise to extend the study of blood groups to stuttering.

Summary:

Group	No. Persons	O	*Per Cent of Groups*		
			A	B	AB
Stutterers	50	46.0	44.0	4.0	6.0
Controls (aver.)	38,000	44.9	38.9	11.6	4.5
Range in U.S. studies		44.5-45.6	36.1-42.3	8.7-14.3	4.0-5.2

Differences in groups A and AB, it was felt, could be partially explained by considering the Scandinavian and Germanic backgrounds of over 60% of the subjects. Blood group studies carried out in Sweden and Germany indicated a higher percentage of A and AB types than had been found in the general American population. It did not explain the low percentage of B type.

Conclusions: It was concluded that there is an approximate parity of distribution among the stuttering and non-stuttering groups. This, the authors feel, does not mean necessarily that there are no blood differences, only that there are no differences in these protein factors which govern red cell agglutination.

TITLE

Johnson, W., Stearns, G., and Warweg, E.: Chemical Factors and the Stuttering Spasm, *Quarterly Journal of Speech,* **19 (1933), 409-414.**

Purpose: To determine if there are any alterations in the chemical composition of the blood in stutterers which might bear a significant relationship to the muscular spasms and heightened muscular tonus, and to the etiological and therapeutical problems involved.

Experimental Design: Blood samples were taken from 15 male stutterers with an age range of 9-28 years. Tests were then made on these blood samples for serum calcium, inorganic phosphorus, the relationship between serum calcium and serum potassium, and fasting blood sugar level.

Summary: Because of heightened muscular tonus it was suggested that stuttering might be due to or associated with latent tetany, in which case, a distinct lowering of serum calcium and an increase in inorganic phosphorus would be present. This was tested in the blood samples of the stutterers and it was found that the serum calcium fell within normal limits (actually being a little high) and that, in general, the inorganic phosphorus was also within normal limits.

Heightened muscular tonus, it was felt, would also have been found if serum calcium remained normal and serum potassium was high. Again, the blood samples were tested and the amount of serum potassium was found to be normal. At this point it was suggested that the serum calcium be increased without the increase in serum potassium (the result would be a lowering of muscular tonus) as a therapeutic measure. This idea was rejected because of possible harmful effects.

Another factor considered was an altered carbohydrate metabolism which would prevail as a result of emotional strain and fatigue that accompanies severe stuttering. This would lead to a lowered blood sugar level. However, no essential abnormality of the carbohydrate metabolism was found in tests of the blood samples. To test the effect of a severe stuttering attack, the following procedure was followed on one subject: a blood sample taken three hours after last meal; a second sample taken after one-half hour rest; after reading to an audience of three people and stuttering severely, a third sample; a fourth taken one-half hour after the reading. On analysis, all the samples had normal blood sugar levels.

Conclusions: The authors suggest that their data make it necessary to interpret tonic and clonic spasms and the heightened muscular tonus during stuttering with reference to factors others than alterations in the serum of stutterers. They conclude that any therapy to effect radical alterations in the chemical composition of the blood of stutterers would be inappropriate and probably dangerous.

TITLE

Kopp, G. A.: **Metabolic Studies of Stutterers I. Biochemical Study of Blood Composition,** *Speech Monographs,* 1 (1934), 117-130.

Purpose: "To determine specifically how the metabolism of the stutterer as evidenced by blood serum calcium, inorganic phosphate, potassium chloride, cholesterol, non-protein nitrogen, total protein, albumin, globulin, and glucose differs from that of the non-stutterer."

Experimental Design: Blood samples were taken from 49 stutterers ranging in age from 6-32 and 23 non-stutterers ranging in age from 6-39 under conditions in which as many factors as possible had been held constant. This blood was submitted to various scientific tests.

Summary: The test results indicated the following:

Total serum calcium is higher (5.59%) in stutterers than in normals.

Inorganic phosphate is higher (14.8) in Ss than in Ns.

Potassium is lower (6.63%) in Ss than in Ns.

Total protein is lower (12.6%), albumin is lower 8.85%), globulin is lower (22.7%) in Ss than in Ns.

There is no appreciable difference in non-protein nitrogen, in diffusible calcium, cholesterol and chlorides for the two groups.

The Ss have a high blood sugar (17.4%) as compared with non-stutterers.

These results were all shown to be statistically significant.

The manner in which these various substances associated with each other was as follows:

Summary of Partial Correlations of Zero Order

	Normals	Stutterers
Total Serum Ca and Potassium	−0.33	−0.288
Total Serum Ca and Phosphate	−0.634	+0.525
Total Serum Ca and Total Protein	+0.595	−0.0306
Potassium and Phosphate	+0.567	−0.188
Potassium and Total Protein	−0.716	−0.834
Phosphate and Total Protein	−0.268	−0.418

The author pointed out that the blood pattern of the stutterer, according to these correlations, was practically the reverse of the pattern of the non-stutterer.

Conclusions: The author concluded "that stuttering is a manifestation of a disturbed metabolism." He expressed the hope that when the metabolic changes which produce and maintain stuttering have been established, such deviations can be controlled by dietary means.

TITLE

Karlin, I. W., and Sobel, A. E.: A Comparative Study of the Blood Chemistry of Stutterers and Non-Stutterers, *Speech Monographs*, 7 (1940), 75-84.

Purpose: To determine if there exists a difference between a carefully selected sample of stutterers and non-stutterers in regard to their respective blood chemistry.

Experimental Design: Twelve non-stutterers were matched as closely as possible in regard to age, height, weight, and sex with twelve stutterers. Both groups were healthy, normal children —the only differing characteristic was that one of each of the matched pairs stuttered.

Blood was drawn simultaneously on each subject after a night of fasting. All chemical determinations were carried out in duplicate. To correlate results, two statistical methods for computing the data were used.

Summary: The results showed that the mean values of the two groups are very close and in some cases almost identical. Both groups fell within the normal range of values for the different constituents in the blood.

When the two statistical methods were applied for significant differences between the two groups, it was found that by one method, using .05 level as a significant difference, there were no significant differences between any of the means obtained. Using the second method there was an apparent significant difference only between the means of the potassium values with stutterers having a lower mean value than the control group. However, it was pointed out that the second method is questionable since only 22 calculations were made and a margin of chance is still present.

Conclusions: All the results fell within the normal range of values established in the Pediatric Research Laboratory, Jewish Hospital, Brooklyn, where the testing was done. There were no significant differences between the results of the two groups except for perhaps the potassium. The blood pattern of the stutterer indicates no statistically significant difference from the non-stutterer.

Statistical procedures used in previous similar research were questioned.

TITLE

Fossler, H. H.: Disturbances in Breathing During Stuttering, *Psychological Monographs,* **40** (1930), 1-32.

Purpose: To study the patterns of stutterers revealed by the pneumograph and laryngograph to see if they are associated with the attempts at production of any particular sound or group of sounds; to study the variability of breathing curves with reference to amplitude of inspiration and expiration differences between stutterers and non-stutterers; and to study descriptively the curve forms.

Experimental Design: Records were obtained by means of a laryngograph attached to the thyroid cartilage. An upper chest pneumograph was placed in the middle of the chest at the level of the armpits and a lower chest pneumograph was placed at the lower end of the sternum. An abdominal pneumograph was placed over the umbilicus after the subject was comfortably seated. Subjects were asked to talk naturally about anything they wished, and were requested not to circumvent troublesome words. An electric marker operated by the experimenter indicated when stuttering occurred. Records were obtained for 13 male stutterers and 13 male controls.

Summary: There were some observable, typical, recurrent patterns which, however, were not definitely associated with an attempt to produce any particular sound or group of sounds. Some patterns were characteristic of several individuals, and some only of one.

Study of variability showed no significant differences between stutterers and normals in amplitude of inspiration and expiration. Stutterers had 52% more variability than normals in time of inspiration and 46% more variability than normals in time of expiration. Speech breathing was approximately three times more variable than rest breathing for both stutterers and normals. The average length of full breath interval during speech was greater than for rest in both stutterers and normals: the gain was 14.6% for stutterers and 7.3% for normals.

Stutterers presented from two to five times more anomalous curves than normals and showed approximately twice as many expirations interrupted by inspirations as normals. (A comparison between severe stutterers and mild stutterers showed a marked difference with severe stutterers being between 35 and 45% more variable in time of inspiration and expiration.)

It appeared that stuttering may or may not be accompanied by tonic or clonic spasms in breathing and the laryngeal mechanism, by temporal opposition of breathing curves, by attempts to speak on inspiration, by greatly prolonged expiration, and by breaking up of the normal rhythm of speech.

Conclusions: It was concluded that a difference does exist between the breathing records of stutterers and non-stutterers, but that there are a great deal of individual differences within the stuttering records.

TITLE

Van Riper, C.: Study of the Thoracic Breathing of Stutterers During Expectancy and Occurrence of Stuttering Spasm, *Journal of Speech Disorders,* **1 (1936), 61-72.**

Purpose: To determine what manifestations of expectancy of stuttering or of experience of stuttering are to be found in objective recordings of thoracic breathing.

Experimental Design: A sample consisting of 43 adult stutterers of which only 37 records were analyzed was used. The S was seated before an exposure box into which he looked and waited for the word to be exposed. A pneumograph placed across the lower end of the sternum was connected with a tambour mounted on a polygraph. The S signaled, by depressing a right or left hand key, whether or not he expected to stutter on the exposed word. The S then attempted the word, depressing the key throughout the duration of the speech attempt.

Summary:

1. There were individual differences in the consistency with which expectation of block is followed by occurrence of block. Generally there was a high correspondence.

2. Stuttering spasms did occur without being preceded by expectancy.

3. Expectancy of stuttering did occur without being followed by stuttering.

4. Expectancy of stuttering tended to reflect itself in a high inspiration-expiration ratio, in increased variability, and in the appearance of breathing irregularities.

5. Definite rehearsals were found during the period of expectancy which had the same form of breathing abnormality as those occurring during stuttering speech attempts. Hence, preparatory sets appeared to be significant in determining the form of the overt spasm.

6. Certain stutterers presented stereotyped breathing abnormalities which were both chracteristic and consistent.

Conclusions: On the basis of the data, the author felt that two things seemed clear:

1. For certain stutterers to have such consistent and characteristic breathing patterns during a stuttering block, an explanation of these reactions on the basis of habit seems mandatory.

2. For some reason it is possible to stutter in many different ways.

It was concluded generally that although certain stutterers seem to have stereotyped spasm patterns which affect their breathing, it does not necessarily follow that stuttering is nothing more than a bad habit. However, when blocks do occur in the speech pattern, the individual experiencing them will react to them, and during a lifetime of such experiences will tend to build up patterns or habits or reaction to both their occurrence and expectancy.

TITLE

Starbuck, H. B., and Steer, M. D.: The Adaptation Effect in Stuttering and its Relation to Thoracic and Abdominal Breathing, *Journal of Speech and Hearing Disorders,* **19 (1954), 440-449.**

Purpose: To investigate the physiological function of speech adaptation with respect to thoracic and abdominal respiratory activity in stutterers and non-stutterers.

Experimental Design: Twenty-two male adult stutterers were matched with twenty-two male adult non-stutterers for age, height, weight, and chest and waist circumference. Two pneumographs were used for recordings, one being attached to the chest and the other to the waist. While seated, each S then read a 200 word passage five consecutive times. The passage contained all common phonetic speech sounds except [ð]. Three judges measured the recordings individually; reliability was .99. The depth and the duration of thoracic exhalation and inhalation, depth and duration of abdominal exhalation and inhalation, and the number of complete thoracic and abdominal breathing cycles were measured.

Summary: Results of the study indicated that during successive oral readings of the same passage.

1. Adult stutterers demonstrated the following statistically significant respiratory alterations accompanying the adaptation effect:
   a. Reduction in the number of complete thoracic breathing cycles.
   b. Reduction in the number of complete abdominal breathing cycles.
2. Adult stutterers do *not* demonstrate a statistically significant alteration in the following functions accompanying the adaptation effect:
   a. Depth of thoracic inhalation and exhalation.
   b. Duration of thoracic inhalation and exhalation
   c. Depth of abdominal inhalation and exhalation
   d. Duration of abdominal inhalation and exhalation
3. Adult non-stutterers demonstrated the following statistically significant respiratory alterations accompanying the adaptation effect:
   a. Increase in depth of thoracic inhalation
   b. Decrease in depth of abdominal inhalation and exhalation
4. Adult non-stutterers do *not* demonstrate a statistically significant alteration in the following functions accompanying the adaptation effect:
   a. Depth of thoracic exhalation
   b. Duration of thoracic exhalation and inhalation
   c. Duration of abdominal exhalation and inhalation
   d. Number of complete thoracic and abdominal breathing cycles.

In addition to the respiratory data, significant differences were also found between both groups in the mean total oral reading time.

Conclusions: Similar results were obtained for the duration of thoracic breathing patterns. The non-significant differences noted with respect to duration of thoracic and abdominal inhalation and exhalation could, it was felt, be due to the inherent nature of the two breathing actions. The fact that speech occurs on exhalation could lead to greater mean variation in exhalation measurement regardless of whether stuttering takes place or not. The authors concluded that this greater mean variation makes it necessary for the variation to be extreme before a significant difference is noted.

TITLE

Murray, E.: Dysintegration of Breathing and Eye Movements in Stuttering During Silent Reading and Reasoning, *Psychological Monographs,* **43 (1932), 218-275.**

Purpose: To determine whether the known dysintegrations in stutterers during overt speech are sufficiently deep-seated to be evident in the closely related implicit activities of silent reading and reasoning.

Experimental Design: Three approaches were used: First, a study of the extent and form of the breathing dysintegrations through measurement, analysis and description of kymographic breathing curves; second, an investigation of the rhythms of eye movements through measurement, analysis, and description of eye movements photographically recorded; and third, a study of the dysintegrations as measured by standardized silent reading tests.

In order to bring various factors of the experiment under control, 18 stutterers (17 males, 1 female) and 18 non-stutterers were paired in age, intelligence, and grade level. The same reading and reasoning materials, selected according to the maturity of the individuals, were used under uniform conditions by both members of each pair for the breathing as well as the eye movement records. Data for all subjects were treated by the same quantitative, qualitative, and descriptive procedures for the study of variability.

Summary: In almost every phase of the experiment the results showed various and marked dysintegrations for the stutterers during silent reading and reasoning. In breathing, stutterers showed greater variability than normals in inspiration and expiration. An increase in dysintegrations was proportionate to an increase in difficulty of reading material. The breathing curves of normals followed one or two characteristic patterns while the stutterers followed six distinct patterns. A quantitative study of eye movements showed that stutterers had 22% more fixations per line and 126% more regressive movements per line than normals, while the duration of fixations for non-stutterers was 10% longer than for stutterers. Qualitatively the stutterers used many more patterns of movements than did the normals. The study of dysintegrations as measured by silent reading tests brought out the fact that stutterers were one grade below normal in comprehension and two grades below normal in rate of reading.

It was found that during silent reading both clonic and tonic patterns appeared on the breathing records.

Conclusions: It was concluded that the disharmonies and disturbances so noticeable in the conversation of stutterers extend into the nervous system and cause similar difficulties in activities other than speaking.

TITLE

Moser, H. M.: A Qualitative Analysis of Eye-Movements During Stuttering, *Journal of Speech Disorders*, 3 (1938), 131-139.

Purpose: To determine whether stutterers differ from normal speakers in eye-movements during both silence and speaking.

Experimental Design: Subjects were 52 adult stutterers (5 females, 47 males) and 56 normal speakers (7 females, 49 males). All degrees of severity were represented in the stuttering group. All records were photographed with the Iowa Eye Movement Camera. A signal light was arranged to shine on the edges of the film in order to designate stuttering spasms. Every effort was made to secure the intelligent cooperation of all subjects. Four records were taken in the following order:

1. *Silent fixation:* S was asked to fixate a dot printed on the stimulus paper.

2. *Silent Reading:* S read silently a selection of moderate difficulty.
3. *Oral Reading:* S was asked to read orally another selection of
moderate difficulty.
4. *Fixation during propositional speech:* S was asked to fixate
the same dot used in the first situation. He was instructed
to fixate continuously, and to speak directly to the dot about
anything that came to his mind. In addition to this, the stutterer was asked to produce those sounds and words which
gave him the most difficulty.

Summary:

1. *Silent fixation:* This situation did not reveal any significant
differences between stutterers and normal speakers.
2. *Silent Reading:* Stutterers tended to have more fixations per
line, wider variation in duration of fixation, and more re-
gressions.
3. *Oral reading:* During those parts of the record where the
stutterer enjoyed free speech, his records were quite similar
to those of the normal speaker during speech. Differences
appeared to be associated mainly with stuttering spasms and
speech hesitancies.
4. *Fixation during propositional speech:* About 64% of the normals and no stutterers fixated continuously during these records. The majority of the normal individuals who were unable to fixate continuously were the borderline speech defectives.

Conclusions: It was concluded that eye-movements are in some
way related to the stuttering act, and appear to be due to a generalized inability to manipulate the speech mechanism along with
the eyes. It was suggested that the stutterer possibly moves his
eyes from the dot in order to break a spasm. This, however, was
refuted by the stutterers' introspective reports. It was finally suggested that these random eye-movements during stuttering are an
integral part of a symptom-complex of stuttering itself, and show
the extent to which the stuttering spasms grip the entire organism.
A relationship to this factor and cerebral dominance was suggested.

TITLE

Moore, W. E.: A Conditioned Reflex Study of Stuttering, *Journal of Speech Disorders,* **3 (1938), 163-183.**

Purpose: To investigate the relationship between breathing disturbances and stuttering and to test a theory of stuttering proposed by Bluemel. (See Symptomatology: Abstract 9.) The study is concerned with the following basic questions: (1) Are there differences in the "conditionability" of stutterers and normals which would account for Bluemel's theory? (2) Are disruptions in the stutterer's breathing pattern due to irradiation of inhibition? (3) Is there a cause of breathing abnormalities which if discovered would explain why other investigators failed to get consistent results concerning the relationship between the overt spasm and the disturbance?

Experimental Design: Subjects were 18 stutterers (age range 17-26 years) and 17 normals (age range 18-39 years). The unconditioned stimulus chosen was nonsense syllables. The reaction chosen for conditioning was a respiratory response (shown in earlier studies to be amenable to conditioning). The procedure was split into three sections:

1. In this step the ability of both stutterers and normals to reproduce the time interval between the third and the fourth series of four nonsense syllables was measured. The record was played beween 40 and 50 times before any subject attempted to reproduce the interval by speaking the word. (A record used here excluded the fourth syllable, the S's filling in at the appropriate time.) Each S then had 10 trials, the mean of his responses being the index of his ability. Throughout both the listening and the speaking intervals, breathing records were taken by means of a kymograph and two pneumographs placed around the thorax and abdomen. The mean of the records taken during speaking represented a measure of before conditioning respiration.

2. Next, the conditioned respiratory response was established. The subjects were first tested for sensitivity to electric shock. The maximum level possible was used. The S's then listened to the

complete record played three times, followed by 14 trials of pairing the fourth syllable with shock. A 12 minute silent interval ensued, followed by the replaying of the record six to eight times without shock. Breathing records were taken continuously, and the mean of the records during the replaying of the recordings served as an index of after conditioning respiration—during silence..

3. Finally, the effect of the conditioning on the ability to reproduce the interval between the third and fourth syllables was measured again. The syllable was reconditioned 15 times followed by 10 trials of interval estimation. The mean of the breathing records taken here was an index of AC during speaking.

Summary: It was found that the stutterers did not differ from the normals in ability to reproduce the time interval. It was noted, however, that both normals and stutterers (who had no spasms) tended to shorten the interval—indicating that the effect of the shock was not inhibitory, but tended to accelerate the response. Subjective reports from the S's corroborated this in that they reported that the acceleration was due to the dread and anticipation of the shock.

It was also found that there were no significant difference between stutterers and normals before or after the syllable was conditioned, in terms of mean amplitude, duration of respiration, irregularity of inspiration or variability of above measures. What effect the conditioning did have on the respiration could not be determined on the basis of the data.

The possible differences between the two groups as indicated by the "r" between errors of response and variability of respiration was negated. It was found, however, that if the shock was severe enough, a general disintegration of breathing movements ensued —but it soon became apparent that this was also conditionable. Consequently, the AC breathing records for both normals and stutterers were checked. Twenty-one and one-tenth per cent of the curves for normal speakers showed anomalies, while 11% was found in the stutterers' records. On supplementary study, it was found that horizontal dysintegration could also be conditioned in normals. The fact that 11 normals but only five stutterers exhibited this asynergic functioning seemed to be explained by the stutterer's refusal to take very severe shock.

The most reasonable interpretation, it appeared, was that breathing abnormalities like those during stuttering are conditioned reactions to some element or elements in the speech situation and not a manifestation of a neurological disturbance. If this interpretation is valid the inconsistencies in the results found in other studies concerning the relationship between frequency or temporal course of breathing abnormalities and the overt spasm can be accounted for.

Lastly, it appeared that asynergic breathing movements are not the result of irradiation of inhibition. This was verified by three normals in the AC speaking records who gave hurried responses with no sign of stuttering or inhibition yet exhibited marked breathing abnormalities.

Conclusions: It was concluded that Bluemel's theory concerning suttering is untenable. It was concluded further that breathing abnormalities appear to be conditioned reactions to the spasms of speech symbols on which the spasm or anticipation occurs. Consequently, these abnormalities may show no more consistent relationship to the spasm than to the grimaces and other accessory movements generally considered to be reactions to stuttering.

TITLE

Robbins, S. D.: **A Plethysmographic Study of Shock and Stammering,** *American Journal of Physiology,* 48 (1919), 285-323.

Purpose: to test the organic reactions accompanying stuttering, with reference to Bluemel's cerebral congestion theory of stuttering, by observing the change in blood volume in the hand.

Experimental Design: Past experiments, it was pointed out, have shown that all emotions and stimuli, pleasant or unpleasant, cause vasoconstriction in the peripheral arteries and vasodilation in the brain. The experimenter attempted to duplicate these conditions by shocking the unsuspecting subjects with such stimuli as a blast of a shrill whistle, a sudden yell, a detonation which went off when the subject opened a book, or a relatively innocuous stimulus as an artificial spider being lowered next to the subject's head. The experimental group was composed of 10 stutterers, and the controls were 13 college students. The apparatus consisted of a pneumograph to measure breathing and a rubber glove arrangement which was sensitive enough to measure increase in the blood volume in the finger and in the hand. No apparatus was used to measure blood volume in the head.

Summary: It was found that if a mild stutterer reads a passage when constriction from shock is at its maximum he will stutter severely; if he reads the same passage a minute later after constriction has ceased, he does not stutter. If a normal attempts to speak a word and a noxious stimulus is introduced, the sound of the word is lost and he is unable to say it until constriction has ceased; that is, he becomes a temporary stutterer. The results demonstrated the fact that finger vasoconstriction occurs both during stuttering and with the presentation of a strong stimulus in stutterers and in non-stutterers. The crucial point, apparently, was that stutterers experienced 80% greater and more rapid vasoconstriction and a 23% longer recovery time than did non-stutterers. Robbins feels that the greater the peripheral vasoconstriction, the greater is the vasodilation in the brain and the more is the verbal imagery impaired. Even a fear of stuttering with no attempt at speaking caused peripheral constriction. The pneumograms showed that all stutterers breathed abnormally while stuttering and that every stutterer had a characteristic form of breathing while stuttering.

Conclusions: It was concluded that stuttering and shock are induced emotional disturbances accompanied by the same vasomotor changes, i.e., vasoconstriction in the periphery and vasodilation in the brain. The cranial dilation causes cerebral congestion which temporarily paralyzes the speech mechanism. The experiment, it was felt, confirms Bluemel's theory that stuttering is caused by transient auditory amnesia in the auditory speech center brought on by cerebral congestion (vasodilation).

TITLE

Travis, L. E., Tuttle, W. W., and Cowan, D.: A Study of the Heart Rate During Stuttering, *Journal of Speech Disorders*, 1 (1936), 21-26.

Purpose: To determine if an involuntary function such as the heart action is affected during stuttering.

Experimental Design: The heart potentials and respiratory cycles were recorded simultaneously on sixteen normal speakers and fifteen adult stutterers during silent periods and oral reading.

Summary: It has been observed that inspiration is accompanied by acceleration of the heart rate and expiration by a retardation. This was shown to occur for both groups of subjects as a group and individually. When inspiration and expiration were considered together (respiration) the heart rate was faster for speech than for silent periods for both groups. In addition, there was also an increase in the variability of the heart beat during speech. The stutterers varied more than the normal speakers, and their heart rate for inspiration and expiration was faster than for normal speech in both reading and silent periods. This, it was suggested, is accounted for by the increased emotionality of the stutterer.

It was noted that during a tonic spasm, two stutterers gave typical cycles in that their heart rate became slower. No adequate explanation was given for this phenomenon.

During stuttering practically all stutterers showed tremors of about ten per second on the cardiograph. Also all previously reported abnormalities during stuttering speech such as prolonged inspiration, interruption of expiration by short inspiration movements, failure of the breathing mechanism to move either in or out, and attempts to speak on relatively empty lungs were found in this study.

Means and SD's for Heart Rate During Silence and Speaking for Normals and Stutterers were as follows:

	Silence		Speaking		Difference	
Group	*Mean*	*SD*	*Mean*	*SD*	*Mean*	*SD*
Normals	74	3.5	84	5.4	10	1.9
Stutterers	82	4.1	95	6.6	13	2.5

Whether these data are statistically significant was not mentioned.

Conclusions: It was suggested that changes in the heart rate during speech of both normal speakers and stutterers were secondary to changes in respiration and general body activity.

The varied and severe respiratory abnormalities symptomatic of stuttering, it was suggested, may produce varied and striking changes in the function of the heart.

TITLE

Palmer, M. and Gillett, A. M.: Sex Differences in the Cardiac Rhythms of Stutterers, *Journal of Speech Disorders*, 3 (1938), 3-12.

Purpose: To offer laboratory evidence on physiological differences between male and female stutterers which should be taken into consideration in further etiological research.

Experimental Design: Pulse beats of 24 stutterers (7 females, 17 males) and 24 matched normals ranging in age from 9 to 26 years recorded by a Lombard radial pulse apparatus and a Miller kymograph were studied. The experiment was controlled by recording normals matched age for age, and sex for sex with stutterers. Records were obtained during a period of silence for 16,325 pulsations.

Summary: The data indicated that all of the female normals had significantly higher pulse rate than all of the male normals. At a younger age level, however, this condition was reversed for stutterers. The general average for all age groups also showed the male stuttering heart to beat more rapidly than the females.

The date were related to other concepts in which pulse rate for males and females during stuttering had been reported. The hypothesis was presented that although the increased irregularity of heart beat is not the cause of stuttering it is part of a mechanism linked to stuttering and the sex metabolism.

Conclusions: Authors concluded that the etiology of stuttering must be sought in a sex-linked metabolic picture.

TITLE

Ritzman, C.: A Cardiovascular and Metabolic Study of Stutterers and Non-Stutterers, *Journal of Speech Disorders*, 8 (1943), 161-182.

Purpose: To compare measures of heart rate, sinus arrhythmia, blood pressure, and basal metabolic rate obtained from a group of stutterers and non-stutterers.

Experimental Design: Twenty-nine stutterers (4 women, 25 men) ranging in age from 17 to 34 years were matched for age, sex, and body surface with a group of non-stutterers. Measures were obtained from each subject during a period of silence, and the null hypothesis was tested for each of the four experimental variables.

Summary:

"1. No significant differences were found for heart rate. These results did not confirm previous research.

2. A significant negative correlation was found between sinus arrhythmia and heart rate.

3. Qualitative analysis of sinus arrhythmia revealed no significant difference between stutterers and non-stutterers, though certain trends were noted which were in agreement with previous research findings.

4. Quantitative analysis of sinus arrhythmia revealed that the male stutterers were not significantly different from their controls, but that the female stutterers tended to have less marked sinus arrhythmia than their controls. These results confirmed previous research.

5. Male stutterers as a group were not significantly different from their controls on basal metabolic rate, but, whereas it is normal for female subjects in given age groups to have lower basal metabolic rates than males, female stutterers presented a higher mean rate than the male subjects in this experiment and presented a definite tendency to have higher basal metabolic rates as a group than their controls.

6. No significant differences were found on diastolic, systolic, and pulse pressure measurements. The female stutterers showed a tendency toward higher pulse pressure than their controls."

Conclusions:

1. "Young adult male stutterers, as a group, are normal in heart rate, sinus arrhythmia, basal metabolic rate, and blood pressure when measures for these variables are obtained during silence under conditions of rest.

2. Female stutterers are likely to have less marked sinus arrhythmia than normal speakers of their sex.

3. Sinus arrhythmia and heart rate are concomitant variables."

TITLE

Starr, H. E.: The Hydrogen Ion Concentration of the Mixed Saliva Considered as an Index of Fatigue and of Emotional Excitement, and Applied to a Study of the Metabolic Etiology of Stammering, *American Journal of Psychology,* **33 (1922), 394-418.**

Purpose: To determine if the hydrogen ion concentration in connection with the CO_2 content of mixed saliva can be employed as an index of sub-breathing, chronic emotional excitement, and transient emotional excitement.

Experimental Design: The hydrogen content and CO_2 content of the saliva of 58 college stutterers diagnosed as sub-breathers and 10 distinctly psychopathic stutterers was determined from specimens collected after the Ss were seated for five minutes spent in a comfortable chair.

Twenty-seven of the 58 sub-breathers and all 10 psychopathic stutterers were then excited as far as possible by a verbal goading of a stereotyped form. This goading, it was felt, would not be offensive to a normal individual but was considered sufficient to disturb a hyper-excitable or psychopathic. Goading was done for five minutes, after which the subject was directed to eject his saliva into a test tube, and then say "Yes sir," immediately. The extent of time was noted and used as an indicator of the degree of his emotional disturbance. The subject was allowed a ten minute rest to quiet down. He was then required to say "Yes sir," again. The extent of time was noted and his saliva was again examined.

Summary: The results showed that sub-breathers (average pH 6.0) were overloaded with CO_2 in their saliva far in excess of the normal individual (average pH 6.8). Therefore, the salivary pH with the CO_2 content of mixed saliva, it was suggested, could be employed as an aid for diagnosis of sub-breathers. Hyper-excitable psychopathic stutterers examined had a much lower hydrogen ion concentration (pH 7.15 - 8.00) than did normal individuals. These findings, it was felt, indicated that a persistently high salivary pH is an index more or less of chronic emotional excitement.

The sub-breathers showed practically no increase in salivary pH as a result of verbal goading but psychopaths did show an increase. All except two of the sub-breathers were able to say "Yes sir" within a two minute period after goading. All except two of the psychopaths were unable to say "Yes sir" within a two minute period after goading. After ten minutes rest, only one sub-breather took longer than two minutes to say "Yes sir." He required 2.28. The psychopaths varied greatly among themselves. Three required more than two minutes; two required less than a minute.

Conclusions: It was concluded that there appear to be four groups of stutterers:

1. Those can be classed as sub-breathers and are over-loaded with CO_2. Their mental faculties are dulled and until this breathing problem is cleared up, it appears useless to try to break old speech habits.

2. A smaller group who are distinctly psychopathic and are hopeless for speech training until their general psychopathic condition is cured.

3. A third group may be both hyperexcitably psychopathic and sub-breathers. Such a subject might effect a saliva apparently

normal, in pH, i.e., the sub-breather lowers it, hyperexcitability raises it. An adequate series of determinations, however, can show the predominant tendency.

4. A fourth group might be neither sub-breathers nor psychopathics, simply hyperexcitable.

TITLE

Hafford, J. A.: A Comparative Study of the Salivary pH of the Normal Speaker and the Stutterer, *Journal of Speech Disorders,* 6 (1941), 173-184.

Purpose: (1) To determine whether the saliva of the stutterer is more acid than that of the normal speaker on the basis of the saliva secreted with as little induced stimulation as possible; (2) if the stuttering spasm causes a higher pH than normal speaking; (3) if there is greater pH change from resting saliva per se to resting saliva which has been activated by the process of speaking; and (4) if the pH of the saliva is significant in diagnosis.

Experimental Design: Equipment consisted of a glass indicator electrode, a calomel reference electrode with a saturated potassium chloride bridge and a Beckman pH meter. Nineteen normal speakers and 19 stutterers (all of college age) participated. Two groups were closely paired as to age, sex, sinus infection and condition of teeth.

A 15 minute rest period void of speech, initiated the experiment. A glass electrode was put under the tongue and a pH reading made. Stutterers were held in conversation designed to evoke a block and again pH readings were made. Another talking period, five minute rest period, then two more reading periods were held. In all cases pH readings were made after rest, speaking or reading. Procedure was identical for the normal group.

A list of 12 conditions were rigorously adhered to in order to obtain the best possible standardization under the conditions of the experiment.

Summary:

1. There was no significant difference between the resting saliva of normal speakers taken on the basis of the 19 cases There was also no significant difference after activation of the oral cavity by speaking aloud or reading.

2. There was no significant difference between stutterers and normal speakers with reference to salivary pH changes from the resting period to various stages of activation and between various stages of activation.

3. The nearest approach to a significant difference between normals and stutterers was in the change in pH produced in the second activation by speaking. The difference of the mean deviation of the changes of the normal speakers and stutterers was .11, with a standarad error of .07.

4. The individual variations in pH seemed to be too large to attach any significance to minor statistical variations.

Conclusions: The author concluded that the data collected in this study seemed to indicate that the saliva of stutterers is not significantly different from that of normal speakers, and that pH change should prove of little value in diagnosing stuttering cases.

TITLE

Berry, M. F.: **A Common Denominator in Twinning and Stuttering,** *Journal of Speech Disorders,* 3 (1938), 51-57.

Purpose: To determine whether stuttering appears more frequently in twinning families than in families without record of duplicate births.

Experimental Design: By personal interview with parents and twins, data were collected and tabulated on 250 duplicate births, i.e., 500 children. The questionnaire covered the following points: nationality of parents, siblings with dates of birth, history of handedness in direct and collateral lines, medical history, and family chart showing the siblings in order of the maternal and paternal lines for three generations.

Summary:

1. The average size of a family containing twins in this study was 4.82 children, in contrast with the mean of 2.3 children set down for families in the U. S. (1926). Twins appear much more frequently among the younger than among the older members of the family.

2. According to the parents' reports, 65.5% of the twins were fraternal, 32.8% identical. (A survey of the U. S. indicated that identical twins form 33% of the total in whites.) There were a larger number of female twins than male twins (267:233), perhaps because of the higher mortality rate among males.

3. There were two and one-half times more sinistrals in the sample of twinning families than in the general population. (Four per cent of the population in the U. S. is reportedly left-handed.)

4. The twins show a retardation in the onset and development of speech. The 500 twins were 6.7 months behind the mean of 15.3 months established by Mead.

5. Instead of the normal expectancy of one stutterer in 100 children, 1 in 18 was a stutterer among all the siblings of twinning families. Considering the twins separately, the ratio was higher; one twin child in 11 is a stutterer.

6. There was a high sex ratio of stuttering in the twinning families, males predominating at a ratio of 3:1 to 4:1.

Conclusions: It was concluded on the basis of this study that stuttering occurs more frequently in twinning families than in families in which twins do not occur.

Connections previously having been established between left-handedness and twinning, and between left-handedness and stutterig, a common denominator for twinning, suttering, and sinistrality is postulated in genetic factors.

TITLE

Nelson, S. F., Hunter, N., and Walter, M.: Stuttering in Twin Types, *Journal of Speech Disorders,* **10 (1945), 335-343.**

Purpose: To develop data by doing research in which possible heritable dysphemic factors are studied by means of a comparative study of monozygotic (identical) and dizygotic (fraternal) twins, or by comparison of members of an identical pair.

Experimental Design: Hunter and Walter accumulated data on 200 twin pairs. Hunter's study classified 100 pairs by the instantaneous method. Walter's study classified 100 pairs using instantaneous identification and dermatolglyphical methods. In collecting the data home calls were made and parents were consulted. In some cases teachers and attending physicians were interviewed. Always both members of each twin pair were thoroughly examined for similarities and speech habits. Ages ranged from 4 to 40 years.

Summary:

1. Of the 200 pairs, 69 pairs or 34.5% were found to be identical —131 pairs or 65.5% were found to be fraternal.

2. Stuttering was found among 30 or 22.7% of the fraternals and among 10 or 14.4% of the identicals, or among 20% of the total 200 pairs.

3. Among the 10 stuttering identicals, 8 were females and 11 males. Among the 30 stuttering fraternals, 21 were males and 11 females.

4. When stuttering occurred among identicals, both members stuttered in all cases except one. When stuttering occurred among fraternals, only one member stuttered in all cases, except two.

5. Walter found that both identicals and fraternals of her stuttering pairs began to stutter during the first year of speech with the exception of one fraternal who began to stutter at the age of three after a severe back injury.

Conclusions: A concordance for the stuttering phenomena was found among identical twins, and a discordance for fraternal twins. The authors recommended the concordance-discordance method used by previous investigators to study heritable factors among twins as an excellent method for further study of dysphemia.

TITLE

Nelson, S.: Personal Contact as a Factor in the Transmission of Stuttering, *Human Biology*, 11 (1939), 393-401.

Purpose: To determine the role which association (constant contact) plays in the transmission of stuttering over a range of three generations.

Experimental Design: Subjects were 204 stutterers and 204 non-stutterers matched for sex and age. Data were gathered on the filial, parental, and grandparental generations.

Summary:

1. Stutterers showed a familial tendency—significantly more stutterers appeared in stuttering families than in non-stuttering families. (One hundred and four stutterers had stuttering strains, and only four non-stutterers had stuttering strains.)

2. No significant difference was found between the percentages of stutterers and non-stutterers who associated with stutterers. There was also no significant difference between the percentages of the two groups who had not associated with stutterers.

3. Sixty of the non-stutterers had had some association with stutterers in the past. If these 60 non-stutterers had not become stutterers through association, the author assumed that an equal number of the stutterers had not begun to stutter due to contact.

4. Of the siblings of stutterers, 421 were found free from stuttering.

5. In 58 cases, the stutterers had ancestors who stuttered, but with whom there had been no personal contact.

Conclusions: It was concluded that personal contact as a factor in the transmission of stuttering is slight, but that some hereditary factor might be operating.

TITLE

Brodnitz, F. S.: Stuttering of Different Types in Identical Twins, *Journal of Speech and Hearing Disorders,* **16** (1951), 334-336.

Purpose: To show the need for separating cases of imitation stuttering from genuine stuttering.

Experimental Design: None.

Summary: Imitation was first described by Froeschels in 1928 as a break in the inner logic of regular development of the disorder. "In imitation stuttering no logical sequence in the development of stuttering can be traced." Imitation stuttering is comparable, it is suggested, to the inadequate attempt of a layman to imitate a stutterer. The imitator produces some symtoms which have impressed him while omitting others which the trained observer will expect. The most characteristic symptom of imitation stuttering is the pseudotonus—a prolonged closure in the production of an initial consonant, followed by an almost normal or even normal explosion.

An example of seven and a half year old male identical twins was cited as follows: Phillip G. showed all the symptoms of stuttering of long standing: clonotonus, protrusion of tongue, looking away and up to the right. Words were sometimes divided by momentary stoppage, and the left corner of the mouth was occasionally raised in tonic-clonic pressure.

Mark G. exhibited typical pseudotonus. When repeating phrases in which words had been previously omitted, he was able to do so. He also looked away or up as his brother did, but used the gesture when no speech difficulty arose.

Delivery of the children was normal. Mark preceded Phillip by about 20 minutes. Both began to talk at the beginning of their second year with normal speech development. Both became highly allergic to grasses at age three and were treated with antihistamines and pollen injections. At age five Phillip was treated with suppositories (antihistaminic?) for a 'cold.' Mark was later treated similarly and lapsed into a coma. Phillip became frightened and refused to speak at first, and shortly thereafter developed his first stuttering symptoms. Mark, after recovery, did not stutter for a number of months, but began to stutter when asked to repeat aloud in school. Phillip stuttered very frequently. Mark stuttered only under stress and excitement, and did not stutter at all during summer vacations. The children were separated in school in an effort to help them. Mark took the separation badly and continued to follow the lead of other pupils. Phillip was diagnosed as the genuine stutterer, Mark as the imitation stutterer.

Conclusions: The author concluded that co-existence of stuttering of different types in identical twins underlines the need for caution in drawing conclusions as to the existence of congenital factors in stuttering. It is suggested that genuine stuttering and development of imitation stuttering might be based on an inherited readiness.

TITLE

Rotter, J. B.: Studies in the Psychology of Stuttering: XI. Stuttering in Relation to Position in the Family, *Journal of Speech Disorders*, 4 (1939), 143-148.

Purpose: To study the relationship between stuttering and position in the family, number of years between the stutterer and his nearest sibling, and the sex of the nearest sibling.

Experimental Design: The family positions (oldest, youngest, middle, only) of 522 stutterers (427 males, 95 females ranging in age from 215 to 44 with a median of 14 years) were compared with 7,738 junior high school non-stutterers whose family positions had been determined in a White House Conference Report.

Summary: The comparisons found are as follows:

Position	Stutterers	Normal	Difference
Only	20.01%	12%	4.48
Oldest	25.29%	26%	.36
Youngest	27.01%	26%	.50
Middle	27.59%	36%	4.14

Statistically, more only children and fewer middle children were found among stutterers than could be expected by chance.

Further comparisons revealed that the mean number of years between the stutterers and their siblings was statistically larger than between non-stutterers and their siblings. There was also a greater number of years between the stutterer and the child succeeding than the one preceding him. A slight tendency was found for the nearest sibling in age to the stutterer to be of the opposite sex. If the child is separated by several years from other siblings, other things being equal, it is fairly certain that his mother has more time and attention to give him than if age differences were less. The data suggested that there might be a direct relationship between pampering and the development of stuttering. In only children, the male to female ratio was 3:1 in contrast to a 5:1 ratio for all other groups.

Conclusions: It was concluded that position in family, number of years between siblings and sex of nearest sibling are independent of hereditary influences. These factors were, however, found to appear significantly in regard to the incidence of stuttering. In certain cases at least, certain environmental factors such as pampering appeared to have a direct relationship to the appearance of stuttering. The author suggested that this may shed some light on the high incidents of stuttering among males—assuming that mothers are more inclined to pamper boys than girls. This, it was felt, would also seem to be compatible with the idea that diagnosis precipitates excessive difficulty. The parent who tends to pamper might also be expected to be especially alert to any deviations by the child in speech development.

TITLE

Gray, M.: The X Family: A Clinical and Laboratory Study of a "Stuttering" Family, *Journal of Speech Disorders*, 5 (1940), 343-348.

Purpose: To answer questions regarding the distribution of stuttering within a family, the definite similarities or the differences among the stutterers, non-stutterers and former stutterers, and the nature of the evaluations or assumptions expressed by the family regarding stuttering.

Experimental Design: Two branches of a stuttering family, one located in Iowa and the other in Kansas, were studied in respect to case histories, tests of laterality, intelligence, silent reading, and the Bell Adjustment Inventory. The Iowa branch consisted of eight stutterers, three former stutterers, and 16 non-stutterers. The Kansas branch consisted of one stutterer and 16 non-stutterers. Information for five generations was collected.

Summary: The only differences found between the stutterers, non-stutterers, and former stutterers were possibly in the birth conditions, speech development histories, "nervous" habits and personality inventory scores. One stutterer was born prematurely, another weighed only four pounds at birth and had difficulty with initial breathing. Birth conditions of the non-stutterers, former stutterers, and six remaining stutterers were normal. There was evidence to indicate on the average a somewhat later development in speech among the stutterers. The group differences, however, were not significant enough to justify the consideration of speech retardation as being related to stuttering. In regard to nervous habits, two of the 16 non-stutterers showed some form of nervous behavior, while five of eight of the stutterers showed one form or another of nervous behavior. The inventory scores favored the non-stutterers as being better adjusted, but again there was overlapping and nothing of significant value as far as cause and effect were concerned.

The difference in incidence of stuttering could not be explained on the basis of a sheer hereditary hypothesis because the stuttering was divided almost evenly between the sexes in the family and the ratios most frequently reported are from three to one to five to one. There appeared more evidence for a semantogenic etiology. All stutterers believed that stuttering was hereditary in their family. The difference in incidence between the two branches might, it was suggested, be explained by the fact that one individual who was comparatively the most dominant member of the family remained in Iowa and influenced the Iowa branch attitudes while he was non-influential in Kansas.

Conclusions: Many questions were raised by the author who favored a semantogenic interpretation in that "it suggests more possibilities for further investigations and has more hopeful remedial implications."

TITLE

Wepman, J. M.: Familial Incidence in Stammering, *Journal of Speech Disorders,* 4 (1939), 199-204.

Purpose: To study the familial incidence of stuttering.

Experimental Design: Two hundred and fifty stutterers were matched with 250 non-stutterers for age, sex, and social environment. The author personally interviewed the families and solicited known facts concerning their ancestry. The facts consisted of the number of stutterers, their sex, and position in the family. Family charts were made for each family showing the position, age, sex of each stutterer and his immediate family.

Summary: Of the 250 families of the stutterers, 63.8% showed some incidence of stuttering. In the 250 families of the non-stutterers only 15.6% showed the same disorder. Stuttering appeared more frequently in males than females. The ratio was 4:1.

The results obtained were considered reliable since the various differences were from four to twenty times as great as their probable errors.

Conclusions: The author concluded that certain individuals in the general population are stutterers because of the incidence of that disorder in their family background; others are potential stutterers, and certain others will stutter before the year is out. He suggests that stuttering if inherited from both parents may be permanent. Stuttering inherited from one parent, he feels, may be temporary and can be treated.

TITLE

Fagan, L. B.: The Relation of Dextral Training to the Onset of Stuttering, A Report of Cases, *Quarterly Journal of Speech*, 17 (1931), 73-76.

Purpose: To report cases of speech disturbances ensuing upon imposed right-hand training of amphi-dextrous individuals.

Experimental Design: None. Nine case histories of left handedness and dextral training and four cases of amphi-dexterity and dextral training were cited.

Summary: Case reports were classified into two groups. Group one contained nine cases (7 males and 2 females), and compared left-handedness and dextral training. All of the S's were at one time or another natively left-handed. Each of them was forced to change from this left-handedness to right-handedness. Onset of stuttering in each case began within a year after the change occurred. Group two consisted of four males, each of whom was at some time ambidextrous. When two of S's were forced to change this ambidexterity to right-handedness stuttering occurred within a short time. The other two S's stuttered while being ambidextrous but stuttering became more severe when the right-handedness was forced upon them.

Conclusions: From this data the author concluded that stuttering and change in handedness are definitely linked and suggested that right-handedness should not be imposed on left-handed individuals and the amphi-dextrous should be taught to use their left hand, especially for writing and avoid the acquisition of dextral skills.

"Articulate speech is a product of bi-lateral neuro-muscular groups under the functional dominance of the left cerebral cortex in normal right-handed individuals and vice versa for left-handers. When graphic speech is imposed on the right hand . . . in the left-handed and amphi-dextrous the corresponding cerebral cortex acquires by training a function that places it in active opposition to its homologue in speech production, be it graphic or articulate, making for the peripheral disturbance known as stuttering."

TITLE

Bryngelson, B.: Sidedness as an Etiological Factor in Stuttering, *Pedagogical Seminary,* **47 (1935), 204-217.**

Purpose: Because handedness has been considered a major sign of cerebral dominance, the author felt that there appeared to be a good deal of confusion in the literature as to the relationship between handedness and stuttering. This paper attempts to clarify the problem.

Experimental Design: The findings on 700 clinical cases of stuttering were presented. The ages of the stutterers ranged from 4 to 42 years, the majority falling between 9 and 16 years of age. The data were gathered by interview and clinical observation. In most instances, the parents of these cases were questioned as to the facts about the patient, and as to his stuttering and left-handed relatives. Frequently the parents, and often the adult cases themselves, did not know the facts of early sidedness, and, consequently, one had to seek information from relatives, baby pictures, etc.

Summary:

1. 57.3% of this group of 700 S's were left-eyed. The normal right-handed people have been found to have 25% left-eyedness.

2. 10.3% were amphiocular—twice as many as found in the normal population.

3. 61.1% were ambidextrous. The normal population reveals only 5%.

4. 80.1% wrote mirror script. The highest percentage found in the author's university population was 15%.

5. In the shifted cases, i.e., from left-handedness to right-handedness, there was a rather high percentage of reading, spelling, writing and articulatory disabilities, in addition to the stuttering which they manifested.

Conclusions: It is important, the author feels, to remember that the diagnosis in cerebral dominance is made primarily on the fact of sidedness and not on the fact of handedness. Sidedness represents a unilaterality of nervous organization. Maturation and growth are basic factors of behavior. Growth may be considered largely a process of differentiation, and one-sidedness is a good criterion of this growth process. If this growth process is retarded or interfered with, a one-sided nervous organization may be delayed in developing, or may never develop, in a normal way. Hence, the author feels that the best guarantee for normal reading, writing and speaking is one-sidedness, and that tampering with a child's natural neurological expression is a dangerous procedure.

TITLE

Quinan, C.: **Sinistrality in Relation to High Blood Pressure and Defects of Speech,** *Archives of Internal Medicine,* 27 (1921), 255-261.

Purpose: To review the literature and to present the results of an investigation of left-handedness in relation to high blood pressure and speech defects.

Experimental Design: A survey was made of approximately 600 men between the ages of 44 and 89 years who were inmates of the San Francisco Home for the Aged. Blood pressure observations were made, and each man was questioned as to his handedness and as to whether he had been a stutterer in childhood or had suffered from other defects of speech.

Summary:
1. About 7% of the sample were sinistrals.
    a. Group 1—left-handed, left-eyed, pure sinistral.
    b. Group 2—left-handed, right-eyed, crossed sinistral.
    c. Group 3—right-handed, left-eyed, crossed sinistral.
2. Compared with a group of 100 right-handed, right-eyed, pure dextrals, the mean blood pressure values observed in the sinistral groups were from 7.8 to 17.8% higher.

3. A mean value of 154.5 mm. was obtained for the dextral group. The mean value obtained for the crossed sinistrals of Group 2 was 182.1 mm.

4. In the 3 sinistral groups blood pressure values higher than 150 mm. were noted in from 71 to 85% of the men, as against 46% in the dextral group.

5. About 5% of the pure dextrals gave a history of stuttering. The percentage in the group of pure sinistrals was 35.7%.

Conclusions: It was concluded that high arterial tension occurs more frequently in left-handed than in right-handed people.

In view of the evidence that left-handedness is hereditary, and that it indicates a defective organization of the central nervous system, it was suggested that hereditary predisposition is a definite factor in the etiology of high blood pressure and that high arterial tension is suggestive of constitutional inferiority.

Since stuttering occurs reportedly from three to seven times more in sinistrals than in dextrals a possible relationship was suggested.

TITLE

Johnson, W., and Duke, L.: Changes in Handedness Associated with Onset or Disappearance of Stuttering, *Journal of Experimental Education*, 4 (1935), 112-132.

Purpose: To investigate case histories of stutterers in which there is a more or less clear indication that changes in handedness are associated with the onset or disappearance of stuttering.

Experimental Design: In the 16 cases studied, ages ranged from 5 to 71; I.Q.'s from 87-134. The case histories contained as much pertinent information as possible. Hospital records were used whenever possible. Mental, as well as neurological and physical examinations were made. Motor lead tests were used to determine handedness index in all cases in which it was possible. Data were not statistically analyzed.

Summary: In each case there was evidence of a significant temporal relationship between change of handedness and stuttering. The authors pointed out, however, that certain things could not be adequately evaluated nor completely dismissed.

Some subjects reported diseases or injuries which occurred prior to or concomitantly with the onset of stuttering. Various emotional problems and evidence of delayed motor and mental development were present in some of the case reports. The factor of heredity was not within the realm of evaluation and in some cases the factor of imitation could not be disregarded. It was suggested that perhaps emotionality, which in some cases resulted from change of handedness, was an important cause of stuttering. In some cases, the subjects believed that a change to the originally preferred hand would improve their speech and therefore the power of suggestion could not be dismissed. Such factors, as age and maturation, improved personal relations, etc. were noted as having a temporal relationship with improved speech in some of these cases.

A number of individuals who had almost or completely overcome the stuttering problem were tested and revealed a high degree of ambilaterality. For them it seemed that either stuttering had been overcome without benefit of handedness change or that the measurements of handedness were not accurate.

Conclusions: It was concluded that in the 16 cases studied there appeared to be evidence of a temporal relation between stuttering and change of handedness.

TITLE

Bryngelson, B., and Rutherford, B.: A Comparative Study of Laterality of Stutterers and Non-stutterers, *Journal of Speech Disorders,* 2 (1937), 15-16.

Purpose: To establish a control group for a previous study done by the senior author in which 73% of the stutterers had experienced a shift in handedness, and 61% were ambidextrous at the time of their entrance into the speech clinic.

Experimental Design: Seventy-four of the non-stuttering and 74 of the stutterers were matched for sex, age, social status and school achievement. Each group was tested clinically. Controls, recommended by public school principals, were non-stuttering normal children. Age range varied from 4 to 16, with 41 females and 33 males in each group.

Summary: The data obtained are as follows:

Present Handedness	Stutterers	Non-stutterers
Right	61.6%	75 %
Left	4.1%	16.7%
Ambidextrous	34.3%	8.3%
Shifted left to right	71.6%	9.5%
History of left handedness in family	74.0%	63.0%
History of stuttering in family	46.0%	18.0%

The above data indicated that the two groups differed in ambidexterity and shifting of handedness. There was over four times as much ambidexterity in the stuttering group, and approximately eight times as much shifting of handedness.

Data from a previous study of 1,374 stutterers were presented to show the consistency of the above differentiating factors:

No. of Stutterers	Ambidextrous	History of Shift
700	61%	73%
374	40%	71%
168	77%	81%
111	45%	68%

That fewer stutterers are not as strictly one-sided as normal speakers was shown when footedness, eyedness, and handedness were correlated. Only 12% of the stutterers were strictly one-sided while 55% of the control group were one-sided in the three correlated motor functions.

Conclusions: The authors concluded that there is a tendency for stutterers to fall into a mixed sidedness group, and that neither cerebral hemisphere in stutterers has a dominant lead control over peripheral midline speech structures.

TITLE

Bryngelson, B.: A Study of Laterality of Stutterers and Normal Speakers, *Journal of Social Psychology,* **11 (1940), 151-155.**

Purpose: To ascertain possible differences between a group of stutterers and normals at a higher age level than studied in earlier research.

Experimental Design: Seventy-eight stutterers (29 males and 49 females) ranging in age from 17 to 31 years, were paired with a comparable number of normals on the basis of CA, MA, and social status. Similar case history questions and clinical tests were administered to both groups. Five speech pathology majors helped the author in doing the clinical studies to lend diversification and increase the reliability of the study.

Summary: The two main differences between the groups were: (1) the shift in handedness, and (2) ambidexterity. These differences were statistically significant.

	(1) Normal	Stutterers	(2) Normal	Stutterers
Right handed	94%	69%	83%	63%
Left handed	6%	6%	11%	3%
Ambidexterity	0%	29%	4%	34%
Left-right shift	1%	58%	5%	61%
History-left	42%	49%	53%	64%
History-stutterers	6%	54%	13%	51%

In (2) in the table above, data from the present study were combined with a former one. There were 62 males and 90 females in each of the two groups, with an age range of 4-31 years when all data were pooled.

In the present study, it was also found that there were 50% more enuretics among the stutterers than normals, and fewer diseases in the stuttering group. Former studies by Travis point out that the central mechanism in stuttering is the lack of cerebral dominances. When the pooled group was analyzed for footedness, eyedness, and handedness, 19% of the stutterers were one-sided and 51% of the normals were one-sided. The CR was 6.15, and significant.

Considering either study, it was felt that apparently there is not as great a difference as formerly thought in family history of left-handedness. The CR between the two groups on this characteristic in the pooled group produced an insignificant CR. The differences for stutterers vs. non-stutterers on family history of stuttering, however, showed a significant CR of 7.76.

Conclusions: In normal speech it was postulated that because of dominant hemispherical control the midline speech structures function synchronously. In a stutterer no such cortical superiority of function seems to be present. The possibility is suggested that the central mechanism of bihemispherical antagonism in neural discharge is present at birth in some children causing peripheral myospasms of the speech mechanism to occur when the child first attempts speech communication. But to say that this is the condition in all children who stutter, and consequently that there is nothing to do about it, the author cannot accept at present. Further research was recommended.

TITLE

Van Dusen, C. R.: A Laterality Study of Non-stutterers and Stutterers, *Journal of Speech Disorders*, 4 (1939), 261-265.

Purpose: To investigate differences in handedness between stutterers and non-stutterers and to test further the brain dominance theory regarding stuttering.

Experimental Design: Laterality tests were given to 40 college male right-handed non-stutterers and 40 college male right-handed stutterers. A questionnaire study of hand usage and tests of strength, speed, accuracy, and laterality lead were also given. In addition to this, hand clasp and eye fixation were studied. Dextrality quotients were determined by the following formula:

$$D.Q. = \frac{R + \frac{B}{2}}{N}$$

This was computed on the basis of the usage questionnaire. A person with a quotient of 75% or more was considered right handed; and 25% or less was considered left handed.

The Collins' dynamometer was used in testing for strength. Eye fixation was tested by having the S look at the experimenter's nose through a hole in a card.

Summary: D.Q.'s of non-stuttering subjects were 75% or higher in 97.5% of the cases; whereas, the D.Q.'s of the stutterers were 75% or higher in 100% of the cases. Of the stutterers, 17.9% were found to be ambidextrous as compared with only 7.5% of the non-stuttering group. One of the non-stutterers had a stronger left hand; six of the stutterers had stronger left hands. A slightly greater percentage of the stutterers was found to be right-eyed than were non-stutterers.

In the stuttering group, there was a greater tendency toward sinistrality, and ambilaterality in the hand clasping test, strength test, accuracy test, and laterality lead test. Non-stutterers tended to be more definitely right handed in regard to strength. No significant differences were obtained for speed or accuracy.

Conclusions: It was concluded on the basis of this battery of tests that significant differences in laterality between non-stutterers and stutterers are present only in strength and usage. In both strength and usage, non-stutterers tend to be more definitely right-handed than stutterers. There were no significant differences between the two groups in laterality lead, speed and accuracy.

In general, it was felt that these findings do not support the assumption that there is a lack of dominant lead in the stuttering person.

TITLE

Heltman, H. J.: **Contradictory Evidence in Handedness and Stuttering,** *Journal of Speech Disorders,* 5 (1940), 327-331.

Purpose: To explore the relationship between handedness and stuttering by comparing data from several studies.

Experimental Design: The author compared three sets of data (Daniels, Van Dusen, and Bryngelson) but presented only the data of Daniels and Bryngelson. (Daniels and Van Dusen agreed basically in their studies.)

Summary: Daniels checked all entering students at Syracuse University in 1939 for dextrality tendencies. Of 1,594 students, 216 were found who were either left-handed, ambidextrous, had been shifted, or who stuttered. The breakdown for the entire population studied was as follows:

1,594 students	20 stutterers	1.3% of total
1,422 right-handed	15 stutterers	1.1% of rh gp.
34 left-handed	1 stutterer	2.9% of lh gp.
138 ambidextrous	4 stutterers	2.9% of ami gp.
77 had been shifted for writing	1 stutterer	1.3% of shifted

These data were then compared with the Bryngelson data as follows:

Per cent of stutterers who are:	Bryngelson	Daniels
Right-handed	63%	75%
Left-handed	3%	5%
Ambidextrous	34%	20%
Shifted	61%	5%
Family-history left	64%	not taken
Family-history stuttering	51%	not taken

On the basis of the Daniels' data the following observations were made: (1) Since only 1 of 77 shifted from L to R stuttered, there appeared to be no hazard in making such a change. (2) Since only 1 of 77 shifted stuttered and this 1.3% does not differ significantly from the 1.1% of right-handers who stutter or 1.3% of the entire 1,594, it suggested that a change in handedness was not a significant factor. It was suggested that since 2.9% of the ambidextrous group stuttered (twice as many as in the shifted group) that it might be advisable as a preventative measure against stuttering to have encouraged all the ambidextrous students entering in 1939 to use their right hands for writing.

Conclusions: It was concluded that probably more research was needed in this area before any final conclusions relative to handedness and stuttering could be safely made.

TITLE

Spadino, E. J.: Writing and Laterality Characteristics of Stuttering Children, *Columbia University Teachers College Contributions to Education,* **Columbia University, New York, 1941.**

Purpose: To determine the relationship between laterality and stuttering.

Experimental Design: A series of tests designed to test laterality were administered to matched groups of 70 stutterers (58 males, 12 females) and 70 non-stutterers. The mean C.A. was 12 years. All the laterality tasks were unimanual and designed to deceive the subjects into believing that quickness and skill were being measured and not laterality. The only actual measurements pertinent to the experiment were the choice of hand which the subject used in carrying out the task. Tasks which determined handedness were such things as pointing, tossing an object, spinning a top and touching the end of the nose with a ruler. Eyedness was tested by five different eyedness tests, such as sighting an object through a cone which precluded the use of more than one eye. Footedness was tested by such tasks as kicking a ball or walking a line. If the right foot moved first, it was scored as a "right"; if the left foot led off, it was scored as a "left."

Summary: In none of the tests on laterality was a statistically significant difference between stutterers and non-stutterers found. Trends noted: a few more stutterers than non-stutterers were left-handed, left-eyed and left-footed; and a few more stutterers than non-stutterers were ambi-eyed. Only one of the 140 subjects was ambidextrous. None of the differences concerning crossing of preferences, such as right-handed and left-eyed were statistically significant. Actually, considering the factors which indicate one-sidedness, the stutterers were slightly superior, i.e., both left-handed and left-footed.

Conclusions: It was concluded that "unilaterality or the lack thereof can be associated with stuttering in only an insignificant minority of cases. Left-handedness, ambilaterality and crossing of hand, eye and foot preferences, if they are to be considered to have any relationship to stuttering in children, must be considered as playing a small contributing part in which one or more other factors are of greater importance."

TITLE

Travis, L. E., and Knott, J. R.: Brain Potentials from Normal Speakers and Stutterers, *Journal of Psychology*, 2 (1936), 137-150.

Purpose: "To determine the relationship, if any, between stuttering and the activity represented by the cortical potentials called the "Berger Rhythm." Berger has implied that the distributions of duration and amplitude of the potential waves are bimodal. One mode is formed by waves having a duration of about 0.10 sec., and an amplitude of 20 to 60 microvolts (alpha-waves). The other mode is formed by waves having a duration of about 0.04 sec., and amplitude of 10 to 15 microvolts (beta waves)."

Experimental Design: Thirty-six subjects, 19 normals and 17 stutterers, were used. Needle electrodes were inserted through the scalp, one over the left visual area, the other over the left motor area—each approximately two cms. from the midline. Subjects were in a dark, semi-soundproof and shielded room, lying comfortably on a cot with eyes closed. Records were taking during silence and during simple propositional speech. For the stutterers the experimenter signaled overt spasm as heard through the voice recording circuit.

Summary: For all subjects under all conditions a total of 3,533 waves were studied for frequency and amplitude.

In so far as duration of potential was concerned, all four distributions (normals silent, normals speaking, stutterers silent, stutterers speaking), there was much overlapping. Thus, the theory of discrete classes of wave duration seemed to be refuted. The increase in percentage of waves was significant with respect to speech vs. silence in the case of normals but not in the case of stutterers. The percentage difference between normals (silent) and stutterers (silent) was not significant. Also, the difference of wave duration between normal speech and stuttering speech was not significant.

The four distributions for amplitude were unimodal and continuous. The waves had greater amplitude during the stuttering speech of the stutterers than during the speech of the normals and non-stuttering speech of the stutterers. The waves were significantly larger for the non-stuttering speech of the stutterers than for the speech of the normal speakers.

The above were all in terms of average differences between groups. There were also many individual differences within each group. Because of certain factors, two stutterers were given particular consideration. Both of these showed marked changes in brain potential activity during their complete tonic spasm in which there was no voice. Large peaked spikes appeared on their graphs. These discharges, however, never appeared during a clonic block or during a tonic block with voice. They always seemed to occur after the onset of the stuttering spasm.

Conclusions: The authors concluded that since the differences which were significant were small and trends were often in the same direction between silence and speech for both normal speakers and stutterers, interpretations must be reserved until further observation and experimentation have been carried out.

TITLE

Travis, L. E.: **Brain Potentials and the Temporal Course of Consciousness,** *Journal of Experimental Psychology,* **21** (1937), **302-309.**

Purpose: To determine what the relationship is, for a given person, between the size of his brain waves and the temporal course of consciousness as revealed by his introspective reports.

Experimental Design: Eight persons (six men, two women) served as subjects. The subject while lying on a cot with eyes closed was instructed to permit his mind to wander. At certain moments the subject was given a signal to report what conscious state, if any, the signal had interrupted. His brain potentials were recorded in another room where the experimenter also remained.

Summary:

1. Introspective reports could be categorized into: imagery (of light, of objects, auditory), sensation (kinesthetic, etc.), mental effort, abstract thinking, and mental blankness.

2. Visual images, kinesthetic sensations, and mental effort, it was found, were associated with relatively small brain potentials.

3. Mental blankness and abstract thinking were associated with relatively large brain potentials.

4. Organic sensations and mixed images were not related significantly to any one size of wave.

5. From the few available reports, verbal ideas and anxiety were associated mainly with small waves.

Conclusions: It was concluded that factors which are effective in disturbing the normal alpha rhythm of ten cycles per second are those which focus consciousness. This, it was felt, suggests that large regular brain potentials indicative of a state of cortical equilibrium represent a *generalized* psychic activity while a break-up of this collective action into more rapid and irregular oscillations of much smaller amplitude represent a relatively high degree of *specificity* in psychic activity.

TITLE

Freestone, N. W.: A Brain-Wave Interpretation of Stuttering, *Quarterly Journal of Speech*, 28 (1942), 466-468.

Purpose: To interpret the results of brain waves based on 44 significant differences and 37 trend differences between stutterers and non-stutterers.

Experimental Design: Brain waves records were taken from 20 adult normal speakers and 20 adult stutterers. Recordings were made of 14 separate brain areas for each individual for comparison of functional conditions of silence, speech, and stuttering speech.

Summary: The normal brain wave, it was pointed out, is classified into two general forms: (1) the alpha wave (sinusoidal waves of relatively high amplitude which emerge from the brain at about 10 per second, an increase of which is an indication of reduced consciousness); (2) the beta waves (formless waves of low amplitude emerging from the brain at about 20 waves per second). A disruption of alpha waves into beta is an indication of a focus of mental activity.

The results showed that stutterers have larger waves than normals. The stutterer's wave in speech was larger than his silent wave; the stuttering act gave the largest wave of all. Following the criterion that larger waves mean a loss of mental specificity, stutterers may be said to be functioning in a state of reduced consciousness.

Comparing opposite sides of brain areas, the voltages (amplitude) of the two areas are more alike for stutterers than for normals. This may be construed as meaning that since the two sides are so alike for stutterers, a condition of dominance for one side, necessary for speech, cannot develop.

Normals were found to have a greater per cent of alpha interruption from silence to speech than stutterers. This could be interrupted as meaning that the stutterers failed to have a focus of attention great enough to eliminate as many alpha rhythms as did the normals, and that stutterers function in a relative state of reduced consciousness.

Less than 10 per cent of the total measures gave significant statistical results although those were consistent by a ratio of 40 to 1. The question arose whether the differences caused stuttering or whether stuttering made the differences detectable.

Conclusions: It was concluded that stutterers, as a class, are neurologically different from normals. Stutterers and stuttering tend to function in relative states of reduced consciousness. The author felt that neural differences act as a sub-soil out of which stuttering may arise, but that any child is a potential stutterer and may stutter if given an environment suitable for stuttering. Because one has a weak neurological inheritance is no guarantee he will stutter or will not. Everything being equal, there will be a tendency for those with weak neurological sub-soils to succumb to the average social pressures found in every home. These individuals are more likely to stutter, the author felt, if, stuttering does result.

TITLE

Lindsley, D. B.: **Bilateral Differences in Brain Potentials from the Two Cerebral Hemispheres in Relation to Laterality and Stuttering,** *Journal of Experimental Psychology,* 26 (1940), 211-225.

Purpose: To study the bilateral differences in the simultaneously recorded electrical activity of the two cerebral hemisphere in relation to laterality and stuttering, taking into consideration the two factors of phase relationship of the alpha waves and the amount of unilateral blocking of the alpha rhythm of the two sides of the head. (Unilateral blocking was defined as the absence of alpha waves on either side of the head while the rhythm of the other side was distinctly present.)

Experimental Design: Subjects were 65 normal children ranging in age from 5 to 16 years and two male adult stutterers. Fortyeight of the children were right-handed, eight, left-handed, and nine, ambidextrous on the basis of a laterality index. One of the two stutterers was 25 years old and had severe spasms. Four series of experiments were carried out with him. The other was 23 and had far less spasms. Only one experiment was performed with him. During the recording the subject sat comfortably in a dark and relatively sound-proofed room with eyes open. Records were obtained for the stutterers during silence and during speech. Speech was recorded on a separate voice line on the oscillograph record.

Summary: An analysis of the 65 children's records revealed that the alpha waves in the two hemispheres are out of phase a greater per cent of the time in ambidextrous and left-handed subjects than in right-handed subjects. There was also less unilateral blocking in the right-handed group. Unilateral blocking was slightly greater in the left hemisphere for the right-handed group, and the opposite for the left-handed group. The difference, however, was not significant enough to permit a differentiation between the hemispheres in terms of dominance or laterality. The two adult stutterers' records showed a degree of asynchronism comparable to that of the ambidextrous or mixed laterality groups.

Per cent of asynchronism did not change consistently or significantly during speech. Unilateral blocking of alpha waves was increased during speech. Preceding almost every recorded stuttering episode, there were periods of asynchronism of the alpha waves in the two hemispheres (both occipital and motor speech areas) as well as frequent periods of unilateral blocking or phase reversals of the alpha rhythm.

Conclusions: The results led the author to conclude that asynchronism and blocking of the alpha rhythm in the two cerebral hemispheres may interfere with the formulation and expression of speech. Therefore, the higher degree of asynchronism and blocking in individuals lacking a definite and complete laterality is apt to make their speech more subject to interference. The author formulated the following hypothesis: "In order for bilaterally paired speech muscles to work together in a synchronous manner to produce well regulated speech sounds, motor impulses from the respective contralateral hemispheres must reach them almost simultaneously."

TITLE

Douglass, L. C.: A Study of Bilaterally Recorded Electroencephalograms of Adult Stutterers, *Journal of Experimental Psychology*, 32 (1943), 247-265.

Purpose: To investigate the EEG characteristics of stutterers and non-stutterers during speech and silence.

Experimental Design: Twenty adult stutterers (18 males, 2 females) were matched with 20 non-stutterers. Recordings were taken from four different cortical areas simultaneously. The order of recording was as follows: (1) a five minute silence period, (2) the subjects silently read a passage (no record taken), (3) the subject verbalized the material just read and continuous recordings were taken.

Summary: Results were divided into intergroup differences (non-stutterers vs. stutterers) and intragroup differences. Intergroup differences indicated that normals have a higher percentage time alpha present in both the right and left occipital areas during speech than do stutterers for either fluent or stuttering speech. Non-stutterers have a higher per cent time alpha present in the left motor area during speech than stutterers in non-stuttering speech. All differences were significant at the .01 level.

There was no difference in the EEG between stuttering speech and non-stuttering speech of the stutterer. This made it difficult to interpret the stutterer-normal differences in casual terms. A decrease in per cent time alpha present, it was suggested, might be regarded as a symptom of being a stutterer and not a contributing cause.

The increased interhemisphere similarity of the group during speech might, it was felt, be evaluated in terms of Henry's findings that individuals different in unilateral characteristics (EEG) during silence present a significantly more similar set of measures when they are all introduced to a common activity (speech).

Conclusions: It was concluded that:

1. Intergroup comparison showed that stutterers and normals could not be differentiated on the basis of mean per cent time of unilateral blocking of alpha rhythm either in silence or speech. A greater bilateral blocking of per cent alpha rhythm did appear in occipital areas for stutterers than non-stutterers in speech.

2. Intragroup comparisons indicated no significant difference in normals between silence and speech, but for stutterers bilateral blocking in occipital areas was greater during speech than silence.

3. Interhemisphere relations indicate significant differences between normals and stutterers during silence.

4. The interhemisphere differences in unilateral blocking during silence which distinguishes the stutterers from the non-stutterers seems to point to the existence of a physiological difference between the two groups.

TITLE

Scarborough, H. W.: A Quantitative and Qualitative Analysis of the Electroencephalograms of Stutterers and Non-stutterers, *Journal of Experimental Psychology,* **32 (1943), 156-167.**

Purpose: To investigate electroencephalographic behavior of the dominant hemisphere with peripheral behavior minimal; to discover if there are consistent statistically significant differences in the mean number of cortical potentials per second in the left dominant hemisphere between stutterers and non-stutterers, and in the mean variability of the number of cortical potentials per second between stutterers and non-stutterers; and finally to explore significant differences with regard to the number of records in each group presenting qualitatively abnormal electroencephalographic activity of the type reported in epileptics, psychotics and behavior problem children.

Experimental Design: Subjects were two females and 18 male stutterers with a mean age of 34 and four female and 16 male non-stutterers with a mean age of 23. All subjects were right-handed. Subjects were in a reclining position when records were made.

Two fifteen-minute recordings were made at least a week apart. Only the left hemisphere—presumed to be the dominant one because of the right-handedness manifested by all—was tested. Two 30-second samples were selected for quantitative measurement. Measurements were made in terms of the number of waves per second. The records were also analyzed for the presence of abnormalities known to be related to neuropathological activity.

Summary:

1. No significant statistical difference between the groups in the mean number of waves per second or in the mean standard deviation of the mean number of waves per second was found.

2. No significant difference between the two groups in the values of correlations between sample and sample and records and records was found. That is, stutterers were not more variable.

3. Qualitative abnormalities were few. This occurred only once among the non-stuttering group and three times among the stutterers. The percentage of the stutterers in this group was not considered significant.

Conclusions: It was concluded that under conditions designed to minimize activity the stutterer's dominant cortical hemisphere does not differ from that of the non-stutterer.

TITLE

Bilto, E. W.: A Comparative Study of Certain Physical Abilities of Children with Speech Defects and Children with Normal Speech, *Journal of Speech Disorders*, 6 (1941), 187-203.

Purpose: To determine: (1) the characteristic difference, if any, in certain physical abilities between children with normal speech and those who stutter or have an articulatory defect; (2) the characteristic difference in certain physical abilities between children who stutter and those with articulatory defects; (3) if a specific type of physical education program is needed for speech-defective children.

Experimental Design: Ninety children (34 stutterers and 56 articulation defectives) between the ages of 9 and 18 years of age were given three tests—(1) Brace Motor Ability Tests—a measure of general motor ability; (2) Nielsen and Cozen's Jump and Reach Test—an achievement test involving jumping and pushing; (3) Bilto's Eye-Hand Co-ordination Test—measurement of ability to coordinate alternate hand movements with a moving object external to the body. The data were statistically analyzed by comparisons between means for normal children and between the means for the two groups.

Summary: (1) Brace Motor Abilities Tests: 29.41% of the stutterers scored above the mean, 70.59% below the mean. 35.71% of the articulation defectives scored above the mean and 64.29% scored below. The stutterer and articulation defective, then, are inferior to children without speech defects in large muscle activities. There was little difference between the stuttering group and the articulation group. (2) Jump and Reach Test: 29.41% of the stutterers scored above the mean and 67.65% scored below the mean—2.94% on the mean. 30.36% of the articulation defectives scored above the mean and 60.72% scored below the mean—8.93% on the mean. Both speech-defective groups were inferior to normals in ability to develop power. Articulation defectives were a little better than the stutterers. (3) Eye-Head Coordination Tests: 32.35% of stutterers scored above the mean and 67.65% scored below the mean. 32.14% of the articulation defectives scored above the mean and 67.86% below. Both groups were inferior to normals. Stutterers were better than articulation defectives.

Conclusions: It was concluded that:

1. Children with speech defects are inferior as a group to children with normal speech in large muscle abilities. They were deficient in such abilities as rhythm, coordination, and strength.

2. On the Brace test there was little difference between the groups. Articulation defectives were better on the Nielsen and Cozen Tests and inferior to stutterers on the Bilto test.

3. It was suggested that a majority of the children would benefit from a general program of physical education; however, no specific types of training were suggested which would answer all needs.

TITLE

Blackburn, W. B.: Study of Voluntary Movements in Stutterers and Normal Speakers, *Psychological Monographs,* **41 (1931), 1-13.**

Purpose: To analyze and compare the performance of stutterers and normal speakers on various voluntary, rhythmical movements of certain peripheral speech organs, namely, the diaphragm, the tongue, the lips, and the lower jaw.

Experimental Design: Thirteen stutterers (2 adult females, 8 adult males, 3 males under 14 years of age) and fourteen normal speakers (all adults, 1 female, 13 males) served as subjects. The kymographic recording technique was used for all tests. The point was stressed that the rhythm selected was to be maintained as nearly as possible throughout the tests. The stutterers were instructed to rest during any test when they felt fatigue was interfering with the regularity of the performance. As a check against the performance of the vocal structures, a simple tapping test involving rhythmical arm-hand coordination was used.

Summary:

1. Stutterers showed a marked inferiority to normal speakers in ability to execute rhythmical, voluntary movements of midline speech structures in a non-speaking situation. This conclusion applied particularly to voluntary movements of the diaphragm and tongue and in a somewhat lesser degree to voluntary movements of lips and jaw.

2. There was no significant difference between stutterers and normal speakers in the performance of voluntary rhythmical movements using structures other than those of speech such as arm and hand.

3. Gross qualitative differences exist between the voluntary performances of the speech structures of stutterers and normal speakers.

Conclusions: On the basis of this study it was concluded that stutterers show a decided inferiority to normal speakers in their ability to control midline speech structures for other than speech activities.

TITLE

Travis L. E.: Dissociation of the Homologous Muscle Function in Stuttering, *Archives of Neurology and Psychiatry*, 31 (1934), 127-133.

Purpose: To record the action current potentials from the two masseter muscles.

Experimental Design: Action currents were recorded simultaneously from the two masseter muscles during speech in easy, unemotional, conversational situations. The subjects discussed current topics of the day, answered questions, and entered into conversation with the experimenters. The subjects were 24 adult stutterers and 24 adult non-stutterers.

Summary: During the apparently normal speech of the 22 non-stutterers the action currents from the two masseter muscles were practically identical in regard to instant of appearance, frequency, intensity, duration and general patterning. Action currents appeared continuously during speaking, presenting variation in intensity with variations in the amount of activity of the muscles. During the stuttering of 18 of the stutterers the action currents from one masseter muscle were strikingly different from those from the other masseter muscle in intensity, appearance, frequency, duration, and general patterning. During the free speech of all stutterers and during the stuttering of six, the action currents from one masseter muscle of the stutterers were not strikingly different from those of the other masseter muscle, nor were they strikingly dissimilar in any other respect to the action currents made by normal speakers. In imitative stuttering neither normal speakers nor stutterers could voluntarily produce abnormalities in the action current similar to those obtained during true stuttering. In true stutterers, it was felt, the shift from voluntary to true stuttering was easily discernible in the action current records.

Conclusions. It was concluded that during normal speech the action currents from the two masseter muscles are identical, while during stuttering those from one masseter muscle are strikingly different from those of the other. A unified control by the central nervous system of the two sides of the speech mechanism during normal speech and a lack of such control during stuttering was hypothesized.

TITLE

Williams, D.: **Masseter Muscle Action Potentials in Stuttered and Non-Stuttered Speech,** *Journal of Speech and Hearing Disorders,* **20** (1955), 242-261.

Purpose: To measure the bilaterally recorded masseter potentials in order to test the hypothesis put forward by Travis and Van

Riper that such measurements show a basic neurophysiological difference betwen stutterers and non-stutterers.

Experimental Design: In order to eliminate variables not considered in former research variations in voluntary jaw movement and differences in electrode placement were employed.

Fifteen adult stutterers matched with a control group were tested under two conditions: (1) speaking and (2) performing voluntary jaw movements. For speaking, 20 two or three syllable words were introduced and read singly; half were underlined for the non-stutterers. They were instructed to fake stuttering on these. The stutterers were preconditioned to use the "bounce," and the words were then introduced to them until they had stuttered on ten and read ten without stuttering. The voluntary jaw movements consisted of opening and closing; moving right to left and left to right; jaw tremor; circular movement of the mandible; and various combinations of these.

Summary: Data were compared with respect to (1) bilateral differences in amplitude (25% or more difference was considered "different"); (2) bilateral difference in instant of appearance of the action current; (3) presence or absence of spikes (more than 100% increase of amplitude); and (4) presence or absence of reversals of bilateral amplitude difference. The following results were found in these four comparisons:

1. No significant differences, except that on one of the eight measures (mean number of words showing greater amplitude of the right masseter) the stutterers were more anomalous than the non-stutterers.

2. No significant differences. Very few words of any of the subjects showed concomitant appearance of action current.

3. Stutterers showed significantly more spiking when stuttering than did either group in non-stuttering speech. However, the non-stutterers' faked stuttering also showed the same thing, demonstrating more spiking than did stuttered speech of stutterers. When stutterer's speech was made more effortless during blocking (by the bounce method) the spiking was reduced to a point below the level of significant difference from the non-stutterers.

4. Same pattern as above.

5. In the jaw movements, one comparison out of forty showed a significant difference.

Conclusions: On the basis of the following, it was suggested that action current anomalies are part of the stuttering syndrome, and not a cause of it.

1. Stutterers while stuttering can be equated with both stutterers and non-stutterers during non-stuttered speech by instructions given the subjects.

2. Non-stutterers faking stuttering show the same anomalies as stutterers' stuttering.

3. Specific action current anomalies can be produced by specific jaw movements by both stutterers and non-stutterers.

TITLE

Strother, C. R., and Kriegman, L. S.: Diadochokinesis in Stutterers and Non-Stutterers, *Journal of Speech Disorders*, 8 (1943), 323-335.

Purpose: To determine if there are significant differences between stutterers and non-stutterers with respect to rate of diadochokinetic movements of the lips, mandible, tongue, or fingers. Past studies have produced mixed results with respect to these characteristics.

Experimental Design: The stuttering sample consisted of 15 adults (11 males, 4 females). The stutterers were matched with a control group of sex, dextrality quotient (Iowa Laterality Index), and rhythm discrimination (Seashore Test). A technique was used which permitted a study of the course and amplitude, as well as of the rate, of movement.

Measurements of tongue movements were obtained by means of a face mask in which there was a rubber tube (bulb attached to the end of it) leading to a Macey recording tambour. The movement of the jaws was recorded by placing a rubber bulb with tongue depressors on either side and fastened on each end by a rubber band, between the teeth. Metal stops were also put between the depressors at each end. This procedure provided better control over the amplitude of the movement.

Lip movements were obtained by pneumographic recordings made when S had tip of balloon between teeth. For a measure of finger tapping, a tambour with a small contact plate glued to the diaphragm was used. Overall reliability .95.

Tongue movements were measured first. The S was told to say "t" as fast as he could, the mask was then placed lightly against his face and the "t" sound again said as rapidly as possible. Three trials of three seconds were recorded. The procedure was the same for mandible, fingers, and lips.

Summary: Stutterers were found to be superior to non-stutterers in rate of movement for all structures studied, though the differences were not statistically significant. To see if the severity of stuttering affected the results, the severe stutterers were singled out and compared with the normals. This did not change the former results.

As there had been much research on these mechanisms in the past, the authors felt that it would be advantageous to pool the data of the studies on the various mechanisms and analyze them as a whole. This was done by analysis of variance. No significant differences were found between stutterers and non-stutterers in rate of movement of tongue, jaw or lips. A significant difference in favor of the non-stutterers was found in the comparison of the studies ($F = 56.13$, less than .01) for finger tapping. This difference was attributed to the lack of matching samples in some of the studies, and other variables such as instructions, etc.

Conclusions: It was concluded that further research is needed on different age groups, the factors related to finger tapping, and the possibility of brow movements as an important discriminatory factor.

TITLE

Kopp, H.: The Relationship of Stuttering to Motor Disturb-ances, *Nervous Child,* **2 (1943), 107-116.**

Purpose: To show the relationship between stuttering and motor disturbances.

Experimental Design: Kopp carried on research on stuttering at the University of Paris from 1934 to 1939, during which time 450 stutterers (pre-school to adult) were observed and studied. Family history, personal history, psychologic observation and measurement, anthropometric research, and neuropsychiatric, endocrinologic, hematologic, radiologic, and general medical examinations were made. Observations were also made at the children's homes and in special experimental social situations. The first psychomotor developments of early childhood were studied with special attention given to the appearance of the first word and the first sentence, as well as to bowel and bladder training. The motor system was not studied by the usual neurologic method, but by scaled tests developed by Oseretzky. This scale investigates static coordination, dynamic coordination of the hands, general dynamic coordination, speed of movements, associated movements and synketic movements.

Summary:

1. There are two types of stuttering:
   (a) Stuttering that dates from the first manifestations of speech and that never stopped throughout the child's language development—this may be called "constitutional stuttering"; and
   (b) Stuttering that appeared more or less tardily, the child's language development being normal during the early period.

2. Kopp stressed the importance of the motor disturbance demonstrated in stuttering children of both categories, i.e., 1 (a) and 1 (b).
   (a) The child's early neuromuscular development is retarded.

(b) A motor retardation or disturbance exists while intelligence may be normal or even above-normal.

3. Neurologic examination alone did not detect any neuro-
pathologic signs, in spite of the fact that all S's exhibited motor
deficiencies.

4. Certain cases exhibited a fairly regular motor development,
but the majority presented in various degrees a lack of correlation
between normal and even above-normal intelligence and motor
development.

Conclusions: It was concluded that:

1. Gross hereditary defects of the motor function and disturbances of various motor systems are almost always found
among stutterers. "They are especially manifest when stuttering
is constitutional; and they are still very distinct when stuttering
is acquired."

2. These motor disturbances are so significant, the author felt,
they suggest that stuttering is not fundamentally a psychologic
disorder.

TITLE

**Finkelstein, P., and Weisberger, S.: The Motor Proficiency of
Stutterers,** *Journal of Speech and Hearing Disorders,* **19 (1954),
52-58.**

Purpose: To duplicate, with certain modifications, a study reported by Helene Kopp, concerned with the performance of stutterers on the Oseretsky Tests of Motor Proficiency.

Experimental Design: Subjects were 30 children, 4 to 10 years of
age, 15 stutterers and 15 non-stutterers, matched for age, sex, and
laterality. Each group was composed of 12 boys and 3 girls, 10
right-sided, 4 left-sided, and one mixed laterality. The groups
presented approximately the same socio-economic backgrounds,
and were drawn from the same locale.

The subjects were instructed and then given the Oseretsky
Tests under constantly controlled conditions. The tests included
six measures of motor proficiency: 1. General static coordination,

2. Dynamic coordination of hands. 3. General dynamic coordination. 4. Motor speed. 5. Simultaneous voluntary movement. 6. Synkinesia (performing a function without extraneous movements).

Summary: As a group, the stutterers were slightly, though not significantly, superior to the controls in five of the six tests. The test in which the controls were superior was simultaneous movements; they were superior by an amount smaller than any of the other differences, and the difference was not significant.

The average stutterer was 1.2 months younger than his control in chronological age, but was 7.3 months older in motor proficiency for the mean of all the tests.

When the stuttering group was compared with Oseretsky's norms (as were Kopp's subjects), they showed a mean retardation of 3.5 months. The control group, when thus compared, showed a mean retardation of 12 months. By Oseretsky's criteria, 10 of the stutterers and seven of the controls were "normal" or "superior"; five of the stutterers and eight of the controls were below "normal" on Oseretsky's norms.

Conclusions: These findings are in direct contrast to Kopp's and the disparity is difficult to account for. Perhaps of importance are the facts that Kopp used Oseretsky's norms as control, and may have used a different translation of the test literature than that employed in the present experiment.

It was concluded that stutterers are not retarded in motor proficiencies, but tend to be slightly superior to non-stutterers in such abilities.

TITLE

Hunsley, Y. L.: **Dysintegration in the Speech Musculature of Stutterers During the Production of a Non-Vocal Temporal Pattern,** *Psychological Monographs,* 49 (1937), 32-49.

Purpose: To investigate whether stutterers are markedly inferior to normal speakers in the use of speech musculature in a non-speech act.

Experimental Design: Subjects were 20 stutterers (17 male and 3 females) and 20 normal speakers (15 male and 5 females). Almost all subjects were undergraduate college students. Recordings, by means of an elaborate apparatus, were taken of their jaw, lip, tongue, and breathing movement while producing a rhythmic pattern of clicks. A stimulus pattern consisted of four clicks produced by one revolution of a disk. There were 12 different speeds ranging from 30.7 rpm to 91.3 rpm. The subject produced each pattern three times. The average for the three and the optimal were used in computing the results.

Summary: The data revealed that at every speed in each muscle group, the non-stutterers' performance, with one exception, was better than the stutterers' performance. This one exception was at 89.3 rpm on the performance with tongue movement. For both groups there was an increase in difficulty as the stimulus pattern speed increased as shown by increases in sizes of scores. The data also showed that as speed increased the difference between the two groups decreased. This, it was felt, might be due to the fact that both groups were approaching the upper limit of performance capacity.

The optimal score made by each S at each speed for each musculature gave the same general pattern as did the average score for each speed for the group. The tabulations and graphs showed that stutterers are not able to perform a pattern of movements in time as well as normal speakers and both stutterers and normals perform less accurately when the rate of movement is increased. The differences were statistically significant. This was interpreted as meaning that the speed factor was not the element that differentiated stutterers from normal speakers.

While the major contribution of the study was that stutterers and normals are quantitatively different, there were many qualitative differences which the author felt were appropriate to acknowledge.

In general, the recordings of the stutterers were very irregular when compared with the normals. These irregularities were classified into six categories: (1) breaks, i.e., failure to reproduce the clicks at certain speeds, (2) reversal of temporal intervals of the pattern, (3) too many movements (four or more), (4) too few movements (three or less), (5) small movements superimposed on large movements and (6) blocks, tonic and clonic, in the performance pattern.

In general, both stutterers and normal speakers in the first three categories listed showed an increase in the number of irregularities with an increase in rate of movement. For all speeds, stutterers showed a greater number of irregularities than normals. These results demonstrated that in performance of a pattern of movements in time, stutterers are qualitatively inferior to normal speakers.

Conclusions: It was concluded that stutterers were inferior to normal speakers in their ability to perform a silent pattern in time with the speech musculature. The author suggests that, in part, this supports Travis' theory that stutterers lack a dominant gradient sufficient to integrate the bilateral speech musculature.

TITLE

Strother, C. R., and Kriegman, L. S.: Rhythmokinesis in Stutterers and Non-stutterers, *Journal of Speech Disorders*, 9 (1944), 239-244.

Purpose: To investigate the ability of stutterers and non-stutterers to reproduce a given rhythm pattern by movements of the lips, jaws, tongue, and finger.

Experimental Design: Experimental group consisted of 15 adult stutterers (11 male). A control group, obtained from a university population, was matched with the experimental group on the bases of age, sex, dextrality quotient on the Iowa Laterality Test, and rhythm discrimination on the Seashore Test. Mean chronological age of stutterers was 23 years; the controls, 24. Mean dextrality quotient of stutterers was 80; of the controls, 81. Mean rhythm score of stutterers was 22; of the controls, 22.

Tongue movement was recorded by means of a face mask which was connected by a rubber tube to a tambour. The subject repeated the "t" sound with the mask fitted tightly against the face.

Jaw movements were recorded using a rubber bulb fixed between two tongue depressors, held together by rubber bands.

In obtaining lip movements, the tip of the balloon was placed between S's teeth, and the apparatus was so arranged that unless the teeth were held together, the balloon would not remain between the lips. This eliminated jaw movements and obtained a sensitive record of lip movements.

A tambour with a small circular contact plate glued to the middle of the tambour diaphragm was used for recording finger-tapping.

Stimulus pattern was produced by disks fitted on a phonograph turntable. The disks were so placed that they would contact with another piece of metal, producing an audible click, in a pattern of ¾ time, two eighth beats followed by two quarter beats. Turntable was set for 33 rpm. Records of stimulus and response were obtained simultaneously. This general procedure was followed for each movement: five stimulus patterns produced while the S merely listened to rhythm, five more which he accompanied by tapping his knuckles, five patterns combining knuckle-tapping and the movement to be recorded, five practice trials with stimulus accompanied by movement to be recorded, and, finally, three recorded trials of three patterns each.

Summary: The results showed that stutterers were consistently, although not significantly, superior to non-stutterers on all movements. Individual differences among the non-stutterers were greater than the individual differences among the stutterers. Stutterers are slightly, but not significantly, superior to non-stutterers with respect to the ability to reproduce a given rhythm pattern with the tongue and finger, and they probably do not differ significantly from the non-stutterers with respect to reproduction of rhythm patterns with the lips and jaw.

Conclusions: It was concluded that although stutterers are consistently slightly superior to non-stutterers in ability to reproduce a rhythm pattern, the difference is not statistically significant. No evidence of arrhythmokinesis among the stuttering group was obtained.

TITLE

Eisenson, J., and Winslow, C.: The Perseveration Tendency in Stutterers in a Perceptual Function, *Journal of Speech Disorders,* 3 (1938), 195-198.

Purpose: To determine the relationship between stuttering and the perseverating tendency in a perceptual task.

Experimental Design: Subjects consisted of 15 adult male stutterers and 20 male non-stutterers. Equipment consisted of seven cards prepared for tachistoscope exposure. On each card squares of color were pasted—the number of colors ranging from four on Card I progressively to nine on Card 7. The number of squares exceeded the number of colors (duplication of same color on same card). Exposure time was ⅕ of a second. Subjects were asked to fixate on a card and record the number of colors seen, not the number of squares.

Summary: Non-stutterers saw more colors than the stutterers on the average and were more variable. The difference approached reliability.

Stutterers recorded more completely the names of the colors from the number than did the non-stutterers; the difference was not reliable, however, due to the small number of subjects.

No difference was found between the stutterers and non-stutterers on the average number of omissions in cards. The greater variability of the non-stutterers, however, was of interest.

Stutterers inserted the wrong names of colors in the records more frequently than did the non-stutterers; however, the difference was not statistically reliable.

Erroneous insertions were analyzed to determine the perseverating characteristic, and a statistically reliable difference was found indicating that stutterers did perseverate considerably more frequently.

Conclusions: Perseveration was concluded to be at least one of the characteristics of stutterers which accounts for the phenomena of stutttering, i.e., stutterers continue to react to stimuli when the stimuli are no longer present, and cannot adjust themselves to changing situations as readily as non-stutterers.

It was further suggested that stuttering may be an indication of an inability on the part of the stutterer to adjust his speech organs quickly and easily to the production of the various sounds in the stream of speech. "Stuttering is a manifestation of the perseverating tendency, which, at least in part, causes the stutterer to stutter as his normal way of speaking."

TITLE

Eisenson, J., and Pastel, E.: A Study of the Perseverating Tendency in Stutterers, *Quarterly Journal of Speech*, 22 (1936), 626-631.

Purpose: To test the hypothesis that the stutterers' repetition of sounds or perseveration constitutes what is called stuttering.

Experimental Design: Thirty male stutterers, ranging in age from 10 to 16, were matched with 30 non-stutterers. The subjects were given the Mahler-Elkin Test which is divided into a series of timed sub-tests each containing initial and final tests of the function considered. Sub-test I is a simple task in which the S is required to copy the letter "b." In Sub-test II the S is required to make a different response, i.e., letter "B." The Final Test is a combination in random order of both situations. The S here is required to change his reactions quickly and suddenly. Failure to make these changes is a failure in responding to a new situation. A failure means that the S continued to react to a situation which was no longer present. This is taken as a measure of the perseverating tendency. The fewer the items completed in changing from one task to another, the greater the amount of time needed for the adjustment to the new task or the larger the degree of perseveration.

Summary: Statistically significant differences in the groups showed that the stutterers slowed down in their tasks more than the non-stutterers and made more errors while working. The slowing down arose out of the stutterer's difficulty adjusting himself to the changing situation.

Conclusions: It was concluded that stutterers perseverate more than non-stutterers. The perseveration is an indication of a resistance to change and lack of adaptability on the part of stutterers. It was suggested that the phenomena of stuttering may be considered symptoms of a perseverating tendency.

TITLE

King, P. T.: Perseverative Factors in a Stuttering and a Non-Stuttering Population, *Pennsylvania State Review of Educational Research*, 5 (1953), 10-12.

Purpose: To determine if stutterers are more perseverative than non-stutterers. Three parts to the question were evolved, namely: Are stutterers more perseverative than non-stutterers on (1) tests designed to measure alternating motor perseveration? (2) tests designed to measure dispositional rigidity but which involve a motor element? (3) tests designed to measure sensory perseveration?

Experimental Design: Ten tests were selected from three perseverative areas: the alternating motor area, the dispositional rigidity area, and the sensory area. These tests were administered to 82 non-stuttering males, 55 non-stuttering females, 72 stuttering males, and eight stuttering females. A test of general intellectual ability was given to all groups. Non-stuttering males were compared to stuttering males, and non-stuttering females were compared to stuttering females as to the significance of the difference between the mean perseverative scores on each test. An intercorrelation matrix was made for the stuttering and non-stuttering groups, using the ten perseverative tests and the tests of intellectual ability to see if a group perseverative existed.

Summary: On the tests designed to measure alternating motor perseveration, male stutterers were found to be more perseverative at the .01 level of confidence than male non-stutterers on three of four tests, and between .01 and .02 level of confidence on the fourth test. Female stutterers were not found to be significantly more perseverative than female non-stutterers in this area with the exception of one test. However, when results of the tests in this area were pooled, the females were more perseverative at the .05 level of confidence.

On the test designed to measure dispositional rigidity motor perseveration, neither male nor female stutterers were found to be more perseverative than non-stutterers when tests were considered individually. When the three tests were combined, stuttering males were more perseverative than non-stuttering males at the .05 level of confidence. Female stutterers were not more perseverative when tests were considered collectively.

On tests designed to measure sensory perseveration, two of the three tests in the area discriminated between stutterers and non-stutterers below the .02 level of confidence. One of the two tests indicated stutterers to be more perseverative, and the other two demonstrated non-stutterers to be more perseverative. The test area as a unit did not seem to point in any consistent direction.

When all tests were viewed collectively, 17 comparisons showed that stutterers indicated a greater amount of perseveration. A perseverative general group factor does not seem to exist in either male or female non-stutterers. No areas of perseveration seemed to stand out as units.

Conclusions: On the basis of the results, it was concluded that: (1) Stutterers demonstrate significantly more perseveration tendencies generally than non-stutterers and are significantly more perseverative on specific tests which demand a contiguous change of set. (2) The tests used do not significantly discriminate between non-stuttering males and females. (3) No strong general group perseveration factor apparently exists in the stuttering or non-stuttering populations. (4) Performance of subjects on these tests indicates that perseverative areas do not stand out as units.

TITLE

Travis, L. E., Malamud, W., and Thayer, T. R.: The Relationship Between Physical Habitus and Stuttering, *Journal of Abnormal and Social Psychology*, 29 (1934), 132-140.

Purpose: To investigate the question of how much a certain personality (physically and mentally considered) may be the proper
subsoil for the development of stuttering.

Experimental Design: Subjects were 47 male stutterers ranging
in age from 15-30, and 128 normal speakers ranging in age from
17-37. The mean age for stutterers was 21.7, for normals 19.7.
The identification of body types was made on the basis of general
observation and Kretschmer's types: *Pyknoid habitus*—presence
of pyknic components in conjunction with characteristics indicative of other physical types; *Leptosome habitus*—presence of long,
narrow, flat thorax; narrow shoulders, bones, muscles thin and
delicate; pale skin; egg shaped face; *Athletic habitus*—strong
skeletal development; broad shoulders; narrow hips and slender
lower limbs; hard muscles; *Leptosome-athletic*—mixture; *Dysplastic*—pronounced length of extremities; broad hips and often
characteristics of opposite sex present; dwarfism, disproportion
in body parts.

The classification of stutterers as to mental types was made by
evaluating the following traits in each subject: good mixer, cheerful, moody, flighty, tenacious, stubborn, self-centered, shy, asocial,
holds deep grudges, suspicious, industrious and nervous.

Summary: The results showed that a larger per cent of stutterers
than normals were classified in the leptosome and leptosome-
athletic groups (76.5% of the stutterers as compared to 24.2% of
the normals). Also a much larger per cent of normals fell into
the athlete and dysplastic groups than did stutterers—62% to
14.9% for the stutterers. Not a single stutterer was diagnosed as
a pyknic. However since the pyknic habitus is not clearly defined
in an individual until 30 years of age, it was suggested that some
of the athletic types might eventually develop a more easily observable pyknic type.

From the mental classification of the stutterers, it was found that the great majority of leptosomes were introverted and a great majority of the pyknoids were extroverted. About half of the leptosome-athletics were introverted, the other half ambiverted.

The major finding was that stutterers as contrasted with normal speakers seemed to fall into a single major body group, the leptosome. This suggested that not only the stutterer's personality, but also his stuttering may be constitutionally determined. Acquired causative factors could not be ruled out but it appeared that if they operate, they do operate with a constitutional predisposition.

Conclusions: It was concluded that:

1. A majority of stutterers fall into the leptosome and leptosome-athletic groups.

2. The great majority of stutterers indicate introverted tendencies.

3. Because of the striking relationship between the stuttering and physical habitus, it would seem logical to assume that constitutional determinants play an important role in stuttering.

TITLE

Karlin, I. W.: A Psychosomatic Theory of Stuttering, *Journal of Speech Disorders,* **12 (1947), 319-322.**

Purpose: To present the theory "that the primary or basic cause for stuttering is a delay in the myelinization of the cortical areas in the brain concerned with speech."

Experimental Design: None.

Summary: Most of the nerve fibers of the central nervous system are invested with myelin sheaths. These sheaths are regarded as "having an insulating function" and perhaps a nutritive value to the enclosed axon. "Myelinization is regarded as correlated with function. A nerve fiber that has not been completely myelinated may transmit impulses but the resulting action will lack precision and fine coordination." The author states Flechsig's view that "the degree of myelinization of the fibers of the central nervous system is an index of their functional capacity." The average age of onset of speech is 19 months for boys and 18 months for girls. Speech becomes more comprehensible with age and is perfected at an earlier age by girls than by boys. This normally takes place around the age of three or three and one half years of age. Various cortical areas are myelinized at different stages of development. The stages of development are more delayed in some than in others. At the same time, around the age of three, when the speech mechanism normally becomes capable of smooth functioning, there is a natural negativistic period in the personality development of the child.

Conclusions: The author concluded that the development of stuttering is the result of a combination of organic and psychological factors. Myelinization—and therefore perfect functioning of the speech area—is delayed. This results in inability to function with desired efficiency and usually causes great emotional strain during the negativistic period. If the situation is well handled, the tension can be eased until time allows myelinization to develop and the speech mechanism to improve in functioning. If stuttering continues, emotional factors and habit begin to perpetuate the problem. The theory, it was felt, also offers an explanation for the greater incidence of stuttering among males. Females, reportedly, mature physically earlier than males, and myelinization is probably more normal for them during critical developmental periods.

TITLE

Glasser, E. M.: **Possible Relationship Between Stuttering and Endocrine Malfunctioning,** *Journal of Speech Disorders,* 1 (1936), 81-89.

Purpose: To determine whether there is any scientific evidence to indicate a relationship between endocrine pathology and stuttering, and to obtain information as to the use and effect of endocrine therapy in cases of stuttering.

Experimental Research: Questionnaires as follows were sent to 35 individuals prominent in the field:

1. "Have you ever used endocrine therapy for the treatment of stuttering or stammering? If so, in approximately how many cases?

2. "What was the nature of this therapy?

3. "About how many of the patients you have treated do you consider to be improved? How many cured?

4. "Was the endocrine therapy the only treatment employed for the disorder? If not, in how many of the cases were additional means of treatment used, such as the patient's attending a speech correction clinic or psychiatric treatment? Of these latter cases, how many were improved? Cured?

5. "Would you kindly state, at whatever length suits your convenience, any theories you may hold as to the possible or probable relationship between glandular malfunctioning and stuttering."

Twenty-nine persons replied. Of these, 19 made some contribution.

Summary: Of the 19 replies, 13 were negative, ranging from doubt of any relationship existing to a rather certain feeling that there was none. The other six ranged in content from the relation of certain experiences in the area which might be of some significance to one reply expressing the opinion that there was a causal relationship between stuttering and thyroid activity.

Conclusions: It was concluded that there was no scientific evidence presented which would tend to show a definite causal relationship between endocrine pathology and stuttering. No evidence was reported which would warrant the conclusion that glandular treatment of childhood hypothyroidism will result in an improvement in stuttering in cases where the two happen to go together.

It was suggested that stimulation of the sympathetic nervous system by a drug such as epinephrine may occasionally cause stuttering; however, it was felt that psychological stimuli, inferiority feelings, apprehension, or other subjective factors may also affect the cerebral processes and tend to make the individual more susceptible to stuttering.

TITLE

McCroskey, R.: Effect of Speech on Metabolism: A Comparison Between Stutterers and Non-stutterers, *Journal of Speech and Hearing Disorders,* **22 (1957), 46-52.**

Purpose: To study the Basal Metabolic Rate of stutterers and non-stutterers; to see the effect of speaking on BMR for both, and the effect of various stages of therapy on BMR for stutterers.

Experimental Design: Subjects were 20 stutterers (17 males, 3 females) with a mean age of 21.7, and 20 non-stutterers (17 males, 3 females) with a mean age of 30.5. Stuttering group included 9 individuals who had completed therapy and eleven who were receiving therapy.

A US army gas mask was adapted to fit the regular air lines of the Benedict-Roth apparatus in obtaining scores. All S's were required to rest for 30 minutes before actual testing. After a six minute period of testing apparatus, S's were then tested for score during a four minute period during which they lay in a supine position breathing quietly. At the end of this four minute period S's were instructed to recite the Pledge of Allegiance continuously for an additional four minutes from the same supine position. Scores were taken for this situation.

Summary: Results were analyzed statistically via analysis of variance. There appeared to be no difference between stutterers and non-stutterers in the non-speaking situation. The BMR scores during speaking were significantly different for both groups at the .01 level; however, there was no difference between stutterers and non-stutterers. The two sub-groups within the stuttering group were different in BMR scores during the speaking situation, with the post-therapy group showing a comparatively lower BMR. This difference was significant beyond the .01 level. It was noted that the effect of the speech activity could be observed in BMR scores for a period of four minutes after speaking had stopped. It was suggested that the physician or technician should require the patient to be silent for a ten or fifteen minute period before BMR testing.

Conclusions: It was concluded that there is no significant difference between stutterers and non-stutterers with respect to basal metabolic rate. Both groups do show a significant difference between BMR scores taken while resting quietly and while speaking orally. Stutterers who have completed therapy showed a significantly smaller rise in BMR scores than stutterers who are still in the process of receiving help.

TITLE

Kenyon, E. L.: The Etiology of Stammering: The Psychophysiological Facts Which Concern the Production of Speech Sounds and Stammering, *Journal of Speech Disorders*, 8 (1943), 337-348.

Purpose: To relate the psychophysiologic origin of voice production to stuttering.

Experimental Design: None.

Summary: The author feels that there are four primary principles of action determining vocal cord movement: (1) Vocal cords abducted for breathing. (2) Vocal cords in a balanced abducted-adducted position for the production of the whispered voice. (3) Vocal cords in a balanced abducted-adducted position for production of the loud voice (cords are more closely approximated for the loud voice than for the whispered voice). (4) Vocal cords completely adducted for prevention of breathing and in swallowing food. Number (4) position is the position in which the cords are, it is felt, during the act of blocking.

The author feels that all of these positions can be voluntarily controlled by setting the chest musculature into action by compressing or expanding it. After a period of time this control can become as natural as the involuntary movements.

For the production of any speech sound the breathed air must pass through the vocal cords. In stuttering, the entire speech sound mechanism (chest, vocal cords, articulatory organs) is in action with movement stopped and no sound forthcoming. This, he feels, signifies that the passage of air through the vocal cords has been prevented. For all but six sounds (p, b, t, k, g) vocal adduction is the only answer. For these six sounds, he feels that vocal adduction is present with the blocking of the nose and mouth passages.

Conclusions: It was concluded that stuttering is fundamentally a specific disorder of the psychophysiologic accomplishment of the vocal function of speech. The basic act of stuttering consists of the following: when the mechanism of speech production is in action, a compulsory interpolation of a normal but misplaced psychophysiological act, vocal adduction, is caused to occur. This prevents the passage of air and sound production. This misplaced act, voluntarily accomplished, through repetition becomes habit and results in the act of stuttering.

TITLE

Harms, M. A., and Malone, J. Y.: The Relationship of Hearing Acuity to Stammering, *Journal of Speech Disorders*, 4 (1939), 363-370.

Purpose: To determine if hearing acuity is an etiological factor in stuttering. To determine the status of stutterers among the deaf and hard of hearing in schools for such individuals, and to evaluate the hearing acuity of known stutterers not in schools for the deaf and hard of hearing.

Experimental Design: The following questionnaire was sent to 209 oral schools for the deaf and hard of hearing in the United States:

1. "In your experience, have you found any deaf children who stammer?

2. "Have you found any stammerers among those with some percentage of hearing? What percentage? What test was used to calibrate the acuity?"

Sixty-two stutterers were given pure-tone hearing acuity tests.

Summary: Approximately 45% of the schools representing 74% of the total enrollment in oral schools responded.

1. There were eight known cases of stuttering among 14,458 subjects. Four of these acquired speech and had stuttered before becoming deaf. The remaining four had no available history.

2. Among those with residual hearing, 34 stuttered. Hearing loss in these cases varied from 22 to 80% within an average loss of 46%.

In 100% of the 62 stutterers given a hearing test, a hearing loss ranging from 10-22% in the better ear was found. Of these cases 93.5% remembered having had such childhood diseases as otitis media, mumps, measles, scarlet fever, diphtheria, whooping cough and other related diseases. All cases reported the appearance of stuttering before the end of the eighth year.

Conclusions: It was concluded that stuttering among the deaf is negligible. Where usable hearing is present, however, stuttering does appear.

Hearing impairment may exist where known stuttering exists, even though the stutterer may not be aware of it.

A theory suggesting that loss of hearing acuity during the period of speech formulation is a cause of stuttering was presented.

TITLE

Bills, A. G.: The Relation of Stuttering to Mental Fatigue, *Journal of Experimental Psychology,* **17 (1934), 575-584.**

Purpose: To answer the following questions: (1) What is the relation between the frequency and the length of the blocks of stutterers and normals? (2) How does fatigue effect the blocking in stutterers?

Experimental Design: Subjects were 33 normals and 28 adult stutterers (26 males, 2 females).

The task was naming five colors. First (A), the subjects gave vocal responses for five minutes, then (B) gave five minutes of manual responses by pressing keys corresponding to the colors. This order was reversed for half the subjects.

Summary: Since the stutterers performed the act of pronouncing the names of colors without stuttering, all delayed responses were considered to be mental blocks.

The stutterers' reaction records were much more irregular than the normals'. They also showed greater variability among themselves than did the normals. There was apparently a lack of rhythm in reacting which was greatly improved by having the stutterers react in time with a metronome.

A study of the fatigue curves for both the stutterers and normals showed that normals increased 30% in manual delay frequency and 35% in vocal frequency, while the stutterers only increased 7% on manual, and 8% on vocal blocking frequencies. The author suggested that this phenomenon could be accounted for by the fact that the stutterers started at such a high rate and had little room to increase.

It was found that those members of the stuttering group with slower reaction time delayed more frequently and longer than those with faster reaction time. This, however, was also true of the normal group and could not be considered a distinct variable.

Conclusions: The author concluded that there was a relationship between delayed reaction and stuttering and that an increase in one goes with an increase in the other. He felt that it was safe to assume that there is a common neurological basis involving a loss of control or coordinating ability. Stutterers, he felt, showed a constant mental fatigue and a low emotional threshold.

TITLE

Curtis, J.: **A Study of the Effect of Muscular Exercises Upon Stuttering,** *Speech Monographs,* **9** (1942), 61-74.

Purpose: To test the clinical observation that "fatigue" has an adverse effect on the speech of stutterers.

Experimental Design: Subjects were 21 male stutterers ranging in age from 17 to 26. The experiment was conducted in three cycles, the first and third being utilized as controls and conducted one week prior to and one week following the second. In all three cycles the subjects read six 500-word passages of factual prose, in the same order, each cycle for each individual, but differing in order from each other by the use of three reading orders. In the first and third (or control) cycles, the readings were interpolated by periods of rest or neutral activity. In the second (experimental) cycle, the readings were interpolated by periods of rather strenuous physical exercise, which were carefully matched and controlled for all subjects. For all readings, the subjects' stuttering was recorded by an experimenter by means of depressing a key when blocking occurred; subjects were asked to make no effort to refrain from blocking at any time in the experiments. The reliability of the judge in observing stuttering was determined to be .92 as to whether or not a word was stuttered, and .98 as to the duration of the block. Amount of stuttering in each of the three cycles was computed by four measures: 1. Frequency. 2. Total duration of stuttering. 3. Mean duration of stutterings. 4. Per cent of total time stuttered.

Summary: With the exception of mean duration of stuttering, the trends shown by the data were very similar for both experimental and control conditions. Mean duration of stuttering showed an increase, of a minor order, during the experimental condition. Adaptation effect was observable from the first to the sixth readings in all three cycles.

Conclusions: Attention was called to the fact that the results of physical exercise are only one aspect of "fatigue," but that one purpose of the experiment was to isolate this variable as far as possible and measure its effect.

It was concluded that no statistically significant effect upon stuttering as a result of physical exercise had been found by the experiment.

ETIOLOGY—PHYSIOLOGICAL

Additional Reading References

Anderson, L.: Stuttering and Allied Disorders—An Experimental Investigation of Underlying Factors, *Comparative Psychology Monographs*, 1 (1923), 1-78.

Backus, O.: Incidence of Stuttering Among the Deaf, *Annals of Otorhinolaryngology*, 47 (1938), 632-635.

Berman, A. B. and Train, G. J.: A Genetic Approach to the Problem of Stuttering, *Journal of Mental and Nervous Diseases*, 91 (1940), 580-590.

Berry, M. F.: Developmental History of Stuttering Children, *Journal of Pediatrics*, 12 (1938), 209-217.

———:Twinning in Stuttering Families, *Human Biology*, 9 (1937), 329-347.

Bluemel, C. S.: The Dominant Gradient in Stuttering, *Quarterly Journal of Speech*, 19 (1933), 233-242.

Brown, S. F., and Shulman, E. E.: Intra-Muscular Pressure in Stutterers and Non-Stutterers, *Speech Monographs*, 7 (1940), 63-74.

Bryngelson, B.: Investigation in the Etiology and Nature of Dysphemia and Its Symptom: Stuttering, *Journal of Speech Disorders*, 7 (1942), 15-28.

———, and Clark, T. B.: Left-Handedness and Stuttering, *Journal of Heredity*, 24 (1933), 287-390.

Cross, H.: The Motor Capacities of Stutterers, *Archives of Speech*, 1 (1936), 112-132.

Daniels, E. M.: An Analysis of the Relation Between Handedness and Stuttering with Special Reference to the Orton-Travis Theory of Cerebral Dominance, *Journal of Speech Disorders*, 5 (1940), 309-326.

Eisenson, J., and Berry, M.: The Biological Aspects of Stuttering, *Pedagogical Seminary and Journal of Genetic Psychology*, 61 (1942), 147-152.

Fagan, L. B.: Certain Reflexes During Stuttering, *Archives of Neurology and Psychiatry*, 19 (1928), 1006-1013.

Finklestein, P., and Weisberger, S. E.: The Motor Proficiency of Stutterers, *Journal of Speech and Hearing Disorders*, 19 (1954), 52-58.

Gordon, M. B.: Stammering Produced by Thyroid Medication, *American Journal of Medical Science*, 175 (1928), 360.

Graf, O. I.: Incidence of Stuttering Among Twins, *Stuttering in Children and Adults*, University of Minnesota Press, Minneapolis, 1955.

Hill, H.: Stuttering: I. A Critical Review and Evaluation of Bio-Chemical Investigations, *Journal of Speech Disorders*, 9 (1944), 245-261.

———: Stuttering: A Review and Integration of Physiological Data, *Journal of Speech Disorders*, 9 (1944), 289-324.

Jasper, H.: A Laboratory Study in Diagnostic Indices of Bilateral Neuromuscular Organization and Normal Speakers, *Psychological Monographs,* 43 (1932), 1.

———, and Murray, E.: A Study of Eye-Movements of Stutterers During Oral Reading, *Journal of Experimental Psychology,* 15 (1932), 528-538.

Johnson, W.: The Dominant Thumb in Relation to Stuttering, Eyedness and Handedness, *American Journal of Psychology,* 49 (1937), 293-297.

———, and Duke, L.: Change of Handedness Associated with Onset or Disappearance of Stuttering, *Journal of Experimental Education,* 4 (1935).

———, and King, A.: An Angle Board and Hand Usage Study of Stutterers and Non-Stutterers, *Journal of Experimental Psychology,* 31 (1945), 293-311.

Knott, J. R., and Tjossem, T. D.: Bilateral Electroencephalograms from Normal Speakers and Stutterers, *Journal of Experimental Psychology,* 35 (1943), 357-362.

Malhant, M.: The Relation of Stuttering to Cerebral Associated Reflexes and Conditioned Reflexes, *Mental Hygiene,* 30 (1935), 153-156.

Milisen, R., and Johnson, W.: A Comparative Study of Stutterers, Former Stutterers and Normal Speakers Whose Handedness Has Been Changed, *Archives of Speech,* 1 (1936), 61-86.

Nelson, S. E.: The Role of Heredity in Stuttering, *Journal of Pediatrics,* 14 (1939), 642-654.

Oates, D. W.: Left-Handedness in Relation to Speech Defects, Intelligence and Achievement, *Forum of Education,* 607 (1929), 91-105.

Ojemann, R.: Studies in Handedness: III. Relation of Handedness to Speech, *Journal of Educational Psychology,* 22 (1931), February.

Orton, S. T.: Physiological Theory of Reading Disability and Stuttering in Children, *New England Journal of Medicine,* 119 (1928), 1046.

———: Studies in Stuttering, *Archives of Neurology and Psychiatry,* 18 (1927), 671-672.

———, and Travis, L.: Studies in Stuttering: IV. Studies of Action Currents in Stutterers, *Ibid,* 21 (1929), January.

Palmer, M., and Gillett, A.: Respiratory Cardiac Arrhythmia in Stuttering, *Journal of Speech Disorders,* 4 (1939), 133-141.

Quinan, C.: Stammering and Left-Handedness, *Journal of Experimental Psychology,* 23 (1938), 304-312.

Rheinberger, M. B., Karlin, I. W., and Berman, A. B.: Electroencephelographic and Laterality Studies of Stuttering and Non-Stuttering Children, *Nervous Child,* 2 (1943), 117-133.

Ross, F. L.: A Comparative Study of Stutterers and Non-Stutterers on a Psychomotor Discrimination Task, *Stuttering in Children and Adults*, University of Minnesota Press, Minneapolis, 1955.

Rotter, J. B.: A Study of the Motor Integration of Stutterers and Non-Stutterers, *Ibid*.

Scripture, M. K., Glogow, O., and De Bra, A. H.: Left-Handedness as an Etiological Factor in Speech Defects, *Laryngoscope*, 27 (1917) 157-169.

Shackson R.: An Action Current Study of Muscle Contraction Latency with Special Reference to Latent Tetany in Stutterers, *Archives of Speech*, 1 (1936), 87-111.

Shohara, H.: A Contribution to the Genesis of Speech Movements and the Etiology of Stuttering, *Journal of Speech Disorders*, 7 (1942), 29-32.

Starr, H. E.: Psychological Concomitants of High Alveolar Carbon Dioxide; A Psycho-biochemical Study of the Etiology of Stammering, *Psychological Clinic*, 27 (1928), 1.

Steer, M. C.: A Qualitative Study of Breathing in Young Stutterers, a Preliminary Investigation, *Speech Monographs*, 2 (1935), 1-5.

Stratton, L. D.: A Factor in the Etiology of a Sub-Breathing Stammerer: Metabolism as Indicated by Urinary Cretine and Creatinine, *Journal of Comparative Psychology*, 3 (1924).

Strother, C.: A Study of the Extent of Dyssynergia Occurring During the Stuttering Spasm, *Psychological Monographs*, 39 (1937), 108-127.

Tompkins, E.: Left-Handedness and Stammering, *Quarterly Journal of Speech Education*, 5 (1919), 6-11.

Train, G., and Berman, A.: A Genetic Approach to the Problem of Stammering, *Journal of Nervous and Mental Diseases*, 91 (1940), 590-594.

Travis, L. E.: A Comparative Study of the Performance of Stutterers and Normal Speakers in Mirror Tracing, *Psychological Monographs*, 39 (1938), 45-50.

———:Dissociation of Homologous Muscle Function in Stuttering, *Archives of Neurology and Psychiatry*, 31 (1934), 127-133.

———: A Neurological Consideration of Stuttering, *Spoken Word*, 1 (1933), 8-11.

———: Studies in Stuttering, *Journal of American Medical Association*, 89 (1927), 2142.

———, and Fagan, L. B.: Studies in Stuttering: III. A Study of Certain Reflexes During Stuttering, *Archives of Neurology and Psychiatry*, 19 (1928), 1006-1013.

———, and Herren, R. Y.: Studies in Stuttering: V. A Study of Simultaneous Antitropic Movements of the Hands of Stutterers, *Ibid*, 22 (1929), 487-494.

———, and Johnson, W.: Stuttering and the Concept of Handedness, *Psychological Review*, 41 (1934), 534-561.

———, and Knott, J. R.: Bilaterally Recorded Brain Potentials from Normal Speakers and Stutterers, *Journal of Speech Disorders*, 2 (1937), 239-241.

———, and Lindsley, D. B.: An Action Current Study of Handedness in Relation to Stuttering, *Journal of Experimental Psychology*, 16 (1933), 258-270.

———, and Malamud, W. M.: Brain Potentials from Normal Subjects, Stutterers, and Schizophrenic Patients, *American Journal of Psychology*, 93 (1931), 929.

———, and Orton, S. T.: Studies in Stuttering: IV. Studies of Action Currents in Stutterers, *Archives of Neurology and Psychiatry*, 21 (1929), 60-68.

Twitmeyer, E. B.: Stammering in Relation to Hemo-Respiratory Factors, *Quarterly Journal of Speech*, 16 (1930), 278.

Van Dusen, C.: A Study of the Relation of the Relative Size of the Hands to Speech, *Speech Monographs*, 4 (1937), 127-133.

Van Riper, C.: The Quantitative Measurement of Laterality, *Journal of Experimental Psychology*, 18 (1935), 372-382.

Weller, H. C.: Blood Examinations in the Diagnosis and Treatment of Speech Disorders, *The Central States Speech Journal*, March, 1952.

Wepman, J. M.: Is Stuttering Inherited? *Yearbook American Speech Correction Association*, Wisconsin College Typing Company, Madison, 1934.

West, R.: A Neurological Test for Stutterers, *Journal of Neurology and Psychopathology*, 10 (1929), 114-118.

———: The Pathology of Stuttering, *Nervous Child*, 2 (1943), 96-106.

———, Nelson, S., and Berry, M.: The Heredity of Stuttering, *Quarterly Journal of Speech*, 25 (1939), 23-30.

———, and Nusbaum, E.: A Motor Test for Dysphemia, *Ibid.*, 15 (1929), 469-480.

Westphal, G.: An Experimental Study of Certain Motor Abilities of Stutterers, *Child Development*, 4 (1933), 214-221.

Woldstad, D.: Stuttering and Left-Handedness, *School and Community*, 17 (1931), 310-313.

UNIT IV

ETIOLOGY—PSYCHOLOGICAL

TITLE

Krausz, E. O.: Is Stuttering Primarily a Speech Disorder?
Journal of Speech Disorders, 5 (1940), 227-231.

Purpose: To explain stuttering in terms of psychological dynamics.

Experimental Design: None.

Summary:

1. "Speaking" is defined as the ability to articulate; "talking," as conveying a message to another person by the instrument and vehicle of speech.

2. The stutterer is able to "speak," his deficit becoming manifest in social situations when he has to "talk." Such social situations necessitate that a special *effort* be made when conveying a message to another person, and it is this effort that the stutterer regards himself as being unable to make.

3. A *Compulsion Neurosis* is a condition in which the patient, without any doubts of his ability to do something, knows that he should *not* do something which, however, he believes he cannot avoid doing and which he believes he is compelled to do, e.g., seeing that the door is locked or that his hands are spotlessly clean.

(a) *Positive Compulsion*—refers to the condition in which one never doubts that he *can do* what he thinks he *should not do*. (b) *Negative Compulsion*—refers to the condition in which one is convinced he *cannot do* something which he knows he *should do* or *should be able to do*.

4. Hence, the stutterer engages in the process of *re-ification* (a Latin derivative meaning to make a thing out of something which is not a thing). The stutterer re-ifies again and again his doubt that he cannot *speak* while actually he cannot *talk* in certain situations.

5. Origin of this Compulsion Neurosis in stutterers:

(a) The stutterer develops a somewhat distorted idea of what normal talking is like. He believes that talking normally means speaking without an effort. In fact, he regards making an effort almost as a sign of a speech defect, and in the process of re-ification uses "making efforts" as a means to further discourage himself. (b) *Time factor.* The patient more or less consciously gives himself a certain time within which he expects to make some improvement. The closer he comes to the limit he gave himself the more discouraged he gets because he will find that he still cannot talk *effortlessly;* hence, relapses occur. (c) In the infantile phase of the stutterer's personality development one meets with a phase of *unwillingness-to-talk* unless certain stipulations appear to him fulfilled. In other words, at a time when speech and the ability to convey messages through talking should be developed we discover a personality-in-the-making whose seemingly effortless attempts at articulation had been hailed either as the signs of brilliancy or had failed to make an impression as in the case of a nervous, highstrung, unresponsive early environment. Hence, the belief in his inability to speak developed from the inevitable environmetal reaction to the more and more manifest defect, i.e., from secondary gains of attention and privileging concern of parents and teachers, and from the discouraging cruelties of thoughtless, sneering remarks which both only contribute to reinforce the growing individual in the confusion of his evaluational standards.

Conclusions: The author suggests that (1) by bearing this factor of re-ification in mind, the therapist can almost confine his activity to pointing out the dynamics of his case, and, in addition, thus win his cooperation to an unexpected degree.

(2) Once the stutterer is convinced that the effort he has to make is comparable to the one which normal speakers must make when conveying a message under strain (such as during an oral examination or when fatigued), much of his emotional sur-charge will be removed.

TITLE

Coriat, I. H.: Stammering as a Psychoneurosis, *Journal of Abnormal Psychology,* **9 (1915), 417-430.**

Purpose: To present a theory for the cause of stuttering based on the concept that stuttering is one of the manifest forms of an anxiety-neurosis or anxiety-hysteria.

Experimental Design: None.

Summary: In the few cases treated by the psychoanalytic method conclusions were drawn which indicated that the "disturbing mechanism" was mental rather than physical; that is, it took the form of morbid anxiety due to unconscious emotional complexes which manifest themselves in speech disturbances.

Coriat theorizes that the hesitation of stutterers on certain words or "letters" is due to disturbing complexes. "The stammering does not cause the inhibition, it is the inhibition which is at the bottom of the stammering."

Basic theory: (a) there is an attempt to repress certain thoughts or emotions (usually sexual), (b) there is fear of self-betrayal of these repressed thoughts, (c) the fear of betrayal conflicts with the desire of self-expression, (d) hesitation of speech arises, (e) the repressed thoughts are forced into unconsciousness and, (f) the defective speech pattern becomes automatic.

Some of the types of repressed conflicts which produce stuttering during childhood are: (a) Repression (sexual acts, secrets, fears of betrayal, (b) Oedipus complexes (with fear of betrayal of hate for father), (c) Masochistic fantasies, (d) Fear of pronouncing or saying tabooed words . . . (e) Manifestation of anal eroticism (the holding of faeces so that subject could talk while trying to conceal the act).

Coriat likens the attacks of anxiety in stutterers to that of morbid anxiety to which are added frequent tics of facial and respiratory muscles. The difficulty in "curing" stuttering is due to the strong disinclination (resistance) of the stutterer to give up childhood pleasures of libido, which he attempts to conceal and enjoy as an adult.

Conclusions: It was concluded that "the treatment of stammering must be directed along the lines of breaking down the resistances which lead to constant reversions and stickings to the infantile libido with its tendencies to conceal itself, to an analysis of the various components which lead to a dread of speaking in certain situations and before certain individuals and to a sublimination of the effort to conceal the libido in the unconscious for the pleasure desired."

TITLE

Coriat, I. H.: The Psychoanalytic Conception of Stammering, *The Nervous Child*, 2 (1943), 167-171.

Purpose: To present a theory for the cause of stuttering.

Experimental Design: None.

Summary: In the pregenital stage of libido development, the author feels, there are two important phases, the oral stage and later the anal stage. These enter into the stuttering neurosis and can be demonstrated in practically every stutterer. The motor accomplishments of the attempts to speak can be seen as an act of nursing at an illusory nipple—all followed by a feeling of relaxation after the enunciation of the difficult word. It is a sort of compulsive repetition of primitive and early nursing activities.

The strong oral interest of stutterers gives them a labial nature. This is probably related to early nursing movements. The labials (p, b, m) are usually the most difficult sounds for stutterers to enunciate.

The difficulties in treatment of stutterers are due to three factors:

1. "Stammering is a narcissistic neurosis,
2. "Unwillingness to abandon the pleasure function of nursing activities in speech,
3. "Marked resistance arising from the anal-sadistic level of development."

The anxiety in stutterers is due to the inability of the ego to withstand the primitive oral eroticism.

Speech training treats only an isolated part of the neurosis and therefore is inadequate. It serves as reinforcement of oral-erotic pleasure. Therapy should consist in an abstinence from external forms of oral gratification as these too are reinforcing and increase the stutterer's resistance to analytic therapy.

Choice of the stuttering neurosis is unconscious and results from fixation at the oral-anal level. The development of the libido is slower than the ego and the most satisfactory outlet is the speech difficulty.

In stutterers, early pregenital tendencies appear in characteristic oral-nursing and oral-cannibalistic dreams. The fact that stutterers bite the tongue and mucous membranes is symptomatic of early oral sadism.

In analysis of stutterers there appear the three earliest stages of libido development: the oral-sucking stage; the anal-sadistic (conversion symptom of previtus and constipation) and the oral-sadistic stage (biting movements of lips and cannibalistic dreams).

This also affects the Oedipal complex. In women there is a strong relationship to castration complex. "The tongue has become a displaced phallus: the inner conflict within the libidinal economy has become concentrated on the lingual organ for the purpose of unconsciously satisfying a masculine aim." The symptoms have two opposite meanings: the wish to have a phallus and the wish to incorporate it by a cannibalistic tendency. In deep analysis there emerges a combination of phallic disgust and phallic envy. "Chronologically, the original castrator is the mother and as a consequence female stutterers, as a part of the Oedipus situation, hate their mothers."

Conclusions: It was concluded that stuttering is symptomatic of a fixation at the oral-anal level of libidinal development with Oedipal and castration complexes as components.

TITLE

Bloodstein, O., and Schreiber, L.: Obsessive-Compulsive Reactions in Stutterers, *Journal of Speech and Hearing Disorders*, 22 (1957), 33-39.

Purpose: To study the psychoanalytical concepts which regard the stuttering block as (1) a form of oral-anal eroticism and (2) as a form of repressed hostility.

Experimental Design: Subjects were 15 college stutterers (13 males, 2 females) and 15 college non-stutterers (13 males, 2 females) ranging in age from 17 to 24. All were given the TAT projective-type personality test. Stories were recorded verbatim and then scored independently by three judges. Judges, who were unsophisticated in scoring TAT, used check list of items based on Rapaport's description of obsessive-compulsive behavior as a guide.

Summary: Correlations among judges' scores were .72, .74, and .93. A slightly higher average obsessive-compulsive score was given to the stuttering group by two judges and a slightly lower score by one of the judges. The differences were not statistically significant. Overall obsessive-compulsive scores between stutterers and non-stutterers were not significant.

Conclusions: Recognizing the limitations of the sample and the means for measuring obsessive-compulsive behavior, the authors concluded that college stutterers show no more obsessive-compulsive tendencies than do college non-stutterers.

TITLE

Krout, M.: Emotional Factors in the Etiology of Stammering, *Journal of Abnormal and Social Psychology*, 31 (1936), 174-181.
Purpose: To determine whether stuttering has an emotional etiology.

Experimental Design: Three cases were selected as subjects. In each case, a different type of psychoanalytic treatment was employed.

Summary: *Case I:* male, age 19, college sophomore, I.Q.: 108. Symptoms: minor delinquencies, cynical toward opposite sex, nightmares of falling off high places, frequent daydreams, moody, has feelings of shame connected with body, frequent tonic stuttering; however, never in the presence of women.

Treatment: Hypnotic trance and free association were used, the stimulus words having been abstracted from his autobiography, and from among the words on which he blocked. Automatic writing in the trance was employed to facilitate recall.

Results: After homosexual events were abstracted, there was immediate improvement of speech. However, since no real insight was achieved, the stuttering eventually recurred.

Case II: male, age 18, I.Q.: 112.

Symptoms: frequent conflicts with older brother, no heterosexual contacts, began to stutter at age 8 or 9, left-handed, unsuccessful attempt at changing handedness, mother stutters slightly. He reports that music arouses sadness, professes pessimism, and has few friends. He is inconsiderate of others and resorts to exaggeration to achieve status.

Treatment: passive analysis in which the subject was hidden from view. Subject summarized the achievements of the preceding session, and then revealed the dreams of the preceding nights.

Recovered material: death wishes for the father (this was related to his aversion for music), his brother became a father substitute, strong ambivalence toward mother, (he said that he might be stuttering because he was "like mother"), at the age of 8 he started masturbating and since then has developed guilt feelings.

Results: his relations toward his family have changed markedly and a sudden speech recovery followed. This coincided with the discovery that he had been threatened with castration while annoying his mother. Also, he became right-handed without any suggestion on the part of the therapist.

Case III: female, age 21, I.Q.: 113.

Symptoms: feels apathetic, changeable moods, inability to secure or keep a position, reports headaches, habitual masturbation, irregular menstruations, and stuttering. (Less stuttering in the presence of males.)

Treatment: active analysis was used, the aim being to trace the present behavior to its antecedents.

Recovered material: Earliest recollections were of her oral, anal, and genital functions. Here, too, guilt feelings were uncovered, as well as incest strivings in relation to father.

Results: She has developed some markedly deep attachments (which she could not previously do). She has also become systematic and efficient in her work. Regulation of the menses has also occurred. Her speech is now relatively fluent.

Conclusions: The following were concluded: 1. Deep-seated emotional conflicts have an etiological bearing on stuttering. 2. Stuttering must be regarded as a major type of neurosis, since this conflict persists. 3. The most successful type of therapy is passive analysis which relies on transference as its major aid.

TITLE

Travis, L.: "The Need for Stuttering, *Journal of Speech Disorders*, 5 (1940), 193-202.

Purpose: To advance the theory that stuttering is a defense created and designed to prevent anxiety from developing when certain impulses of which the stutterer dares not become aware threaten to expose themselves.

Experimental Design: None.

Summary:

1. Stuttering, it is suggested, is the expression of a conflict of love or hate or both on one hand and fear on the other. Love, hate, and fear are treated as approach, destruction (attack), and flight respectively. Through speech these impulses become symbolic. Words take the place of approach or destruction or flight.

2. The danger situation arises from a misconcept. An anxiety, the basis for all stuttering symptoms, is not based on a mature

evaluation of realities but develops from an earlier period in the stutterer's life when realities were determined by immature, short-sighted wishes of the fantastic infantile world. Having repressed these impulses by fear, they remain fearful and dangerous. Normally these repressions of early childhood are resolved. But with the stutterer, time and experience do not alter these impulses because he has turned from his original disappointment and never accepted the primitive demands in their original form. These early infantile wishes, hates and fears remain dynamic and force their way into expression as symptoms of stuttering. "What he really fears and what stuttering was developed as a defense against is the dreaded breakdown of control over the overwhelmingness of the pleasure impulses repressed." So we have the need for stuttering.

3. In general, stuttering is a symptom; it gives a disguised expression to repressed impulses in which repressed impulses and repressed forces may be recognized. Since most stuttering begins in early childhood, the symptoms will have to be about infantile preoccupations. These symptoms consist of four main activities of the speech mechanism: (1) retaining—keeping the sounds in (p, b, m, t, d); (2) expelling—the sudden sharp release of air, protruding the tongue, etc.; (3) ingesting—speaking on inspiration and biting, sucking, or chewing movements; and (4) molding—distorting the face, facial starters, etc. "Stuttering is a compromise formation between seeking and inhibiting instinct gratification." So far psychoanalytic work on stutterers, the author feels, is suggestive of anal fixation. Certain words are stuttered more because they are better love or hate objects because of their phonetics and possible symbolization.

Conclusions: The author concludes that the treatment of stutterers can take one of two courses: (1) The stutterer must discover for himself the real nature of the impulses repressed, eliminate them and then he cannot go on stuttering even if he wants to; (2) one may give him a substitute pattern, an objective attitude, and relaxation exercises. This too frequently, however, the author feels, leaves the individual emotionally impoverished.

TITLE

Wischner, G. J.: Anxiety-Reduction as Reinforcement in Maladaptive Behavior: Evidence in Stutterers' Representations of the Moment of Difficulty, *Journal of Abnormal and Social Psychology,* **47 (1952), 566-571.**

Purpose: To discuss "the nature and identification of the reinforcing mechanism . . . in maladaptive or non-integrative behavior with special reference to the problem of stuttering." The hypothesis under consideration follows: Stuttering is reinforced by its close association with anxiety-tension reduction accompanying the removal of a feared word which causes the tension and anxiety. This becomes a vicious cycle.

Experimental Design: Subjects were 30 males and three female stutterers. The majority were of college age with a few of elementary and high school age. Subjects met in small groups and were instructed to draw whatever they thought adequately represented their behavior immediately before, during and after a moment of stuttering. Representations were analyzed in terms of content and spontaneous written language used by the subjects.

Summary:

Verbal Analysis

Twenty-two of the thirty-three drawings contained some descriptive language. The following states were expressed: Physiological or emotional disturbance, shame or embarrassment, fear, tension, exhaustion, relaxation or relief.

EXAMPLES OF LANGUAGE EMPLOYED BY SS IN THEIR REPRESENTA-
TIONS OF BEFORE, DURING, AND AFTER-PERIODS OF THE STUTTER-
ING MOMENT.

Before	During	After
1. Breath-chest tight	Tense	More relaxed
2. Normal-nervous condition arising	Nervous condition remains	....
3. Water-dike	Dike broke, Water floods land	Flooded, calmed down
4. Tensing	Tense	Gust of air ejected; ease
5. Anticipation-conscious preparation	Struggle	Weary sound-exhaustion ad infinitum
6. Hardly any tension	Great tension grows with more stuttering	Tension diminishes though stuttering as great
7. All worked up	Block-excited-trying to force	Embarrassed, glad it's over
8. Nothing there	Hits block, gets word	Look like before, feel embarrassed, doesn't bother any more, feel like did not stutter.

Process Analysis

The process or cycle of events and the number represented in each were:

tension—release	16
normal, climax, normal	12
fear, release, fear	3
avoidance—escape	1
physical, mental tension	1
	—
N	33

Conclusions: It was concluded that both language and content demonstrated a strikingly similar process in practically all subjects. There was progressively mounting tension, anxiety, or stress followed by a reduction in these states after completion of the stuttering act.

TITLE

Luper, H. L.: Consistency of Stuttering In Relation to the Goal Gradient Hypothesis, *Journal of Speech and Hearing Disorders,* **21 (1956), 336-342.**

Purpose: To test the hypothesis that the anxiety reduction accompanying the end or release of a stuttering block tends to reinforce the specific behavior occurring immediately prior to the release, thus causing this specific behavior to be a consistent component of stuttering for the subject.

Experimental Design: Subjects were 33 persons (sex not stated) judged by themselves and by speech therapists to be stutterers; their ages ranged from 18 to 35 years. The subjects read phrases designed to elicit stuttering, and their actions and speech were recorded by motion picture camera and tape recorder. Each phrase was repeated if necessary until it was read fluently.

Judges noted different behavior present in stuttered readings, and the sequence in which it occurred; they then noted behavior occurring in subsequent readings of the same phrases, looking for consistently recurring patterns in the stuttering of each subject.

Summary: Data were analyzed by chi square, testing the hypothesis that there is no consistency beyond chance, i.e., that reinforcement of behavior immediately preceding release of a block does not cause this behavior to be more consistently a part of the stuttering of a subject than can be accounted for by chance.

The chi square values were not significant at the .05 level of confidence, and the hypothesis could not be rejected.

It was noted that the agreement between the judges "did not run as high as might be desired for the testing of the hypothesis." Some of the agreements were as low as 53% for particular pairs of judges.

It was suggested that if the data can be considered conclusive, it might follow that the occurrence of specific behavior in stuttering is a matter of chance.

Conclusions: It was concluded (1) that stuttering behavior may not be reinforced by anxiety reduction accompanying the release of a block and (2) that anxiety reduction may serve to reinforce stuttering behavior in some way or ways not tested by this experiment.

TITLE

Abbott, J.: **Repressed Hostility as a Factor in Adult Stuttering,** *Journal of Speech Disorders,* 12 (1947), 428-430.

Purpose: ". . . to suggest a mechanism by which repressed hostility toward his listener may in some cases generate guilt feelings which may interfere with the success of the stutterer's therapy."

Experimental Design: No design, merely a discussion divided into two parts. The first part describes how hostility comes about; the second, how to resolve the hostility.

Summary: A consideration of the conscious attitude of the stutterer to his listener at the moment of stuttering must include, the author feels, his great fear of rejection accompanied by an anxious desire to be accepted unconditionally by his listener. Any implied or expressed disapproval is reacted to by increased anxiety and insecurity.

The stutterer also has another attitude, one of repressed hostility toward the listener at the moment of stuttering. This attitude is reasonably arrived at by considering the multitude of rejections, the lost opportunities, the embarrassing moments, the feelings of inadequacy and other emotional traumata which years of stuttering have produced.

However, this hostility must be repressed because of the need for acceptance and affection on the part of the listener. Since affection and hostility are opposites, one would have to be repressed. Such repressed hostility often leads to a feeling of guilt which carries with it a feeling for self-punishment to atone for the guilt.

The author suggests that in some cases the unconscious reluctance of the stutterer to give up his secondary symptoms may be explained by the need for self-punishment to atone for guilt feelings toward the therapist.

How this knowledge can be applied is first to attempt to render this hostility conscious, if it exists. This is a delicate task and not safe in unskilled hands. The safest way is to direct the therapeutic interviews so that the stutterer will "discover" it himself and accept it.

Once the hostility is conscious, use of an objective approach is suggested which shows the stutterer the advantage of disregarding his listener's immediate embarrassment for a farsighted view of the benefit society will receive from his eventual habilitation.

Conclusions: It is suggested that in some cases the stutterer's reluctance to part with his secondary symptoms may arise from guilt feeling arising out of repressed hostility toward the listener.

TITLE

Solomon, M.: Stuttering as an Emotional and Personality Disorder, *Journal of Speech Disorders*, 4 (1939), 347-357.

Purpose: To present certain relationships to the thesis that: "Stuttering is a specifically conditioned personality, emotive behavior and speech disorder in the struggle for equilibrium during social speaking."

Experimental Design: None.

Summary: Speech, the author feels, is the highest type of integrated response of the total human organism. During social speaking or excitement, excessive tension occurs, and a state of undifferentiated emotion with a feeling of disintegration, disorganization or dis-equilibrium results. One of the possible types of responses to one of these situations is stuttering. Therefore, stuttering is a type of adjustive behavior—a clinical syndrome.

The author attempts to explain some of the inconsistencies of stutterers in the following manner:

1. During singing, the stutterer is more apt to be absorbed in the melody or tune and be free from the fear of a speech block, unless his attention wanders.

2. Whistling is a less complex activity than speaking, accompanied by less tension and excitement—the same goes for whispering.

3. The stutterer feels buried in a mass of individuals when speaking in concert, and, therefore, less conspicuous.

4. The stutterer can repeat a word just blocked upon because there is a momentary change in emotional attitude.

5. Males stutter more than females because in addition to biological factors their lives are more stimulating and their activities more exciting.

6. The increase of stuttering after the first grade is due to increased tension from various causes.

Conclusions: It was concluded that many factors may be responsible for the state of emotional excitement at the time of the first moment of stuttering and its recurrence.

The treatment of stuttering, it was felt, should concern the total personality and not merely the speech phenomena. Intensive personality study and reorganization leading to a better peace of mind and social adjustment are recommended for the stutterer.

TITLE

Brown, F. W.: Stuttering, Its Neuro-Physiological Basis and Probable Causation, *American Journal of Orthopsychiatry*, 2 (1932), 363-371.

Purpose: To present the theory that "stuttering *may* occur, and so far as anatomical, physiological, and clinical evidence permits us to ascertain, does *usually* occur on the basis of the *normal* neuro-physiological mechanism."

Experimental Design: None.

Summary: Brown reviews the researches of Cannon which show that "emotional expression results from action of subcortical centers." Speech is a learned activity and as such it is generally under the control of the motor cortex. So long as the individual is trying to say something which is in accord with his emotions and social customs, the cortex and the lower centers which control emotion

are free of conflict. Under conditions of intense emotions, however, disturbances of speech—even stuttering—can sometimes
be noted in the speech of "normals." The lower area controlling
emotions is said—in such cases—to be inhibiting the cortical
process of controlled speech.

Brown believes that stuttering is a response to an emotionally
conditioned stimulus—the social situation. "The degree of dominance of motor cortex over thalamus depends directly upon the
nature of the associational process involved. . . . the associational
process of the stutterer is of such a nature that in the situation
where stuttering occurs, the control exercised by the motor cortex
and that exercised by the thalamus are equal or nearly equal.
The attempt to speak, that is, the attempt to exercise voluntary
motor control, is blocked by an involuntary attempt to prevent the
motor activity." The external situation is not in itself capable of
producing such conflict through great emotion; the author theorizes that it is the subject's subjective evaluation of the situation
which gives rise to the great emotion that serves in turn to inhibit the cortical process of controlled speech. The author terms
this subjective feature "emotional conflict" which he considers a
conflict between the stimulus to speak and the stimulus not to
speak. This later stimulus is the "fear" of speaking so common
among stutterers.

The author feels that this theory holds good in the light of so
many cases first manifesting symptoms after sickness and other
trumatic situations. He feels that such a background of emotional
stress would be a sort of preparation period for the appearance of
this inner conflict. He also feels that the high degree of incidence
of stuttering among those whose handedness had been shifted
may be explained by the fact that excessive emotional strain may
have been caused by such a shift. The author concludes that the
neurophysiological mechanism of any person is capable of becoming so involved under certain conditions.

Conclusions: The author suggests for therapy "the resolution of
the emotional conflicts producing the undesirable behavior pattern and the substitution of an adequate pattern of meeting the
realities of social intercourse through speech."

TITLE

Glasner, P.: **Personality Characteristics and Emotional Problems in Stutterers under the Age of Five,** *Journal of Speech and
Hearing Disorders,* 14 (1949), 135-138.

Purpose: To present data concerning the personality characteristics and emotional problems in stutterers under the age of five.

Experimental Design: Observations were made during the examination and treatment of 70 stutterers under the age of five. A detailed case history was obtained for each child from the parents,
and a careful appraisal of the child's personality was made by
direct study during personal interviews. In most cases, the
author's observations and findings were supplemented and correlated with examinations made by other members of the staff of
the Children's Psychiatric Service at the Johns Hopkins Hospital.
The median age was 3 years, 6 months. The children were evenly
divided into three age groups: 2-3 years; 3-4 years; 4-5 years.
Their speech was characterized by a change in muscle tonus,
pitch, speed, and rhythm.

Summary:

1. Many children under five years when stuttering, it was felt,
do not exhibit the same calm, totally unconcerned attitude characteristic of normal children when they speak with speech in-
accuracies and the usual childhood repetitions.

2. All the children studied had exhibited some degree of emotional manifestation other than stuttering.

(a) 54% were characterized as "feeding problems."

(b) 27% were enuretic.

(c) 20% had exaggerated fears and/or nightmares.

(d) Over half of the children showed two or three other indications of emotional disturbance, e.g., thumbsucking, nail biting,
masturbation, exaggerated sibling rivalry, emotional vomiting.

3. As obtained from the mothers' reports:

(a) 33% were described as sensitive or nervous.

(b) Other descriptions in smaller percentages were: timid,
shy, high-strung, stubborn, unsocial, excitable, restless, tense.

(The author's clinical findings corroborated these non-scientific and instinctive opinions of the parents.)

4. Clinical experience, the author feels, supports the view that *any* condition or situation which produces fairly constant emotional disturbances in a child may produce a change in the speech pattern. It was therefore not believed that there is any specific "typical stuttering environment."

Conclusions: It was concluded that stuttering children under the age of five can be roughly divided into three classes:

Type I: The child may be a relatively healthy child whose stuttering closely follows the introduction of a disturbing element into his environment. No basic personality maladjustments as yet seem to have taken place. The removal of the disturbing element removes the emotional disturbance, and the speech returns to normal.

Type II: In addition to stuttering, the child has a whole constellation of neurotic symptoms and tendencies. The child has been emotionally disturbed and insecure for so long that no quick relief is possible. Furthermore, from the practical point of view, the disturbing conditions in the child's home cannot be remedied speedily.

Type III: These children stand somewhere between the first two types. They are not highly neurotic, but they are generally dependent, confused, and fearful; they are shy and emotionally unsteady; they seem anxious and exhibit a constant inner restlessness. In short, they are what are commonly referred to as "sensitive children."

TITLE

Ingebregtsen, E.: **Some Experimental Contributions to the Psychology and Psychopathology of Stuttering,** *American Journal of Orthopsychiatry,* 6 (1936), 630-651.

Purpose: To present results of a series of tests, including psychological profiles of Rossolime-Bartsch, given to a group of stutterers.

Experimental Design: Sixty stutterers varying in age from 8-26 years at the Granhaug School, Germany, were examined. Subjects represented different parts of the country. Psychic processes were combined into three groups: tonus (attention and will); faculty of noticing (noticing and memory); and associate processes (perception). Deficiency in tonus was classified as: hypotonic type; deficiency in the faculty of noticing: amnestic type; defective of associate processes: dement type. Of the 60 subjects, 20 were given the Rossolime-Bortsch and classified as hypotonic-amnestic type. The remaining 40 were given additional examinations; medical, memory, word testing, test of vocal musi of subjects, intelligence (performance tests of Drever and Collins) and psychodiagnostic (Rorschach).

Summary:

Psychological Profile:

Using Bartsch's revision, 20 stutterers (hypotonic-amnestic type) had a low degree of tonus and abnormally high degree of forgetfulness of language. Words were forgotten more than sentences.

Medical Examination: (40 S's)

17 (42.5%) stuttering occurred in family.

5 (12.5%) had rickets.

9 (22.2%) mental or nervous sufferings occurred in family.

24 (60%) began to stutter at age 3-4; 16 (40%) at age 5-13.

16 reported a cause of stuttering: seven were frightened, two, tickled, two began after strong excitement, one grew too rapidly, one after adenoid operation, one after post-war pneumonia, one mimicked a playmate, and one began after a fracture.

Test of Memory: (40 S's)

Items best retained were objects and figures optically impressed, figures auditorily impressed, and certain objects and pictures of certain content optically impressed. Very little was impressed, either acoustically or optically, regarding language. Forgetfulness for language was about seven times greater than that for optical impressions of pictures and objects, and five times greater than for figures. Forgetfulness for objects, pictures, and figures seemed to be normal.

Test of Words

In storage of words 82% were more than two years below normal standard. A tendency for logical displacement also occurred.

Vocal Musi: (40 S's)

Most subjects were able to recognize a melody and most could state where false intervals occurred. 42.5%—faculty to reproduce melody was lacking. Most had no sense of rhythm. Some could reproduce melody with others but not alone. In all S's, finer changing of intensity and accentuation were missing. Regarding vocal musi stuttering never occurred.

Intelligence: Mechanical (40 S's)

All subjects were lowest in memory for certain movements and memory-span for figures. Regarding total score, about 20 subjects were below average.

Psychodiagnostic (also Intelligence): (40 S's)

Only about one-fourth of the S's gave a mediocre number of total answers. A number of total answers indicates the dispositional energy of the working of association and indicates will (conscious and unconscious) to do complicated work.

Twenty-one cases gave no answers of motion, lack of which is indicative of depression. Eight cases gave one answer of motion; four, two answers; three cases, three answers; and four cases gave four answers.

Eighteen cases gave no color responses representative of affection while the remaining subjects gave them sparingly.

Ten cases gave pure "Hell-dunkel" answers indicating abnormally easy change in emotional life.

Most conspicuous (60% of subjects) was the frequent "Versagen," i.e., unanswered plates. Seven had one, and one had nine. "This 'Versagen' is a symptom of affective restriction."

Conclusions: ". . . the developed stutterer presents the following characteristic pictures of symptoms:

1. Reduced attention.
2. Weakness of will—great suggestibility.
3. Reduced memory of language—small storage of words.
4. Logical displacement—amnestic confabulation.
5. Motorial amusi.
6. Stereotyped perception—tendency to perseveration.
7. Indolence—bluntness of affect.
8. Derangements of motility.
9. Signs of depression.
10. Repressions.
11. Restrictions."

TITLE

Moncur, J.: Symptoms of Maladjustment Differentiating Young Stutterers from Non-Stutterers, *Child Development,* **26 (1955), 91-96.**

Purpose: To answer the questions which follow: (1) Do stuttering children have symptoms of maladjustment other than stuttering? (2) Do they have more of these symptoms than non-stuttering children? (3) Which of these symptoms are most characteristic of stuttering children?

Experimental Design: Subjects were 48 children (six females) with a median age of 79.6 months, who had been diagnosed as stutterers by their mothers, teachers, and school speech correctionists. Information was gathered by direct observations by the experimenter. Controls were 48 children (six females) with a median age of 80.2 months, who were matched to the experimentals for age, sex, and school placement. These controls exhibited no symptoms of stuttering.

Summary: Controls averaged 4.0 symptoms of maladjustment and stutterers averaged 8.8. Forty-one of the 48 pairs showed the stutterer to have more maladjustments; two pairs were equal; five pairs showed the control to have more maladjustments.

The following are the differences which were significant at or beyond the .01 level of confidence:

Question	Per Cent of Mothers Answering "Yes"	
	M. of stut.	M. of non-stut.
Is child very nervous?	67	13
Is child very aggressive?	59	6
Does child "scrap" with others?	56	23
Does child need discipline often?	56	13
Is child a "fussy" eater?	more	less*

---

* Percentages not given.

Differences significant at the .05 level of confidence showed the stutterers to be the aggressors in more quarrels, to quarrel more with their siblings, to have more nightmares, to have more "mouth habits" (undefined), to have more nocturnal enuresis, and to display more negativism than the controls. Little or no differences were found in shyness, melancholia, self-consciousness, nail-biting, constipation, vomiting, nervous tics, weeping or daydreaming, fears, self-pity, imaginary playmates, temper tantrums, and thumb-sucking.

Conclusions: It was concluded that stuttering children do display more symptoms of maladjustment than non-stuttering children, and that the symptoms of maladjustment most characteristic of stuttering children are nervousness, enuresis, nightmares, aggressions, fussiness in eating, and frequent need for discipline.

TITLE

Kimmell, M.: Studies in the Psychology of Stuttering: IX. The Nature and Effect of Stutterers' Avoidance Reaction, Journal of Speech Disorders, 3 (1938), 95-100.

Purpose: To determine the types of avoidances stutterers reveal and the effect of these avoidances on specified phases of adjustment.

Experimental Design: Thirty-three autobiographical documents written by 29 adult stutterers were examined, and passages were selected which described avoidance reactions. Two judges, working independently, marked every passage in the autobiography selected as representative of avoidance behavior and classified each according to whether or not it was judged to have affected specified phases of adjustment.

Sumary:

1. *Effects of avoidance reactions on speech behavior:* Of 233 behavior items selected by both judges as avoidance reactions affecting speech, the greatest number were classified under: (a) the effect upon the amount of speech and (b) the effect upon the choice of words. Others included: effect upon rate, irrelevant sounds, and overt bodily movements.

2. *Effects of avoidance reactions on behavior in the home:* Of 18 behavior items, the greatest number were classified under: (a) the amount of time spent in the home but in isolation and (b) the nature of activities indulged in at home. Others included: effects upon relationships with parents, siblings, visitors, age of assuming economic independence, etc.

3. *Effects of avoidance reactions on behavior in school:* Of 83 behavior items, the greatest number were classified under: (a) the amount of oral recitations and (b) the amount of time spent studying. Others included: effects upon grade average, amount of retardation, extracurricular activities, etc.

4. *Effects of avoidance reactions on vocational behavior:* Of 16 behavior items, the greatest number were classified under: (a) effects upon the direction of the stutterer's vocational ambition and (b) degree of agreement between stutterer's ambition and nature of a given job. Others included: effect upon degree to which co-workers were liked, length of time worked at a given job, degree of authority, etc.

5. *Effects of avoidance reactions on heterosexual behavior:* Of 26 behavior items, the greatest number were classified under: (a) effects upon amount of time spent with members of the opposite sex and (b) effects upon the amount of conversation with the opposite sex. Others included: age when dating began, number of individuals dated, age of marriage, etc.

6. *Effects of avoidance reactions on personal behavior:* Of 221
behavior items, the greatest number were classified under: (a)
effects upon the intensity and nature of feeling of inferiority, (b)
effects upon the amount of conversation with strangers, and (c)
effects upon the amount of time spent with others. Others included: effects upon the degree of intimacy in relations with one
or two close friends, physical fitness, sexual practices, day-dream-
ing, smoking, drinking, etc.

Conclusions: In general it was concluded that avoidance reactions
tend to delay, decrease, or prevent speech in certain given situations, and to limit the individual's range of social experience.

TITLE

Richardson, L.: The Personality of Stutterers, *Psychological
Monographs,* 56 (1944), 1-41.

Purpose: To investigate the difference between the personality
of adult stutterers and non-stutterers by means of a questionnaire
and two projection-type personality tests.

Experimental Design: Thirty adult stutterers ranging in age from
17 to 48 with a mean of 27.8 years were matched with a control
group for age, sex and college experience. Three tests were included in the battery: An Inventory of Factors S (Social Introversion), T (Thinking Introversion), D (Depression), C (Cycloid
Tendencies), R (Rhathymia = happy-go-lucky attitude); The
Rorschach Ink Blot Test and The Thematic Apperception Test.
The groups were compared on the basis of the three personality
tests. All testing was conducting and evaluated by the experimenter over a period of 15 months.

Summary: On the Inventory of Factors, the stutterers were found
to be more socially introverted (CR = 2.49), and less happy-go-
lucky (CR = 3.21) than the non-stutterers.

A summary of the stutterers' traits as determined by the Rorschach norms showed them tending to be more detailed in their
approach to problems, average in their stereotypy, more con-

stricted than the average, and tending to recognize their inner life (no M).

Although there were no statistically significant differences, trends on the TAT revealed them to have a desire for achievement and affection in excess of other needs. They are inclined to feel guilty and to punish themselves, and to react aggressively to frustration. Their environment thwarts, punishes, and dominates in excess of being helpful or loving and gives little recognition. They tend to show less adequacy in their story characters and give less proportions of happy endings than the normal group.

Conclusions: It was suggested that these tests be used further to measure possible attitude changes during therapy.

TITLE

Bender, J.: The Stuttering Personality, *American Journal of Orthopsychiatry*, 12 (1942), 140-146.

Purpose: The author posed two questions for study: "Do post-pubertal male stutterers have more disturbances of personality than non-stuttterers?" and "Are post-pubertal male stutterers afflicted characteristically with certain specific pecularities of personality?"

Experimental Design: Personality was defined as ". . . the entire organization of a human being at any stage of his development," and as being manifested in morphology, mental capacity, and temperament.

A large group of college male stutterers were studied intensively in regards to morphology and mental capacity. (No detailed description of the sample or of the procedure was offered.)

In order to determine whether post-pubertal male stutterers have characteristic traits of temperament, an experiment was made upon 249 male college stutterers and a like number of non-stutterers controlled for age, sex, intelligence, and socio-economic background. An experiment was set up using the Bernreuter Personality Inventory.

Summary: Post-pubertal male stutterers differed significantly and characteristically from comparable post-pubertal male non-stutterers in regards to morphology and mental capacity.

1. *In regard to morphology.* Post-pubertal male stutterers were found to present the following significant findings: (a) characteristic body build, tending toward the leptosomic and never being pyknic; (b) more disturbances of a bio-chemical nature; (c) more vasomotor disturbance; (d) afflicted by characteristic tremors; (e) inferior in control of voluntary muscle movement; (f) more disturbances of the breathing function; (g) more disturbances of certain reflexes; (h) more vocal anomalies; (i) more disturbances of eye movement; and (j) more disturbances of motor coordination.

2. *In regard to mental capacity.* Post-pubertal male stutterers were found: (a) to be afflicted characteristically with perseveration; (b) to be more intelligent than non-stutterers; (c) to be less efficient silent readers than non-stutterers; (d) to be more efficient than non-stutterers in mirror reading ability; (e) to differ characteristically in written language ability; and (f) to be more facile at mirror writing than non-stutterers.

3. *In reference to temperament,* post-pubertal male stutterers more often consider themselves "a rather nervous person." They are often in a state of excitement; more often feel self-conscious in the presence of superiors in the academic or business world. Stutterers more often find it difficult to speak in public; often get stage fright; more often express themselves better in writing than in speaking. Stutterers more often prefer traveling with someone who will make all the necessary arrangements. They are slower in making decisions. People come to stutterers less for advice.

Conclusions: It was suggested that any new theory of the etiology of stuttering must take into account at least such well-established facts as the following:

1. There are types of stuttering, and the various types of stuttering symptoms may reflect different etiologies.

2. Stuttering appears to be highly individualistic, i.e., the symptom of stuttering must always be related to the stuttering person —his antecedents, education, physical condition, attitudes, etc.

TITLE

Steer, M. D., and Johnson, W.: An Objective Study of the Relationship Between Psychological Factors and the Severity of Stuttering, *Journal of Abnormal and Social Psychology,* **31 (1936), 36-46.**

Purpose: To test the correlation between psychological factors and the number of stuttering spasms experienced by an individual in a given situation.

Experimental Design: Ten adult male stutterers (ranging in age from 17 to 23) read a passage in 15 situations of varying social complexity. The psychological reactions were tested by introspective ratings and the spasms were recorded by the experimenters. The subjects were made familiar with the reading material and the objective nature of the speaking situations was—insofar as was possible—made constant for all subjects.

Summary: Findings showed that stutterers stuttered more in some situations than in others. The least stuttering occurred before small familiar audiences (one person) or in a no-audience situation. The most stuttering occurred before larger, unfamiliar or indefinite audiences (microphones, recorders). In those situations in which the introspective ratings and the recorded spasms had a statistically significant correlation, the results could be summarized: "Greater intensity of the combined emotional and psychological reactions tend to be associated with increased frequency of stuttering spasms."

Conclusions: "The results of this study tend consistently to suggest a positive relationship between emotional and psychological reactions and the severity of stuttering. . . ." The authors feel that the stuttering *per se* is the result of organic disability, but that the condition is aggravated by emotion. They point out that many of the so-called symptoms of stuttering may be manifestations or results of the emotionality rather than of the stuttering itself. They feel that actual stuttering should be attributed to physiological causes and many of its so-called symptoms to emotionality and that the two should be sharply differentiated.

TITLE

Johnson, W.: The Influence of Stuttering on the Personality, *University of Iowa Studies: Studies in Child Welfare,* **5 (1932), No. 5.**

Purpose: To evaluate the influence of stuttering on the personality of the stutterer. The study is chiefly concerned with: (1) perceptive responses, (2) attitudes, and (3) motor responses.

Stuttering is definied as: ". . . a disorder of rhythm of verbal expression . . . characterized by tonic and clonic spasms . . . in the neuro-muscular mechanisms for the production of sound and speech." Personality is defined as: ". . . the meaning of an individual, derived from the observations that are made of him . . . always relative to the person who makes the observations."

Experimental Design: The method used was that of a functional analysis of case studies, utilizing in the process: case histories, speech clinic examinations, autobiographies, personal documents (introspections and retrospections), questionnaires, the Woodworth-House Mental Hygiene Inventory, personal interviews, and intimate observations of the subjects. In all of these, the major emphasis was placed on the investigation of attitudes and adaptations with regard to school, home, vocational and social situations, toward stuttering, toward self and toward others.

The results were based on a sample of 80 stutterers (61 male and 19 female) ranging in age from 7 to 42, with a mean of 19.2 years.

Summary: The important conclusions with respect to the stutterer's attitudes and reactions toward oral recitations, extra-curricular activities and social activities in connection with school were:

(1) To the extent that teachers were able to empathize with the stutterer they were able to deal successfully with him. The best oral recitation policy found was to expect the stutterer to recite only when he volunteered. The study supported the tenet that extra written work should be required in the absence of recitation.

(2) The most popular extra-curricular activity of the stutterer was athletics. Participation in any kind of activity was circumscribed by the stutterer's attitude toward his stuttering in relation to that activity.

(3) The most important factor related to scholastic difficulties was the humilitating influence of the stuttering.

There was a relationship between the points of view of the parent and of the child toward stuttering. An equilibrium was found to be present in this parent-stuttering child relationship when the situation-as-perceived was of a similar nature. As the disparity toward the evaluation of the speech difficulty increased, increasing degrees of conflict were introduced.

The stutterers ambitions and proposed vocations.

An inverse relationship was found between the choice of occupation and ambitions and the severity of stuttering, i.e., the more severe the less the ambition.

Several interesting results were found in the responses elicited by stutterers on the Woodworth-House Mental Hygiene Inventory (comparisons with normal and psychoneurotic non-stutterers utilized):

As a group, stutterers presented normal emotional and social adjustment (relatively speaking), their number of problems being less numerous than those of the comparison group's, yet being somewhat more extreme than those of the normal non-stutterers, and tending to become more extreme with increasing age. An insignificant difference was found between stutterers and normal non-stutterers in terms of childhood maladjustments. Stutterers had decidedly less psychoneurotic involvement than diagnosed psychoneurotics in terms of number and severity of personality problems.

All but 30% of the stutterers' problems were found to be due largely to the frustrating and humilating influence of stuttering itself. The personality problems of stutterers, more so than those of non-stutterers but less than the psychoneurotics, were featured by shyness, anxiety, depression and nervous instability. Emotional and social maladjustments and stuttering occurred independently of each other to a significant degree.

It was indicated that emotional disturbance may be a contributing cause of stuttering insofar as it disturbs the neurological gradients responsible for speech, probably owing its etiological significance to the relative instability of these gradients. In general, it was concluded that the emotional and social maladjustments of stutterers is in large measure the result of stuttering, insofar as stuttering is pertinently related to it.

The reported phantasies of the stutterers were categorized thusly: (1) success-normal speech; (2) revenge; (3) anxiety; (4) despair. The success-normal speech was the most common of the four. The nature of the phantasy depended largely on the definition that was given reality, and to stuttering as a part of reality.

It was found, furthermore, as the stutterer's evaluation of his stuttering changes, the nature of the phantasy changes. In their daydreams, stutterers often indicate that they are normally sociable individuals, being considerably aggressive. Their apparent introversion appears to be a frustrated extroversion. The most common wish expressed by stutterers is that they be cured of stuttering.

Conclusions: It was suggested that emotional and social maladjustment may be a contributing cause of stuttering (insofar as it aggravates or precipitates more severe spasms). However, it was felt that the great problem is not stuttering *per se,* but the definition that the stutterer gives his disability and his situation in general.

TITLE

Meltzer, H.: Personality Differences Between Stuttering and Non-Stuttering Children as Indicated by the Rorschach Test, *Journal of Psychology,* **17 (1944), 39-59.**

Purpose: To measure personality organization in stuttering children with a test which purports to yield deeper insights than those previously used in this type of experimental problem.

Experimental Design: Fifty of 64 available stuttering children from 23 speech centers were matched with an equal control group for age, sex, grade, school, and intelligence. The other 14 available were not used, since matched controls were not available for them. Both the control and experimental groups had 38 boys and 12 girls, and were of a mean age of 12 plus years. Rorschach tests were administered to both groups in the usual way.

Summary: Factors in which chances of a true difference in the results were 90 or more in 100 were:

Z—organizational response (perceiving and organizing relationships)

W—whole response (capacity for abstract thinking)

Ds—white space details (negativism, resistance, obstinacy)

F(c)—chiaroscure response (absorption in the far-away or disposition to depression)

At—anatomical response (morbidity)

M—movement response (richness of inner life, inner control, or fantasy life, withdrawal)

Ad—animal detail (parallel to A, stereotypy)

ΣCF—numerical of color responses (extratensive trend)

%A—animal responses (stereotypy)

A number of other factors were different in the two group responses at levels less significant than 90 in 100.

Conclusions: The differences discovered were interpreted as indicating:

1. that stuttering children tend to have more creative ability, fantasy, withdrawal, adaptability to outer reality, irritability and manic trend than do non-stuttering children.

2. that many more compensatory adjustments and indications of insecurity and compulsive behavior to compensate for it occur in stuttering children than in non-stuttering children.

TITLE

McDowell, E.: **Educational and Emotional Adjustments of Stuttering Children,** *Columbia University Teachers College Contributions to Education,* **No. 314, 1928.**

Purpose: To learn more about the "psychological" and "mental" aspects of stuttering as determined by finding answers to these questions: (1) Do stuttering children vary from normal children in intelligence and, if so, is the variability more noticeable in language or non-language activities; (2) How do stuttering children compare with non-stuttering children of like intelligence in school achievement; (3) Are stuttering children more emotionally unstable and socially maladjusted than similar but non-stuttering children; (4) Do stuttering children have other speech difficulties more frequently than non-stuttering children; (5) Do stuttering children have marked physical abnormalities more frequently than non-stutterers? For this study stutterers were described as those having hesitant speech accompanied by spasms of the muscles of the throat and diaphragm and showing special inability to produce voiced sounds.

Experimental Design: Seven New York City schools representing different types of economic and social background and racial inheritance were canvassed for stutterers. Out of 7,138 children, 61 stutterers were found and they became the subjects of this experiment. Boys outnumbered girls 2.9 to 1. A control group equivalent in chronological age, mental age, intelligence, sex, language and racial background was matched with the stutterers. Both groups were subjected to a testing program to determine differences in personality, health, achievement and language abilities. Tests used were: (1) Pinter-Patterson Shorter Performance Scale, (2) Stanford Achievement Tests, (3) Woodward-Matthews Questionnaire, (4) Woodward-Cady Questionnaire, (5) Kent-Rosanoff Free Association Test, (6) Wood and Rowell Health and Growth Examination, (7) A special test for correct pronunciation of vowels and consonants devised by the experimenter, (8) Terman's scale for judging personality traits.

Summary: The 61 stutterers registered I.Q.'s on the Stanford Revision of the Binet Intelligence Test ranging from 63 to 156, with a mean of 99.14 and a standard deviation of 20.3. The mean I.Q. for the 50 subjects selected for the experiment group was 101.9; for the control, 102.0.

School Achievement—The results of the standard achievement test in reading, arithmetic, and spelling showed no appreciable differences between achievement quotients (educational age divided by M.A.). The stutterers had a mean score of 100, with SD of 12.64; the controls, 103.06, SD of 12.67.

Language Abilities Selected From Binet Tests—A test in which each subject was required to say as many words as he could within a three minute period was used. In spite of the stutterer's speech handicap he did almost as well as the controls. In the vocabulary test the difference of 2.58 had an experimental coefficient of .097 certainty. This difference, it was decided, was probably not due to special language aptitudes.

Emotional Readjustments—As measured by several questionnaires and association tests and from teachers' judgments, the two groups were found to be very stable.

Physical Traits—Marked similarity of the two groups was evident in comparisons of weight, height, heart rate, nervousness and in those physical traits thought to be more intimately connected with speech skills—lung capacity, chest girth, relative strength of right and left hands, nose and throat condition and missing teeth.

Speech Pronunciation—In total number of errors in speech pronunciation a difference in favor of the controls was found. However, in no one of the groups of speech sounds was a difference found which was large enough to be diagnostic.

Conclusions: It was concluded that the two groups showed a surprising amount of similarity. If the conditions pointed to in these findings can be accepted as true, the procedure for corrective work with stutterers, it was suggested, would naturally swing toward a marked emphasis on the improvement of speech habits rather than upon the eradication of neuropathic or psychopathic tendencies in the individual.

TITLE

Fiedler, F. E., and Wepman, J.: An Exploratory Investigation of the Self-Concept of Stutterers, *Journal of Speech Disorders,* 16 (1951), 110-114.

Purpose: To determine if the self-concept of stutterers is different from non-stutterers.

Experimental Design: Ten adult male stutterers and six controls were matched on the basis of age, socio-economic and educational background. They were instructed to place 76 statements descriptive of personality traits into a forced normal distribution (Q-Sort Technique) (1, 5, 12, 20, 20, 12, 5, 1). Later, a group of 13 clinical psychologists and a group of 13 mental hygiene patients who were not matched with the stutterers and who themselves did not stutter were given the task. Correlation matrices were evolved from the data.

Summary: The results of the study indicated that the stutterers' self-concept showed no characteristic difference from that of the non-stutterers. In comparing the self-concepts of the stutterers against two other non-stuttering groups, it was found that stutterers as a group tend to look upon themselves as being more like a group of psychologists than a group of mental hygiene patients.

Conclusions: It was concluded, on the basis of this exploration of the self-concept in stuttering adults, that one of two inferences can be drawn. Either stuttering, even though it appears during the early formative years of life, does not have as disruptive a force on the personality development as had been previously assumed, or the self-concept is formed prior to the formation of the stuttering symptom.

The advisability of studying stutterers as a group rather than as individuals is questioned.

TITLE

Sheehan, J. G., and Zelen, S.: A Level of Aspiration Study of Stutterers, *American Psychologist,* 6 (1951), 500.

Purpose: To determine whether stutterers suffer from level of aspiration difficulties.

Experimental Design: Design is not mentioned. The article is a short abstract from a paper read for the 31st annual meeting of Western Psychological Association.

Summary: "Comparison of twenty stutterers with twenty non-stutterers on the Rotter Board yielded no significant differences, with the stutterers somewhat lower than the controls."

Conclusions: It was concluded that stutterers were more like the crippled in respect to level of aspiration difficulties.

TITLE

Sheehan, J. G., and Zussman, C.: Rorschachs of Stutterers Compared With Clinical Control, *American Psychologist,* 6 (1951), 500.

Purpose: To compare the Rorschach records of stutterers with non-stutterers.

Experimental Design: Design is not mentioned. The article is a short abstract from a paper read for the 31st annual meeting of Western Psychological Association.

Summary: "Rorschachs of 25 stutterers were compared with Rorschachs of 25 non-stuttering clinic patients. The stutterers showed a greater drive toward achievement, overemphasis or suppressive control, reluctance to accept dependency needs, prevalence of inner resources over channels of communication, and a greater tendency to marshal intellectual defenses against anxiety."

Conclusions: Not mentioned.

TITLE

Quarrington, B.: The Performance of Stutterers on the Rosen-zweig Picture-Frustration Test, *Journal of Clinical Psychology*, 9 (1953), 189-192.

Purpose: To explore the findings of earlier studies which indicated that stutterers are characterized by more intropunitive and submissive reactions than non-stutterers.

Experimental Design: Thirty adult stutterers (23 males) with a mean age of 30.4 years were given the Rosenzweig Picture-Frustration Test, and their scores compared with Rosenzweig's norms.

Summary: The seven categories of responses on the test are Extropunitive, Intropunitive, Impunitive, Obstacle-Dominance, Ego-Defensive, Need-Persistence, and Group Conformity. None of the comparisons of the experimental group with Rosenzweig's normative group yielded differences which were significant at the .01 level.

Earlier studies had found differences significant at the .01 level, indicating that stutterers were less extropunitive and more intropunitive, and showed less obstacle dominance. The findings of this study were interpreted as refuting or at least questioning the earlier work.

Conclusions: It was concluded that:

1. A psychoanalytic explanation of stuttering etiology, borne out by the earlier work, is not justified by the present findings.

2. A hereditary, neuromuscular interpretation of etiology is not incongruous with these findings.

TITLE

Zelen, S. S., Sheehan, J. G., and Bugental, J. F. T.: Self-Perceptions in Stuttering, *Journal of Clinical Psychology*, 10 (1954), 70-72.

Purpose: To determine if the self-percepts of stutterers and non-stutterers differ significantly.

Experimental Design: Subjects consisted of 30 stutterers and a control group of 160 non-stutterers, all of college age. The W-A-Y technique was used in examining self-percepts. The subjects were asked to respond three times to the one question, "Who are you?"

The results fall into eleven categories: name, familial relationship, social positions of prestige, occupation, age, sex, group membership, unit (as me, myself, an individual), positive affect negative affect, and other (misc. responses).

Summary: An over-all F ratio was obtained and the following results were found to be significant at the five per cent level.

1. Positive affect—stutterers showed more positive affect perceptions than did the control group.

2. Unit—control group gave higher unit percepts than stutterers.

3. Sex—control group having more sex identifications percepts.

4. Group membership—stuttering group responded more often; however, if the percept "stutterer" is withheld the difference is not significant.

5. Social status—more successful individuals of the stutterers who terminated therapy successfully gave self-percepts which could be classified under this heading.

Conclusions:

1. The positive feelings of stutterers about themselves, it was felt, may be due to: (a) over compensation, and (b) previously successful therapy in which the therapy had helped to correct any negative self-percepts.

2. The significantly greater frequency of Social-Status relationships in the percepts of successful persons might perhaps be one of the bases for favorable response to group therapy. Those who have strong needs for social status usually become most involved in the group.

TITLE

Walnut, A.: A Personality Inventory Item Analysis of Individuals Who Stutter and Individuals Who Have Other Handicaps, *Journal of Speech and Hearing Disorders,* **19 (1954), 220-227.**

Purpose:

1. To investigate whether the personality deviations of stutterers result from stuttering or whether the stuttering is possibly a result of the personality deviation.

2. To give indications as to the specific areas in which the reactions of crippled, cleft palate, and stuttering individuals may differ from the normal.

Experimental Design: The short form of the Minnesota Multiphasic Personality Inventory was administered to a control group and three experimental groups. The control group contained 52 Ss; the stuttering group, 32; the crippled group, 25; and the cleft palate group, 26 Ss. The age spread for all subjects in all groups was between 15 years and 20 years with the majority in either their junior or senior years in high school.

The test results for all groups were scored and evaluated according to the norms of the MMPI scales. Mean scores for the E and C groups were also ranked and statistically compared. (CR test) Mean scores for males and females were determined and items in the test were categorized for subject content analysis.

Summary: All of the groups measured fell well within the normal range of personality as measured by the MMPI norms. The stuttering group as compared with the C group showed significant differences toward the poor adjustment end of the Depression and Paranoid scales. The cleft palate group as compared with the C group deviated significantly in the Psychopathic Deviation scale toward the better adjustment end of the scale. No clinically significant conclusions were drawn from these deviations.

In the subject content item analysis the stuttering group deviated from the control group in the specific areas of 'Speech-School.' The deviation was uniform in all other areas. The stuttering group demonstrated a marked inability to handle speech and speaking situations. The crippled group deviated from the control group in the area of 'Home and Family.' The deviation was uniform in all other areas. The crippled group felt a greater harmony with their homes and parents than did the other groups. The cleft palate group did not differ from the control group in the area of speech, but they did differ in the areas of 'Opinions' and 'Relations with other People.' The deviation was in the direction of the control group with a small percentage of items answered differently. This, it was felt, indicated that there was less deviation in these areas than would have been expected with the over-all deviation observed.

Conclusions: On the basis of the obtained data it was concluded that the stuttering, crippled, and cleft palate groups are well within the normal range of personality as measured by the MMPI.

In general, it was felt that these data do not indicate whether stuttering precipitated abnormal personality or vice versa, since the so-called pathological groups showed no significant personality deviations.

TITLE

Schuell, H.: **Sex Differences in Relation to Stuttering: Part I,** *Journal of Speech Disorders,* 11 (1946), 277-298.

Purpose: To summarize past investigations of stuttering in relationship to sex differences.

Experimental Design: None.

Summary:

1. A sex difference of from two to 10 males to one female was found. The degree of ratio varied according to age and educational status of the population studied, and according to methods used to obtain samples. Males are more severe stutterers than females. More males reportedly outgrow stuttering than females.

2. Male infants have more difficult births than females and incur more birth injuries. Males are more susceptible to disease than females and have greater statistical probability of meeting

sudden and violent death. Boys develop more slowly than girls both in growth and speech. Boys show more repetitions in speech than do girls. More males are referred to clinics for speech retardation, language disabilities, and articulatory defects. Approximately three times as many boys have reading disabilities. Males make more errors in writing and spelling and have a lower correlation between school achievement and intelligence. In lower grades girls are superior to boys. In high school the difference in achievement drops because of addition of courses in science and mathematics in which males usually excel. However, at this level, girls are still superior to males in language. More males than females quit school prior to graduation. A sex ratio comparable to that found among stutterers is found among behavior problems and also in studies of delinquent and pre-delinquent children.

3. Society tends to reward children for submissive and withdrawn behavior and penalize them for traits of aggressiveness, which males are expected to develop.

Conclusions: It was hypothesized that "the male child, whose physical, social, and language development proceeds at a slower rate than that of the female, experiences more unequal competition, and consequently more frustrations, particularly in relation to language situations, than the female child. As a result he exhibits more insecurity, more hesitancy, and more inhibitions in speech."

If the frustrating situations are too frequent, if the speech behavior is compared unfavorably with that of other children, or if the child becomes aware of unfavorable reactions toward him on the part of other people, it is suggested that anxieties and tensions and the overt behavior regarded as stuttering may develop.

TITLE

Schuell, H.: Sex Differences in Relation to Stuttering: Part II, *Journal of Speech Disorders,* **12 (1947), 23-28.**

Purpose: To explore sex differences in parent-child relations at the pre-school level.

Experimental Design: Subjects were 28 children (ages 26-53 months) divided as to sex (14 boys, 14 girls). At least one parent of each child was interviewed—in most cases, the mother. Parents were asked to record the disturbances in eating, bed, nap, bath, dressing, toilet for periods varying from one to six weeks. Only 18 subjects gave records which were usable.

Summary: More boys than girls were reported to be punished for disobedience, destruction, being noisy, and teasing. More verbal protest and pouting were found in girls. Boys more often responded to the situation by leaving the scene. More boys showed a desire for reassurance and affection, yet boys desired far more freedom and wider experience. Boys showed willingness to initiate conversation with adult strangers but girls were more willing to converse with children their own age.

While no statistically significant sex differences appeared in number or kind of disturbances that arose, the data suggested that if a more comprehensive study of child behavior were made at this age level, sex differences similar to those in older children might be expected to appear. The data also suggested that to some extent parental attitudes are culturally determined rather than based upon actual observation of a child's behavior.

Conclusions: It was concluded that it does not seem probable that there is a direct relationship between stuttering and the higher infant mortality rates for males, the higher incidence of birth injuries or greater male susceptibility to diseases. What these data do tend to make clear, it was felt, is that contrary to assumption, the male child is not sturdier than the female.

Neither does it appear, the author felt, that a direct relationship exists between stuttering and sex differences in physical growth. It appears much too simple also to attribute stuttering to the slower language development in boys. Here, as in the case of physical growth, the crucial point would seem to lie, it was suggested, in the tendency of parents and teachers to expect equal performances from children who are not equally developed mentally.

Nor is it suggested, the author felt, that more stutterers than non-stutterers are delinquent children but rather that the same social pressures which produce a higher incidence of maladjustment among boys also produces a higher incidence of stuttering.

The data analyzed, it was finally concluded, tend to support the hypothesis that stuttering is a semantogenic disorder arising with the repetitions, hesitations and other inadequacies characteristic of speech in young children. It was hypothesized that stuttering and the sex difference in the incidence of stuttering can be accounted for by a combination of physiologically determined factors and responses to culturally-determined stimulus-complexes which are different for girls and boys, men and women.

TITLE

Bloodstein, O., and Smith, S.: **A Study of the Diagnosis of Stuttering with Special Reference to the Sex Ratio,** *Journal of Speech and Hearing Disorders,* **19** (1954), 459-466.

Purpose: To determine whether there are higher standards of fluency for boys than for girls, on the hypothesis that this is a contributing cause of the sex ratio in stuttering. In other words, how far is non-fluency tolerated in the speech of boys and girls as measured by the readiness with which normal children of either sex are diagnosed as stutterers by a sample of adults.

Experimental Design: Approximately 160 fifteen-second tape- recorded speech samples were first collected. The samples represented the spontaneous speech of four to six year old nonstuttering children. From among these, the experimenters chose 65 which seemed to offer least clue to the child's sex in the form of speech content or vocal factors. These were used in a preliminary study in which 68 college students served as judges. Then, of these 65 samples, the 30 samples which showed the greatest ambiguity as to sex (smallest chi-squares) were culled for use in the experiment. These samples, representing 14 different children, were numbered consecutively from 1 to 30. They were then divided into two series of 15 samples each, Series A and Series B.

For the experiment *per se,* the subjects were 44 college students who were divided into two groups, each consisting of 11 males and 11 females. Each group heard Series A and Series B in the same order. Group I was told that Series A was a series of boys and that Series B was a series of girls. These suggestions were reversed for Group II. They were then asked to judge whether or not each voice sample belonged to a "stutterer" or a "non-stutterer."

Summary:

1. "Boys" were regarded as stutterers slightly more often than "girls" by both male and female subjects, but the difference was not statistically significant.

2. A clear tendency, significant of the .01 level, was found for male subjects to make more diagnoses of stuttering than female subjects.

Conclusions: The author felt that this experiment did not furnish sufficient grounds for the conclusion that college students of the type sampled are more likely to diagnose more boys than girls as stutterers on the basis of their recorded speech. An inference readily drawn is that the sex ratio in stuttering is due to factors other than a difference in cultural standards of fluency for boys and girls. If so, the explanation of the sex ratio in accordance with a "diagnosogenic" theory of stuttering would seem to lie essentially in a sex difference in fluency *per se.*

However, it was felt that the emotionalized, self-involved expectations which parents have with regard to their own children may be quite another thing. The hypothesis cannot be dismissed that parents tend to expect more fluency of the boy, that they are more likely to regard his speech interruptions as abnormal, and that, once having made such a diagnosis, they take measures with more determination, vigor and resourcefulness in the case of the boy.

TITLE

Moncur, J. P.: **Parental Domination in Stuttering,** *Journal of Speech and Hearing Disorders,* **17 (1952), 155-165.**

Purpose: To determine the importance of parental domination in a syndrome of environmental factors which seem to differentiate stutterers from non-stutterers.

Experimental Design: The author reevaluated data from an unpublished study of 48 stutterers (42 boys and 6 girls) ranging in age from 62 months to 98 months and a group of non-stutterers, in terms of parental domination. Domination was classified four ways: (1) as revealed by disciplinary action, (2) by over-supervision and over protection of the child, (3) by holding child to excessively high standards and (4) by undue parental criticism. Information was also obtained by personal interviews with mothers of stuttering and non-stuttering children.

Summary: Parental domination may be revealed by disciplinary action such as spanking, threatening, nagging, and blind obedience. Statistically significant results showed that more mothers of stuttering children than non-stuttering children give answers which indicated parental domination. The large number of affirmative answers by both groups indicated that spanking is a popular corrective technique.

It was apparent that the mothers of stutterers held their children to far higher standards than mothers of non-stutterers. This was revealed by the fact that significantly more mothers of stutterers reported that their child was very nervous and felt their child had to struggle hard to keep up to the high standards set by parents or others. More mothers of stutterers indicated dissatisfaction with their children's immature conduct probably indicating a too intense urging of the child to attainment beyond his reach. On the question of attempting perfect toilet training in a short time, more mothers of stutterers indicated that they did attempt this.

In the other two phases which reveal parental domination the same significant results were found—mothers of stutterers gave far more affirmative answers to questions which indicate over-protection and over-supervision as well as undue criticism. Undue criticism was acknowledged by questions of holding up another child as an example of good conduct, criticizing or correcting his speech, and nagging the child.

Of the 59 questions asked, 19 were significant at the .01 level; 9 at the .05 level; and 24 others, while not significant, indicated definite positive trends. It was felt that a difference on one item did not establish dominance on the part of one group but that the results showed a group tendency showing fairly conclusively that the mothers of the stutterers were dominant.

Conclusions: It was concluded that there is a syndrome of environmental factors which precipitate or aggravate stuttering and that syndrome includes dominating parental action among which are domination by discipline, by over supervision and over protection, by holding children to excessively high standards, and by adverse parental criticism.

TITLE

LaFollette, A.: **Parental Environment of Stuttering Children,** *Journal of Speech and Hearing Disorders,* **21** (1956), 201-207.

Purpose: To study certain traits and attitudes of parents of stuttering children, as measured by self administered tests, with those of parents of non-stuttering children.

Experimental Design: From a group of names and case histories supplied by speech correctionists holding the rank of Clinical or Professional Member of ASHA, an experimental group of 85 families, representing 25 states of the U. S. and two provinces of Canada, was set up. The control group consisted of 50 homes whose children showed no significant speech defects. The experimental group were all families who had stuttering children. Subjects' self and social adjustments were measured by the California Test of Personality. Their ascendent-submissive tendencies were measured by the Allport Ascendance-Submission Reaction

Study. Their general mental health was measured by the Psycho-Somatic Inventory of MacFarland and Seitz. Their degree of tolerance for stuttering was measured by the Ammons-Johnson Test of Attitude Toward Stuttering. Another test was conducted for the study; it was designed to measure parental attitudes toward the roles of boys and girls. All tests were mailed to the subjects and self-administered.

Summary: The experimental group showed a significantly greater tendency toward submission than did the control group, when these groups were considered as wholes. The fathers in the experimental group showed significantly greater tendencies toward submission than did the mothers of the group. The fathers of the experimental group were significantly more submissive than the fathers of the control group, and were also significantly more variable among themselves referring to submissiveness. The fathers of the experimental group were significantly less well adjusted (as measured by the Psycho-Somatic test) than the fathers of the control group. The fathers of the experimental group who had stuttering children from 2 to 18 years of age were significantly more submissive, less favorably adjusted (as measured by the California test), and less tolerant of stuttering than were the fathers who had stuttering children from 19 to 30 years of age. An analysis by age within the groups revealed that the older fathers who had stuttering children were less favorably adjusted and more submissive than the fathers of the control group. This was not found to be true of the younger fathers of stutterers, who apparently were similar to their controls.

No dependable differences were found between mothers of the two groups, nor between the parents of male stutterers and those of female stutterers.

Conclusions: None.

TITLE

Bloodstein, O., Jaeger, W., and Tureen, J.: A Study of the Diagnosis of Stuttering by Parents of Stutterers and Non-Stutterers, *Journal of Speech and Hearing Disorders,* **17 (1952), 308-314.**

Purpose: To determine whether parents of stutterers, if given the opportunity to express judgments about the recorded speech of a number of young children, would make diagnoses of stuttering more frequently than a group of parents of non-stutterers. It was designed to afford a partial test of Johnson's "diagnosogenic" theory of stuttering.

Experimental Design: Subjects were 48 parents (24 married couples). Half of these were parents of children who had been referred to a Speech and Hearing Center as stutterers. These children ranged in age from 3.5 to 8 years. The remaining parents had children, ranging in age from 4 to 10 years, who had never been regarded as stutterers.

In addition, 12 subjects were used in making recordings of the spontaneous speech of children. Of these, six were non-stutterers and six were regarded by their parents as stutterers. This group consisted of 10 boys and two girls, ranging in age from 3.5 to 8 years. A series of picture cards was presented to each child, and a tape recording was made as he responded to instructions to "tell a story" about each. The tape was then edited to provide 12 two-minute samples of continuous speech, one from each child. The parents listened to this recording and, after each sample, judged whether the child just heard was a stutterer or a normal speaker.

Summary:

1. Parents of stutterers significantly exceeded parents of non-stutterers in the extent to which they diagnosed both the stuttering and non-stuttering children as stutterers.

2. Among parents of stutterers as well as among parents of non-stutterers, mothers and fathers as groups did not differ significantly in the number of diagnoses of stuttering which they made.

3. There was a tendency for married couples to score somewhat alike, especially parents of non-stutterers.

Conclusions: The results of this study, it was concluded, sub-stantiate a "diagnosogenic" theory of stuttering.

The possibility should be recognized that the perfectionism of parents of stuttering children resulted from, rather than caused their children's stuttering. It was concluded, therefore, that this study did not demonstrate the effect of high standards of fluency on the speech of children—only that such high standards exist.

It was finally suggested that the crucial implication of this study is that the extent to which a child's non-fluency is excessive or conspicuous is determined not solely by the amount of repetition in his speech, but, also, to a significant degree, by who is listening. In so far as this is true, the term "primary stuttering" loses much of its meaning.

TITLE

Duncan, M. H.: **Home Adjustment of Stutterers vs. Non-Stutterers,** *Journal of Speech and Hearing Disorders,* 14 (1949), 255-259.

Purpose: To determine if the responses to items in the 'home adjustment' area of a personality inventory show greater than chance differences between college-age stutterers and non-stutterers.

Experimental Design: The sample consisted of 62 stutterers and a comparable number of non-stutterers (49 men and 13 women). All 124 of the subjects were under treatment at the time of the study. The non-stutterers had varying degrees of articulatory defects. The stutterers' age range was from 16 to 27 years, the non-stutterers' from 16 to 25 years. The Mdn for both was 18 years.

The inventory used was the Bell Adjustment. Only the 'home adjustment' section scores, which comprised 35 of the 140 items in the inventory, were used in computing the data. Only those differences which reached the .02 level of significance were accepted as significant in this study.

Summary: The responses to five of the 35 items were significantly different at the .01 level, four were less than the .01 level. The five discriminating questions were:

"1. Have you often felt that either of your parents did not unstand you?

2. Do you feel there has been a lack of real love and affection in your home?

3. Do you think your parents fail to recognize that you are a mature person and, hence, treat you as if you were still a child?

4. Did you ever have a strong desire to run away from home?

5. Do you sometimes feel your parents are disappointed in you?"

On all of these items the differences were in favor of the stutterer. There were eight other questions which yielded differences on a lower significance level: three between .01 and .02, five between .20 and .10.

Conclusions: It was concluded that the significant differences shown to exist pointed toward an unwholesome situation somewhere in the relations between the stutterer and his parents. It may, on the other hand, it was suggested, indicate only a higher incidence of neurotic characteristics among stutterers.

TITLE

Spriesterbach, D.: **An Objective Approach to the Investigation of Social Adjustment of Male Stutterers,** *Journal of Speech and Hearing Disorders,* 16 (1951), 250-257.

Purpose: To determine in a standardized and quantitative fashion the character of certain evaluative reactions which could logically be expected to function more or less significantly in relation to the individual's social adjustment.

Experimental Design: Subjects were 183 normally-speaking college males, 50 male stutterers undergoing therapy, and 20 male institutionalized psychotic patients. The median age of the normal males was 20.5 years, of the stutterers 21.5 years and of the psychotics 47 years. The major considerations in the selection of the psychotic patients were the patients' state of mental deterioration and general cooperativeness.

The procedure required the subject to rate each of a series of pictures with respect to its appropriateness as an example of the meaning of a specified word. Each picture represented one or more persons engaged in some sort of activity. For example, one of the words used in the test was "worthwhile," and as one part of the procedure the subject was instructed to rate each of 15 pictures as an example of people engaged in worthwhile activity. A 7-point scale was used. A rating of *one* indicated that the activity picture was, for the subject, an extremely poor example of what he would mean by "worthwhile"; a rating of *seven* indicated that it was an extremely good example of what he would mean by the word. The intervening scale values were used by the subject to designate intermediate degrees of appropriatenesss. Eleven different words were employed, and for each word there were 15 pictures to be rated.

Summary: ". . . stutterers differed from the normal males in the ratings on only slightly more pictures than could be attributed to chance; both the normal males and stutterers differed significantly from the psychotic patients in the ratings of at least six times the number of pictures that could be attributed to chance." Hence, the evaluation behavior of the stutterers resembles that of the normal males more than that of the psychotic patients.

Conclusions: It was concluded that because of imperfections in the design, i.e., lack of rigid control of the composition of the sample, size of sample, etc., the obtained results could be discussed only in relatively general terms.

Insofar as the test employed measures a basic aspect of social adjustment, the stutterers investigated demonstrated evaluative reactions different from those of presumably normal non-stutterers to an extent suggestive of relatively mild degrees of social maladjustment. The stutterers differed markedly, on the other hand, from the psychotic patients in their evaluative reactions.

"The factors of age and mental ability, insofar as it was possible to study them in this experiment, did not appear to be significant determiners of the deviation scores of the normal males."

The need for further research in this area was suggested.

TITLE

Morgenstern, J.: Socio-Economic Factors In Stuttering, *Journal of Speech and Hearing Disorders*, 21 (1956), 25-33.

Purpose: To answer the questions: (1) What socio-economic strata are affected by symptoms of stuttering? (2) What possible explanation can be offered for any varying incidence?

Experimental Design: Qualified speech therapists interviewed and listened to readings of children reported by the supervisors of their schools to be stutterers. Three hundred fifty of the 29,499 sixth and seventh grade children in the schools surveyed were judged by the therapists to be stutterers. The results of the interviewing were tabulated to furnish data concerning the following questions: Is stuttering incidence related to (1) population density, (2) occupation of father or guardian, (3) crowded housing (determined by the ratio of occupants to number of rooms in dwelling), (4) sibling status, or (5) age of mother?

Norms and other data concerning population density and housing conditions were used from a former survey of 70,000 eleven year old children chosen at random in five different geographical areas.

Summary:

1. Stuttering incidence was not found to vary significantly according to either geographical area or density of population.

2. A significantly high proportion of stuttering was found among children whose fathers or guardians were semi-skilled manual weekly wage-earners, regardless of the area in which they lived. The difference was significant at the .01 level.

3. A significantly high proportion of stuttering was found among children whose fathers or guardians were skilled manual weekly wage-earners living in sparsely-populated areas. The difference was significant at the .01 level.

4. A significant difference was not found among children whose fathers or guardians had middle and upper class occupations.

5. A significantly low proportion of stutterers was found among children whose fathers or guardians were unskilled industrial or agricultural laborers, regardless of the area in which they lived.

6. Crowded housing was found to correlate negatively with stuttering incidence, i.e., the more crowded the housing, the lower the incidence of stuttering. The correlation was significant.

7. Sibling status (number of siblings, ratio of older and younger siblings, number of first-born, number of last-born, number of only children, position in family) was found to have almost no relation to stuttering incidence, except that there was a greater difference (significant at the .01 level) in number of years separating stutterer from next preceding or succeeding sibling than for normals.

8. Age of the mother was unrelated to incidence of stuttering in the 46 cases which were investigated on this point.

Conclusions: It was concluded that the relation of certain socio-economic factors to the incidence of stuttering may be explained by means of Johnson's theory that parental anxiety, placing a premium on speech fluency, may cause children of parents with upwardly oriented cultural ambitions to suffer from higher incidence of stuttering. It was also suggested that the child separated by a larger than usual number of years from his siblings may suffer in the same fashion because his mother has more time and concern to give to his speech. This later conclusion, however, was not borne out in cases of only children.

TITLE

Rosenberg, S., and Curtiss, J.: The Effect of Stuttering on the Behavior of the Listener, *Journal of Abnormal and Social Psychology,* **49 (1944), 355-361.**

Purpose: To present some responses of the listener which may be influenced by stuttering, namely, eye contact, hand movement, and other bodily movement.

Experimental Design: Twenty college students (13 males and 7 females) with a mean age of 24.3 years were subjects in the experiment. The experiment consisted of observing their reactions, while they thought they were waiting for the experiment to begin, to five minutes of random conversation with one experimenter who posed as another subject and spoke normally, and five minutes of random conversation with another experimenter posing as a subject, who simulated stuttering. Observations were made without the knowledge of the subjects, and were classified as to frequency and duration of eye contact, hand movement, and other bodily movement.

Summary: Significant differences were found in five of the six measures:

1. Increased duration of loss of eye contact during stuttering.

2. Decreased frequency of loss of eye contact during stuttering.

3. Decreased frequency of initiating hand movement during stuttering.

4. Decreased duration of other bodily movement during stuttering.

5. Decreased frequency of initiating other bodily movement during stuttering.

After tests of reliability, a statistical control was applied which reduced all the differences below the level of significance except one, namely frequency of loss of eye contact. It was suggested that the data might cause one to concur in the hypothesis that stuttering is "noxious" or punishing stimulus to the listener, and he reacts to the stuttering as if it were a behavior depressant, constraining his actions.

Conclusions: It was concluded that:

1. Listener behavior is affected by stuttering.

2. The frequency of loss of eye contact was significantly less during stuttered than during non-stuttered speech.

3. Stuttering seems to act as a behavioral depressant to the listener, a type of "noxious stimulus" or negative reinforcer.

TITLE

Bloodstein, O., and Bloodstein, A.: Interpretations of Facial Reactions to Stuttering, *Journal of Speech and Hearing Disorders,* 20 (1955), 148-155.

Purpose: To examine certain aspects of the stutterer's response to listener reaction behavior.

Experimental Design: Ten subjects (seven males), all college students, and one severe stutterer participated in the making of a motion picture film. The suttterer, a 19 year old severe case, spoke to each of the 10 students in an experimental situation. The reactions of the students were recorded on film, unknown to them. They had had no previous knowledge of what the experiment was. These 10 subjects afterwards listed their subjective opinions of their own reactions to the stutterer on a questionnaire.

Twenty-five stutterers and an equal number of controls viewed the film. Both these groups were composed of twenty-three males and two females, median age 19, all students in college. All subjects rated the pictured reactions on a prepared form which allowed them to interpret the reaction of the person(s) filmed as one of: "no unfavorable reaction—embarrassment—amusement—impatience—pity—annoyance—superiority—shock—morbid curiosity—studied unconcern—any other." All the stuttering subjects has some time previously indicated what reactions people usually made to their stuttering (this was at the time of their enrollment in the clinic).

Summary: The following results were obtained:

1. Subjects disagreed widely among themselves as to what reaction was pictured on the films.

2. Stutterers and non-stutterers were not essentially different in the evaluations they made of the films.

3. Both groups' interpretations were essentially "incorrect" when compared with the reactions the pictured listeners indicated they had made.

4. Stutterers did not tend to find the reactions they had listed as the one usually made to their own stuttering.

Conclusions: Stutterers, as this experiment sees them, seem to be more objective about listener reactions than has been previously believed. They also do not appear to project their own ideas into the reactions they see in their listeners.

TITLE

McDonald, E., and Frick, J.: **Some Store Clerks' Reactions To Stuttering,** *Journal of Speech and Hearing Disorders,* **19** (1954), 306-311.

Purpose: To determine how one group of listeners (store clerks), feel while listening to a severe stutterer.

Experimental Design: A list of probable reactions to listening to a stutterer was obtained by means of having students in a beginning speech correction class listen to a speech by a stutterer and then describe their feelings. Their answers were classified into eight categories: surprise, embarrassment, impatience, pity, amusement, curiosity, sympathy, and repulsion. To these were added a few others based on stutterers' evaluations of the feelings of their listeners. The questions compiled from these were submitted to several "trial interviews" with clerks in order to clarify and eliminate confusing questions or phraseology. The final questionnaire resulting from this contained 25 items under the eight headings listed above and one other entitled, "Unclassified." The test was administered to a total of 50 clerks (28 men and 22 women) in three towns, immediately after a severe stutterer had talked with them.

Summary: From introductory questions asked the clerks before administering the questonnaire the following information was secured:

1. Twenty-two clerks described the speaker's difficulty as "stuttering" or "stammering."

2. Seven used the phrase "speech defect."

3. Fifteen said they didn't know what was wrong with the speaker.

4. Three made highly emotional responses, such as, "My God, wasn't that awful?"

5. Three described the difficulty as some kind of "nervous disorder."

6. A total of 57% recognized the difficulty as a speech defect.

7. Forty said they had talked before with someone like the speaker; 10 said they hadn't.

To the questionnaire itself, the following responses were made:

	Yes to All	Yes to at Least One	No to All	Don't Know to All
SURPRISE (3 questions)	9	32	18	0
EMBARRASSMENT (4 questions)	0	26	22	2
IMPATIENCE (2 questions)	1	11	39	0
PITY (3 questions)	2	47	3	0
AMUSEMENT (3 questions)	0	11	3	0
CURIOSITY (3 questions)	4	36	14	0
SYMPATHY (2 questions)	21	42	8	0
REPULSION (3 questions)	0	1	49	0

Conclusions: It was concluded that the data indicate that feelings of impatience, amusement, and repulsion will be encountered only rarely by the stutterer, while feelings of surprise, embarrassment, pity, curiosity, and sympathy will be experienced with varying degrees of frequency. It was suggested that these findings have implications for therapy.

TITLE

Travis L., Johnson, W., and Shover, J.: The Relations of Bilingualism to Stuttering, *Journal of Speech Disorders*, 2 (1937), 185-189.

Purpose: To ascertain whether there is any relation between bilingualism and stuttering.

Experimental Design: This survey was conducted in the public schools of East Chicago, Indiana. A total of 4,827 children were surveyed individually, approximately 50% being boys. The age range was from 4 to 17 years with an average of 8.54 years. Of the 4,827 Ss, 2,399 spoke English only. There were 2,322 who spoke English and one other language, these being classified as bilinguals. There were 37 boys and 52 girls who were polyglots who could also speak English, while 27 foreign speaking Ss could not speak English. There were 126 stutterers found among the 4,827 Ss. A questionnaire was used in connection with the interview with each S.

Summary:

1. There were significantly more stutterers among the bilinguals than among the children who speak only English—the respective percentages were 2.80 and 1.80—both significant at the .02 level.

2. The age of onset of stuttering in 13 of the boys coincided with the introduction of a second language; for four girl stutterers the same was true. These cases constitute 26% of the total group of bilingual stutterers.

3. Of the bilingual stutterers 66.2% were boys and 33.8% girls. Of the English speaking group 77.4% were boys and 22.6% girls.

4. The evidence seemed to indicate that bilingual stutterers were on the average less intelligent than the English-speaking stutterers.

Conclusions: Though it appeared that significantly more stutterers are found among the bilinguals than among the children who speak only English, the authors felt that it was not certain that this difference was due solely to the factor of bilingualism. It might be due, they suggested, to the economic insecurity and emotional instability found in many foreign homes as a result of the economic depression, or to a confusion which arises from being placed in a totally strange and new environment. A check on several factors other than bilingualism indicated that the somewhat lower average IQ of the bilinguals should be considered in evaluating the significance of bilingualism as such in relation to stuttering.

"That there is a difference between the bilinguals and English speaking subjects may be no more significant than the fact that the difference is really quite small." That 97.2% of the bilinguals do not stutter, the authors feel, cannot be overlooked.

TITLE

Swift, W. B.: A Psychological Ananlysis of Stuttering, *Journal of Abnormal and Social Psychology,* **10 (1915-16), 225-235.**

Purpose: To investigate the activities which occur in the central nervous system above the level of the lower sensory and motor areas during speech.

Experimental Design: Some preliminary normative data were obtained from 20 stutterers and some normal speakers. Each S was asked: (1) "Where do you live?" and (2) "Say after me, 'The dog ran across the street.'" The resulting data warranted the tentative conclusion that stutterers have a loss or diminished power of visualization.

A more exhaustive investigation was then executed with the following points in view: (a) To what extent is visualization weak? (b) Is it weaker in the worst cases? (c) Is it less and less weak as cases appear less severe? (d) Is it the same for past, present and future memories? (e) Is visualization equally at fault in all sensory areas of the cortex? (f) Do cases approach normal visualization processes in proportion as they progress in their cure? (g) Numerous and other minor questions presented themselves.

In order to answer these questions, a series of 24 tests were formulated and administered to 19 stutterers. Tests involved asking questions concerned with speech, motor performances, general sensory perception, hearing, sight, smell, taste and muscle sense. Introspective reports were obtained from each S.

Summary: Severe stutterers never appeared to visualize at all. "In direct proportion that these cases became less severe, did visualization increase in frequency, strength, and continuation in consciousness before and during speech." In general, when visualization was present stuttering was absent; when visualization was absent stuttering was present. Visualization appeared to be slightly more frequent for past and future memories than for present ones. Stuttering, it was felt therefore, is an indication of absent or weak visualization.

Conclusions: The author concluded that all the intricate phenomena of stuttering can be explained in terms of visualization theory. Visualization processes, it was felt, are a matter of growth through exercise and development and use from the sensory area —mostly the eye. These processes may receive a setback through the treatment of people in the environment, such as interruptions of early speech efforts, or hearing other stutterers interrupt their own visualization processes as they stutter. When the habit of visualization is lessened, the action upon speech is the same as the withdrawal of an inhibiting reflex arc.

Visualization processes, it was suggested, act like reflex inhibition. On concrete matters that can be easily visualized the stuttering is gone; on abstract matters that are difficult to visualize, stuttering again appears. In anger, when an intense visual picture is presented and occupies the mind; there is no stuttering. In singing, an auditory image of a melody may be more easily applicable as supplying the needed inhibition reflex arc than the visual because it is nearer to the speech center. For the same reason, prayer is uttered without stuttering when there is enough faith in a God to hold an image of Him during utterance. Swift gives this condition of defective visualization the name of *asthenia*.

ETIOLOGY—PSYCHOLOGICAL
Additional Reading References

Ainsworth, C.: Studies in the Psychology of Stuttering: XII. Empathic Breathing of Auditors While Listening to Stuttering Speech, *Journal of Speech Disorders*, 4 (1939), 149-156.

Ammons, R., and Johnson, W.: Studies in the Psychology of Stuttering: XVIII. The Construction and Application of a Test of Attitude Toward Stuttering, *Journal of Speech Disorders*, 9 (1944), 39-49.

Barbara, D. A.: *Stuttering: A Psychodynamic Approach to its Understanding and Treatment,* Julian Press, New York, 1954.

Bender, J. F.: *The Personality Structure of Stutterers,* Pitman, New York, 1939.

Berwick, N. H.: Stuttering in Response to Photographs of Selected Listeners, *Stuttering in Children and Adults,* University of Minnesota Press, Minneapolis, 1955.

Bluemel, C. S.: *Mental Aspects of Stuttering,* Williams and Wilkins, Baltimore, 1930.

————: Stammering and Cognate Defects of Speech, *Journal of Abnormal Psychology,* 9 (1915), 431-432.

————: Stammering and Inhibition, *Journal of Speech Disorders,* 5 (1940) 305-308.

Brown, F. W.: Mental Aspects of Certain Cases of Stuttering, *Journal of Expression,* March, 1930.

————: Personality Integration as an Essential Factor in Permanent Cure of Stuttering, *Mental Hygiene,* 17 (1933), 266-277.

Brown, S. F., and Hull, H. C.: A Study of Some Attitudes of a Group of 59 Stutterers, *Journal of Speech Disorders,* 7 (1942), 323-324.

Bryngelson, B.: Psychological Problems in Stuttering, *Mental Hygiene,* 21 (1937), 631-639.

Bullen, A.: A Cross Cultural Approach to the Problems of Stuttering, *Child Development,* 16 (1945), 1-88.

Cooper, C. A.: Discussion on the Relationship Between Speech Disorders and Personality Defects in Children and How Stuttering May Unfavorably Affect Children's Personality Development, *Journal of Pediatrics,* 21 (1942), 418-421.

Coriat, I. H.: Dynamics of Stammering, *Psychoanalytic Quarterly,* 2 (1933), 244-259.

————: Stammering. A Psychoanalytical Interpretation, *Nervous and Mental Disorders Monograph,* No. 47, 1928.

————: Oral Erotic Components of Stammering, *International Journal of Psychoanalysis,* 8 (1927), January.

Darley, F. L.: The Relationship of Parental Attitudes and Adjustments to the Development of Stuttering, *Stuttering in Children and Adults,* University of Minnesota Press, Minneapolis, 1955.

Dickinson, E. D.: Educational and Emotional Adjustments of Stuttering Children, *Teachers College Contribution to Education,* No. 314, Columbia University.

Dixon, C. C.: Stuttering Adaptation in Relation to Assumed Level of Anxiety, *Stuttering in Children and Adults,* University of Minnesota Press, Minneapolis, 1955.

Dorsey, J. M.: Psychology of Person Who Stutters, *Psychoanalytic Review,* 22, (1935), 25-35.

Dunlap, K.: The Stuttering Boy, *Journal of Abnormal Psychology,* 12 (1917), 44-48.

Fletcher, J. M.: An Experimental Study of Stuttering, *Journal of Applied Psychology,* 25 (1914), 201-249.

Font, M. M.: A Comparison of the Free Associations of Stutterers and Non-stutterers, *Stuttering in Children and Adults,* University of Minnesota Press, Minneapolis, 1955.

Fraiser, J.: An Exploration of Stutterers' Theories of Their Own Stuttering, *Ibid.*

Freund, H.: Psychosis and Stuttering, *Journal of Nervous and Mental Disorders,* 122 (1955), 161-172.

Friedman, G. M.: A Test of Attitude Toward Stuttering, *Stuttering in Children and Adults,* University of Minnesota Press, Minneapolis, 1955.

Gardner, W. H.: The Study of the Pupillary Reflex, With Special Reference to Stuttering, *Psychological Monographs,* 49 (1937), 1-31.

Glauber, I. P.: Psychoanalytic Concepts of the Stutterer, *Nervous Child,* 2 (1943), 172-180.

Goodstein, L. D., and Dahlstrom, W. G.: MMPI Difference Between the Parents of Stuttering and Non-Stuttering Children, *Journal of Consulting Psychology, October,* (1956), 365-370.

Goss, A. E.: Stuttering Behavior and Anxiety as a Function of Experimental Training, *Journal of Speech and Hearing Disorders,* 21 (1956), 343-351.

Goss, H.: Stuttering Behavior and Anxiety as a Function of the Duration of Stimulus Words, *Journal of Abnormal and Social Psychology,* 47 (1952), 38-50.

Greene, J., and Small, S. M.: Psychosomatic Factors in Stuttering, *Medical Clinics of North America,* 28 (1944), 615-628.

Heilpern, E.: A Case of Stuttering, *Psychoanalytic Quarterly,* 10 (1941), 95-115.

Heltman, H. J.: Psycho-Social Phenomena of Stuttering, *Journal of Social Psychology,* 9 (1938), 79.

Johnson, W.: The Influence of Stuttering on the Attitudes and Adaptations of the Stutterer, *Ibid.,* 5 (1934), 415-420.

———: The Problem of Stuttering from the Point of View of General Semantics, *Papers of the Second American Congress of General Semantics,* 2 (1943), 189-193.

———: Psychological Considerations of Stuttering, Journal of Exceptional Children, 43 (1936), 22-24.

———: The Role of Evaluation in Stuttering, Journal of Speech Disorders, 3 (1938), 85-89.

———: Some Semantic Aspects of Stuttering, Proceedings of American Speech Correction Association, 9 (1939), 39-40.

———: Stutterers' Attitudes Toward Stuttering, Journal of Abnormal and Social Psychology, 29 (1934), 32-44.

———, and Sinn, A.: Frequency of Stuttering with Expectation of Stuttering Controlled, Journal of Speech Disorders, 2 (1937), 98-100.

Kenyon, E.: A Critical Examination of the Foundation of the 'Recoil of the Vowel' Theory of the Cause of the Impediment of the Speech in Stammering, Journal of Speech Disorders, 5 (1940), 97-112.

———: The Etiology of Stammering, Ibid., 7 (1942), 97-104.

———: The Nature and Origin of Stammering, Transactions of American Laryngological Association, 1919.

Krugman, M.: Psychosomatic Study of Stuttering Children, IV. Rorschach Study, American Journal of Orthopsychiatry, 16 (1946), 127-133.

Leutenegger, R.: Adaptation and Recovery in the Oral Reading of Stutterers, Journal of Speech and Hearing Disorders, 22 (1957), 276-287.

Marinesco, G.: Stuttering and Conditioned Reflexes, Mental Hygiene, 44 (1935), 30-42.

Meyer, B.: Psychosomatic Aspects of Stuttering, Journal of Nervous and Mental Diseases, 101 (1945), 127-157.

Meyer, S.: Remarks Upon Dr. Coriat's Paper 'Stammering as a Psychoneurosis,' Journal of Abnormal and Social Psychology, 10 (1915), 120-137.

Milisen, R.: Frequency of Stuttering with Anticipation of Stuttering Controlled, Journal of Speech Disorders, 3 (1938), 207-214.

Moncour, J. P.: Environmental Factors Differentiating Stuttering Children from Non-Stuttering Children, Speech Monographs, 18 (1951), 312-325.

Murray, E.: The C. S. Bluemel Collection on Stuttering, Journal of Speech and Hearing Disorders, 22 (1957), 761-763.

Pitrelli, F. R.: Psychosomatic and Rorschach Aspects of Stuttering, Psychiatric Quarterly, 23 (1948), 175-194.

Satterfield, V.: Psychiatric Aspects of Stammering, Journal Mo. Medical Association, 31 (1934), 117-121.

Seth, G.: An Experimental Study of the Control of the Mechanism of Speech, and Particularly that of Respiration, in Stuttering Subjects, British Journal of Psychology, 31 (1934), 275-288.

Sheehan, J. G.: Fear-Reduction During Stuttering in Relation to Conflict, 'Anxiety Binding' and Reinforcement, *American Psychologist,* 7 (1952), 530 (Abstract).

———: A Theory of Stuttering as Approach-Avoidance Conflict, *Ibid.,* 5 (1950), 469 (Abstract).

———, and Voas, R.: Tension Patterns During Stuttering in Relation to Conflict, Anxiety-Binding and Reinforcement, *Speech Monographs,* 21 (1954), 272-279.

Snidecor, J. C.: Tension and Facial Appearance in Stuttering, *Stuttering in Children and Adults,* University of Minnesota Press, Minneapolis, 1955.

———: Why the Indian Does Not Stutter, *Quarterly Journal of Speech,* 33 (1947), 493-495.

Solomon, M.: The Psychology of Stuttering, *Journal of Speech Disorders,* 3 (1938), 59-61.

———: Stuttering, Emotion and Struggle for Equilibrium, *Proceedings of the American Speech Correction Association,* 6 (1936), 221-239.

Spring, W.: Words and Masses: Pictorial Contirbution to Psychology of Stammering, *Psychoanalytic Quarterly,* 4 (1935), 244-258.

Staats, L. C.: Sense of Humor in Stutterers and Nonstutterers, *Stuttering in Children and Adults,* University of Minnesota Press, Minneapolis, 1955.

Steer, M. D.: General Inteligence of College Stutterers, *School and Society,* 44 (1936), 862.

Swift, W. B.: Mental Imagery of Stutterers, *Journal of Abnormal and Social Psychology,* April, May (1917).

Thorpe, L. P.: Psychological Mechanisms of Stammering, *Journal of General Psychology,* 19 (1938), 97-109.

Travis, L. E.: The Influence of the Group upon the Stutterer's Speech in Free Association, *Journal of Abnormal and Social Psychology,* 23 (1928), 45-51.

———: Muscular Fixation of the Stutterer's Voice under Emotion, *Science,* 62 (1925), 207-208.

———: Recurrence of Stuttering Following Shift from Normal to Mirror Writing, *Archives of Neurology and Psychiatry,* 21 (1929), 386-391.

Trotter, W. D., and Kools, J. A.: Listener Adaptation to the Severity of Stuttering, *Journal of Speech and Hearing Disorders,* 20 (1955), 385-387.

Usher, R. D.: A Case of Stammering, *International Journal of Psycho-Analysis,* 25 (1944), 61-70.

West, R.: Is Stuttering Abnormal? *Journal of Abnormal and Social Psychology,* 31 (1936), 76-86.

Will, N.: A Six-Month Report on the Personality Development of a Thirteen-Year-Old Stuttering Boy, *Quarterly Journal of Speech,* 30 (1944), 88-95.

Wischner, G. J.: An Experimental Approach to Expectancy and Anxiety in Stuttering Behavior, *Journal of Speech and Hearing Disorders,* 17 (1952), 139-154.

————: An Experimental Approach to Stuttering as Learned Behavior, *American Psychologist,* 3 (1948), 278-279.

————: Stuttering Behavior and Learning: A Preliminary Theoretical Formulation, *Journal of Speech and Hearing Disorders,* 15 (1950), 324-325.

UNIT V

THERAPY

TITLE

Heltman, H. J.: Remedial Training for Speech Deviates in the Elementary School, *Elementary School Journal*, 46 (1946), 283-287.*

Purpose: To present certain theoretical concepts concerning speech therapy for elementary school children.

Experimental Design: None.

Summary: The author feels that one of the most disturbing problems the elementary teacher is called on to meet is that of the stutterer. The teacher feels unqualified to offer remedial assistance but when specialists are available the teacher usually expects flat "yes" and "no" answers in regard to techniques to be used.

Before any specific remedial measures are adopted even by the professional therapist it is imperative to know, it is felt, just *when* a pupil is really a stutterer, or as Johnson has said, "to treat certain phenomena of speech in children as if they were true stuttering is possibly the commonest cause of the onset of the disorder."

There are two symptoms of stuttering, it is suggested, which distinguish it from all other speaking irregularities involving lack of fluency. They are: (1) anxiety lest the speaker will hesitate and repeat, (2) spasm of organs of speech, particularly breathing muscles.

Therapy, the author points out, should be structured so that the child *never* comes to look at the act of speaking as an unpleasant experience. Some special recommendations are made as follows:

1. Speech games for schoolroom so speaking becomes a pleasure.

2. Choral reading.

---

*Copyright (1946) by the University of Chicago.

3. Action games using nonsense or nursery rhymes recited in time to rhythmic movement of the body.

4. Dramatizing the speech of animals in stories.

5. Use of hand puppets talking back and forth.

All of these devices, it is felt, are useful in building confidence in the pupil's ability to use his speech "machine" without difficulty.

The most difficult situations, according to teachers, occur in ordinary classroom situations. Some suggestions are offered:

1. Meeting the child with encouraging patience when he attempts to speak.

2. Encouraging recitation to be voluntary.

3. Observing situations where the stutterer expresses himself most easily and making such occasions available to him.

4. Providing group projects where he can forget his speech for a time.

5. Allowing him to read orally frequently if he is a good reader.

Conclusions: It is concluded that it is not the responsibility of elementary teachers to "cure" stuttering and perhaps they shouldn't try; however, they can offer invaluable "vocational-rehabilitation" in which the pupil becomes an integral part of school life and is as welcome as any other person in social groups. This, it is suggested, will probably do more to alleviate the child's distress than any other method.

TITLE

Knudson, T. A.: **A Study of the Oral Recitation Problems of Stutterers,** *Journal of Speech Disorders,* 4 (1939), 235-239.

Purpose: To determine the various types of methods used by teachers in handling stutterers in the oral situation and to determine the effect of these methods upon the stutterers.

Experimental Design: Seventy-two stutterers and 50 teachers served as subjects. The stutterers were 60 boys and 12 girls ranging in age from 9 to 27 years. The teachers were 10 men and 40 women from grade one through senior high school. Information was secured from the stutterers by means of personal interviews, supplemented by a questionnaire. A second questionnaire was used to secure information from the teachers.

1. Twenty-nine stutterers made use of written work to compensate for their shortcomings in oral recitation.

2. Sixty-two stutterers felt they made poorer oral recitations than they were intellectually able to make.

3. Thirty-one stutterers reported having been retarded in school because of stuttering. Eleven of these blamed the teacher.

4. Six stutterers admitted having played truant because of stuttering.

5. Six stutterers felt they should be excused from oral recitations.

6. Most felt that it would be more satisfactory to recite when they volunteered to do so.

7. A survey of teachers' responses showed that the most common reactions that the teachers have toward stutterers are sympathy and pity.

8. Forty teachers felt stuttering to be beyond their ability to cope with therapeutically.

9. There was a wide variance of opinion among teachers concerning the cause of stuttering.

Conclusions: The following recommendations were offered:

1. Some type of special consideration should be given the stuttering pupil in regard to oral recitation.

2. The stutterer should not be hurried in oral recitation, or words spoken for him.

3. An atmosphere should be created so stutterers will not feel excluded from, nor inferior to, the rest of the group.

4. It is usually desirable to demand extra written work of the stutterer to the extent that he is excused from oral recitation.

5. It is especially desirable to develop a sincere, friendly interest in the stuttering pupil to gain his point of view and to establish his confidence.

6. It is desirable to prepare the stutterer emotionally and intellectually to meet as many speech situations as possible.

TITLE

Bender, J.: What the Physical Education Instructor Can Do for the Stuttering Student, *Journal of Health and Physical Education*, 6 (1935), 16.

Purpose: To acquaint physical education instructors with the basic facts of stuttering and to recommend to them ways in which they may help the stutterers.

Experimental Design: None.

Summary: By and large, the author states, stuttering starts early in life, sometimes at onset of speech; certainly by adolescence it has begun. Few develop stuttering as adults. The stutterer presents a picture of nervousness and tension, not only of facial and speech muscles, but of the breathing apparatus, and perhaps even the entire body. His carriage and physical appearance are likely to be poor, and certainly his personality development is likely to be somewhat unwholesome, characterized by shyness, anxiety, negativism, restlessness, rebelliousness, obsession, etc. It is rather certain that the stutterer uses his speech difficulty as a compensatory device for various ones of these maladjustments.

Conclusions:

It was concluded that the physical education instructor can help in the following ways:

1. Befriend and understand the stutterer.

2. Learn all he can about the stutterer and his background.

3. Help him with his problems, such as heavy school load, worry over his schooling, home situation problems, and health problems.

4. Employ relaxation exercises for the stutterer (such as Jacobson's).

5. Encourage the stutterer to participate in games which induce relaxation of the large muscles, i.e., swimming, dancing, running, etc.

6. Encourage the stutterer to join in social and group activities.

TITLE

Bryngelson, B.: Prognosis of Stuttering, *Journal of Speech Disorders*, 3 (1938), 121-123.

Purpose: To estimate the prognosis for stuttering.

Experimental Design: None.

Summary: The question of prognosis, the author feels, must be discussed from two points of view—the child whose experience with stuttering has been brief, and the adult whose stuttering experience has persisted through the years with disastrous effects on thought, emotion, and general behavior.

Forty per cent of stuttering children will probably stop by eight years of age. The problem is how to tell which ones.

An absolute cure, the author feels, is very rare in adults. By 'cure' he refers to the elimination of all symptoms such as fear, sensitivity, habit patterns, avoidance and postponement devices, psychologic and physiologic crutches and the short neurological spasms. All, he suggests, are difficult to manage and uproot in clinical procedures, because they have become so deeply imbedded.

Adult patients must set goals for improvement of their speech and personalities. They rise or fall in relation to their points of view of themselves as stutterers. Along this line the so-called secondary reactions can be eliminated. Prognosis for this is hopeful if the patient has:

1. Sufficient intelligence to gain insight into the goals and practices in clinical procedure.

2. A degree of determination which so few people possess, the ability to stick to a task undisturbed by ordinary diversions of the clinic or of society at large.

3. Self-discipline in fulfilling the requisites essential in the performance of duties which often are unpleasant and very difficult.

4. Unimpeded by disturbing and non-cooperative factors in the home and school.

With the younger stutterer, prognosis is very good, it is felt, because here the clinician is dealing with stuttering in the raw;

the primary neurologic spasm, which is his most important consideration. With the young stutterer, speech rehabilitation in a comparatively short time is dependent on:

1. Physical health and care in general.
2. A wholesome mental and emotional environment.
3. Average intelligence.
4. The setting up in the brain of the co-ordinating faculty for easy, unimpeded motor facility by attending to all the factors relevant to inherent stock-brainedness, unilaterality of nervous organization, and the correlated factors of peripheral handedness. Any environmental factor, whether physical or emotional, which operates against the establishment of a unified heirarchic motor control of the cortex over its substructures, is unfavorable to a good prognosis.

Conclusions: As above.

TITLE

Hogewind, F.: Medical Treatment of Stuttering, *Journal of Speech Disorders*, 5 (1940), 203-208.

Purpose: To review past efforts to link stuttering to physiological causes and to present the author's linguo-medical treatment.

Experimental Design: None.

Summary: The author reviews some of the many attempts to connect stuttering to some physical disorder. He remarks on the frequent co-existence with stuttering of such disorders as epilepsy, migrane, vaso-motor catarrh, and allergic exzema. All of these disorders, he feels, are greatly influenced by the para-sympathetic nervous system. The author sought then to treat stuttering, which he assumed was also influenced by the para-sympathetic system, by means of sedation.

The experiment was conducted with older patients who were given oral doses of Bellergal containing "Bellafoline" (vagal sedative), "Gynergen" (sympathetic sedative) and phenobarbital (sedative of the central part of the para-sympathetic nervous system). As a test of suggestive influence, some of the patients were given only the vago-sedative. During this period their speech was not influenced. However, when Bellergal was administered improvement again occurred. The author also reports success in the administration of calcium to children under the age of 12. Although satisfactory results are reported, the author emphasizes that language training must be conducted at the same time for assurance of success.

Conclusions: As above.

TITLE

Hale, L. L.: **A Consideration of Thiamin Supplement in Prevention of Stuttering in Preschool Children,** *Journal of Speech and Hearing Disorders,* 16 (1951), 327-333.

Purpose: To investigate whether observable changes in the fluency of preschool children can be detected during the administration of vitamin B_1 (thiamin).

Experimental Design: As a pilot study, a select group of preschool age stutterers were administered thiamin (10 mg. three times daily) for one month. A control group was given placebo (an inert dose) during the same period. At the end of the month, the two groups were reversed and observations continued for another month. In most cases follow-up observations continued beyond the two month period.

Summary:

1. Observable speech improvement occurred in 55% of all the cases receiving thiamin.

2. There may have been improvement in an additional 20%.

3. No improvement could be claimed in 20% of the cases.

4. Of the two and three year olds, 80% were observably improved.

5. Of the four year olds, only 50% were observably improved.

6. It was doubtful if either of the two five year olds made any improvement.

7. Thiamin seemed to have no effect on the speech patterns of the seven and eight year olds.

8. In four cases there was a regression in the fluency of speech following cessation of the thiamin. Improvement was noted again after thiamin was resumed. With one exception, those who showed improvement with thiamin did so within the first two weeks of treatment.

Conclusions: It was felt that there was enough evidence of improvement in a sufficient number of cases to indicate that administration of thamin might be effective in preventing stuttering among preschool children. Indications were that the younger the child the more effective the thiamin therapy will be.

It was noted that although thiamin therapy may have contributed to the reduction of non-fluency it should not be considered as the only factor that may have been operating. It was suggested as an aid in the eradication of non-fluency pattern along with the customary parental counseling and guidance methods.

TITLE

Owen T., and Stemmermann, P.: Electric Convulsive Therapy in Stammering, *American Journal of Psychiatry,* **104** (1947), 410-413.

Purpose: To present a rather detailed case study involving the administration of electric convulsive therapy to a stutterer.

Experimental Design: None.

Summary: The subject presented in the case was a twenty year old girl, whose case history showed several disturbing relationships with her parents, siblings, and other men. Stuttering onset apparently had followed one of these traumatic experiences.

She was treated in a speech clinic without much success: it was then decided to administer electric shock treatments in much the same manner for various mental disturbances.

It was noted that the *petit mal* treatments were remarkably more beneficial than the *grand mal.* The history indicated that the program of shock produced ensuing periods of fluent speech or of greatly reduced stuttering. It was theorized that the shock acted as a relaxing agent and helped to destroy the tension involved in the stuttering syndrome.

The subject relapsed into her former stuttering behavior when visiting her home, and further treatment by shock therapy was administered, to which she continued to respond favorably. She had no objection to the therapy and said it relaxed her and made her feel less like herself.

Conclusions: It was concluded that this case supports a psychoanalytic theory of stuttering etiology. It was also concluded that the value of electric convulsive therapy in stuttering is that it relaxes the patient, helps him adjust to himself, and thus facilitates the program of psychoanalysis, which is the really important factor in therapy.

TITLE

Solomon, J.: Stammering, Stuttering, Pediatrician's Responsibility, *American Journal of Diseases of Children,* 45 (1933), 1079-1086.

Purpose: To sketch briefly the symptoms of "stammering" and "stuttering"; and to suggest what the pediatrician can do to help the child who manifests these disorders.

Experimental Design: None.

Summary: The author uses "stammer" to refer to articulation defects, particularly those involving the "s," "r" and "k" sounds, and gives some consideration to therapy for such defects. Concerning stuttering, the author offers the following as the progress of the "ailment" from a slight to a severe defect; the first symptom is the "clonus," simple syllable or sound repetitions; then the "tonus" develops; it is a stoppage in the flow of speech. Next is the "fast tonoclonus," a quick combination of stoppage and repetition; it is followed by the "slow tonoclonus," which is a longer stoppage with embolalia (insertion of unnecessary or meaningless sounds or words) and repetitions. The final stage is the *"forme cache,"* a process of interiorizing or attempting to hide the symptoms by various devices. Stuttering is characterized as a "vicious mental cycle." The author states concerning the cause, "A violent mental shock or a slowly developing mental conflict will serve as etiological factors in most cases."

He suggests to the pediatrician that it is unwise to attempt psychoanalysis, but feels that some form of psychotherapy may be helpful. He states, "the minor psychologic aspects" of stuttering "are easily handled, and cure easily effected as soon as diagnosis is made." He suggests, however, that in some more severe cases, a "special nurse or teacher" may be necessary, and perhaps separation of the child from his parents.

The easy clonic type of stuttering should be treated by adjusting the environment; the speech defect itself should not be pointed out to the child. For the more severe cases, "psychic treatment" and exercises, including breath control drill, voice training and consonant drills, should be employed.

Conclusions: None.

TITLE

Bender, J.: Do You Know Someone Who Stutterers? *Scientific Monthly,* 59 (1944), 221-224.

Purpose: To describe some therapeutic methodology for the treatment of stuttering.

Experimental Design: Three cases were presented—each treated by a different method.

Summary: One therapeutic technique used for a six year old girl involved a period of rest for the patient with the instructions that the parents ignore the stuttering behavior. Another technique used for an adult male was called the "rate-control" method. This involved speaking based on phonetic analysis designed "(1) to awaken aural speech consciousness, (2) to permit accurate diagnosis and isolation of habitual articulatory and vocal defects, (3) to relax the organs of articulation and use them economically, (4) to induce mental ease while speaking or reading orally, (5) to improve vocal quality, (6) to develop conscious control of the mechanical factors of articulation, and (7) to enlarge breath capacity." The third technique used for an adult male involved "voluntary stuttering" for therapy.

Success was reported for all three cases. It was pointed out that this was one reason why a speech specialist or psychologist should be familiar with a number of different therapeutic techniques, and therapists may many times want to employ a combination of techniques with one patient. It was noted that two of the three cases were given daily progressive relaxation exercises along with their respective programs.

Conclusions: It was concluded that "perhaps the most significant single item in the correction of stuttering is the rapport established between the stutterer and his correctionist. The value of rapport, the reciprocal feeling of friendliness and confidence, cannot be stressed too heavily. . . . Fundamentally it is because of rapport that so many techniques prove successful."

TITLE

Buckholtz, C. A.: Indigenous Confidence for Stutterers, *Quarterly Journal of Speech,* **19 (1933), 60-64.**

Purpose: To present a method of therapy for stutterers.

Experimental Design: None.

Summary: The author feels that while all stutterers lack confidence in speech, they all have confidence to some degree—nearly all stutterers can speak fluently in certain situations. This phenomenon is termed "indigenous confidence."

Establishment of a basic confidence of utterance, it is suggested, should be the prime objective at the beginning of training. Speech should be as natural as possible. At times, however, it must be of necessity unnatural—slow speech for example.

Awareness of how and why the feeling of complete confidence is operative should be built up in the subject's mind. Detailed and definite training applied consistently over a period of time is required to build up a natural and spontaneous speech reaction. Great care should be taken to preserve the natural indigenous confidence.

There is, it is felt, no one system for training stutterers. In many ways it depends more upon the therapist than the methods. The efficient teacher will, however, seek knowledge of what has proved effective elsewhere. The therapist must deal with each stutterer as an individual and adapt the training to suit his needs.

Conclusions: As above.

TITLE

Van Riper, C.: Do You Stutter? *Atlantic Monthly*, **164** (1939), **601-609.**

Purpose: To discuss the treatment for primary and secondary stutterers.

Experimental Design: None.

Summary: During the primary stage (usually three to four years of age) the symptoms are the same for all stutterers—easy prolongations and unconscious repetitions. The child, it is felt, is seldom permitted to remain in this primary stage long enough to permit nature to solve the problem through maturation. The child's parents usually become worried and show anxiety. Treatment, therefore, is suggested for the parents, not the child. At this point, stuttering is prevented rather than cured.

Treatment may consist of home, school, and playground observations by the therapist. All obvious symptoms and spasms are recorded as are the conditions under which the spasms are precipitated. Removal of the precipitating causes is the goal. "Removal of even one disturbing influence may effectively clear up the speech difficulty."

Parents may occasionally be asked to stutter themselves. Distractions should be used when the child blocks. Parents must learn to hide all reactions to the child's stuttering. The child should feel no pressure and live in an accepting environment.

The treatment for secondary stuttering is exactly the opposite of that for primary stuttering. There should be no distraction; therapy should be aimed at direct control of the stuttering block.

It is recommended that the laws governing the breaking of habits be followed. Assignments should be given which will bring the habit up to consciousness, break up its characteristic pattern, dissociate the cues which set it off, weaken the motive which causes it, place strong penalities upon its occurrence, and substitute other reactions in its place. When a block occurs, with this plan, there will be an intelligent plan of reaction rather than blind groping.

Gradually, it is felt, the habits of postponement, etc., will begin to disappear as the block is revealed in its simplest form. It is stressed that the stutterer must learn to accept his blocks if he is to refuse to react to them.

Conclusions: The author feels that with this approach the stutterer may have to reconcile himself to short blocks; however, they will no longer interfere with his communication.

TITLE

Van Riper, C.: **To the Stutterer as He Begins His Speech Therapy,** *Journal of Speech and Hearing Disorders,* 14 (1949), 303-306.

Purpose: To orient adult stutterers who are beginning their therapy.

Experimental Design: This paper is in the form of a letter to the stutterer.

Summary: The stutterer beginning his therapy for the first time goes through a period of bewilderment and confusion. It is important that he realize that there is no quick cure and that it is his rather than the therapist's responsibility to conquer the speech difficulty. Self-competition should be stressed rather than competition with others. The stutterer cannot be cured on faith alone; nor can he be taught how to talk—he knows how to talk already. He is taught what to do when he gets into a blocking situation. He should realize that stuttering therapy, like all others, is fallible.

The basic aim is to "... teach you how to stutter, and without obvious abnormality, in a way that does not interrupt the flow of your speech." The stutterer should work toward learning to stutter quickly, effortlessly, and unnoticeably.

A plan of therapy is outlined. Basically it is as follows:

1. Stutterer learns to stutter well—quickly, effortlessly.
2. Old reactions, old habits are gradually reduced.
3. Understanding of the over-all plan of treatment is essential.
4. Must be willing to stutter without embarrassment. Stop avoiding feared words and eliminate use of devices.
5. Negative practice must be learned.
6. Stutterer must be willing to accept a good deal of psychotherapy from the therapist.

Conclusions: As above.

TITLE

Van Riper, C.: The Preparatory Set in Stuttering, *Journal of Speech Disorders*, 2 (1937), 149-154.

Purpose: To show the use of the stutterer's preparatory set as a part of therapy.

Experimental Design: None.

Summary: It is suggested that the stutterer's preparatory set be used as a tool for changing his spasm pattern. The preparatory set is described as a pre-stimulus neuromuscular adjustment which selects, determines, and controls the response to the expected stimulus. The author feels that in stuttering, the preparatory set determines the form of the spasm and causes the compulsive aspects of the reaction.

Rather than eliminate the stuttering spasms, it should be modified until it carries little social penality. Say to the stutterer, "Stutter all you wish—but stutter in this way . . ." The stutterer should be shown a way to stutter that provides little abnormality.

The author suggests a method that is essentially stop-go. This "consists of building up a preparatory set at attempt to say the feared word as a whole, but to get in readiness to react to a felt block by stopping immediately and then finishing the rest of the word." The block must serve as the signal to set off the preparatory set—"thus we use stuttering to get rid of stuttering."

It is essential in this method that the stutterer learns to say the whole word and not to split it. If he has trouble with the word 'this' he learns to say it like 'th-is' rather than like 'a-a-a-th-th-this.' He must learn, too, to react with stop-go only when an actual block is felt.

The following principles are suggested for use in tearing down the old preparatory sets and building up new ones:

1. "Get rid of the fundamental cause of the primary symptoms, whether it be a shift of handedness or something else.

2. Change the form of the spasm to one which is neither peculiar nor of long duration.

3. Tear down the old secondary symptoms of avoidance, postponement, starting and release.

4. Use the primary symptoms to set off the stop-go preparatory set.

5. Seek out feared words so as to associate with them these new preparatory sets."

Conclusions: As above.

TITLE

Bryngelson, B.: A Method of Stuttering, *Journal of Abnormal and Social Psychology,* **30 (1935), 194-198.**

Purpose: To discuss voluntary stuttering as a therapeutic technique.

Experimental Design: None.

Summary: The author feels that since cortical control is lacking in the neurology of the stutterer, the therapeutic aim should be to set up a center of speech control on one side of the cortex.

In voluntary stuttering the stutterer is taught to imitate willfully spasms as he studies them in his own speech. Using a mirror he observes his spasms and then tries to reproduce them. It is felt that there is no danger of increasing the symptoms with this method for spasms cannot be accurately reproduced either in rate or form. The neurological advantage of this, it is felt, lies in the fact that the cortex is exercised instead of the sub-cortical levels. Constant repetition of the initial letter, syllable or word mobilizes speech energy on the highest level of response and tends to build ultimately a center of greater dominance in the brain.

It is suggested that clonic-type blocks be imitated first. After the stutterer has made the psychological adjustment he will be in a more objective state of mind when watching the more bizarre tonic-type spasm in the mirror. It is felt that mirror drill should be prefaced with conferences in which the stutterer is encouraged to accept the problem unemotionally.

General rules for teaching voluntary stuttering are given as follows:

1. Repeat the first sound in each word distinctly several times.

2. Vary the number of repetitions in order to avoid the establishment of a set speech pattern.

3. Whenever the stutterer has a spasm while using voluntary stuttering, he should repeat the word until he can say it without difficulty.

4. In longer words, voluntary stuttering can be practiced on each syllable and with various sound combinations.

5. Initially voluntary stuttering should be performed before a mirror. After it has been mastered, it should be employed in all social situations.

Conclusions: As above.

TITLE

Dunlap, K.: Stammering: Its Nature, Etiology and Therapy, *Journal of Comparative Psychology*, **37** (1944), 187-202.

Purpose: To present certain theoretical concepts concerning etiology of and therapy for stuttering.

Experimental Design: None.

Summary: The author feels that stuttering is usually caused by a family situation which produces a neurotic condition. As the child learns to talk he inadvertently stumbles, mispronounces and inverts words, and parents correct, stop and make him repeat. He becomes jittery about speech and expects to make slips and be corrected. Dunlap suggests that parents should be careful to speak correctly, and avoid talking baby talk in infancy, since the child learns speech by imitation.

He feels that no treatment should be undertaken before the age of eight—that treatment before this age merely fixes the habit more firmly. If the condition, however, is treated before age 15-16, he feels the defect can be cleared up in a few months.

Before treatment, the cause which produced the defect, he feels must be discovered and attempts made to eliminate it—until these environmental factors have been eliminated the stutterer will be unable to overcome the habit.

General orientation in therapy includes telling the patient the damaging effects of trying to avoid stuttering—explain to him that a stutterer is not merely a person who stutters, but one who worries about it and as a result can't stop.

It is suggested that a predisposing cause may be physical weakness and malnutrition, and an increase in the amount of meat consumed—especially for very young stutterers is recommended.

The basis of the therapy prescribed is negative practice which should be used in a carefully controlled situation and by a skilled therapist. Three repetitions of each error is recommended. Other techniques suggested are unison reading, solo reading with skipping of troublesome words, study of secondary symptoms, rhythmic reading and beating time to speech, practice in conversational speech, participation in social activities and sports. Negative practice, he feels, should not be used at home where it might be used incorrectly.

Importance of family cooperation is mentioned. Family members should react normally and ignore defect.

Therapy sessions, it is felt, should be held three times a week for 50 to 60 minute periods. As improvement occurrs, sessions may be reduced.

Conclusions: As above.

TITLE

Fishman, H. H.: A Study of the Efficacy of Negative Practice as a Corrective for Stammering, *Journal of Speech Disorders,* 2 (1937), 67-72.

Purpose: To study the effectiveness of negative practice as a treatment for stuttering.

Experimental Design: Four males and one female ranging in age from 12 to 20 years were the subjects. All of the S's except one who was a non-reader read a story and ten minutes later were asked to tell all they could about it. The same procedure was used for the non-reader except that spontaneous speech was used as the sample. Words stuttered on by the subjects were noted and were used in formulating ten sentences used as practice material in the study.

Prior to the beginning of the study of negative practice the E spent two weeks with each S familiarizing himself with the individual and his stuttering pattern. Each S was told that negative practice was a positive cure and that he must learn to stutter voluntarily while at the same time realizing that stuttering was undesirable.

After the E felt that on the basis of the first of the ten sentences the S was imitating his pattern accurately he was directed to (1) stutter each sentence three times; (the sentences contained underlined words on which the S was supposed to stutter) (2) say the sentence correctly three times with the E; (3) say each sentence alone one time. As the ten sentences were mastered, new ones were added. For the S who was unable to read, the same procedure was used except that the sentences were read to him.

The stuttering of three of the S's was characterized by repetition of words, syllables, and letters. Two of the S's (both males, the two oldest of group) had complete (tonic) type blocks.

Summary:

1. The three S's characterized by repetitions showed definite improvement after negative practice.

2. The two S's characterized by tonic-type blocks developed more stuttering after negative practice.

Conclusions: It was concluded that negative practice can be used with beneficial results with stutterers who evidence a repetition-type block. For stutterers who evidence the tonic-type block negative practice does not appear to be advisable—may even make the condition worse.

It was felt that a tonic block is difficult to simulate without having the involuntary pattern appear. This, it was felt, suggests that negative practice may not be applicable to the correction of certain speech blocks, and that this type speech block may not be essentially a habit.

Stuttering characterized essentially by repetitions, it was concluded, appears to be a habit and as such may be eliminated by the application of the proper laws of learning.

TITLE

Sheehan, J. G., and Voas, R. B.: Stuttering As Conflict: 1. Comparison of Therapy Techniques Involving Approach and Avoidance, *Journal of Speech and Hearing Disorders,* **22 (1957), 714-723.**

Purpose: To test approach-avoidance theory in relation to stuttering by comparing the effectiveness of three types of negative practice in reducing stuttering behavior.

Experimental Design: Twenty four stutterers (3 females), ranging in age from 15 to 40 years, each read four test passages six times in an adaptive situation. Eight used the Dunlap technique of imitating their own stuttering after the first reading of each passage. Eight used voluntary bounce after the first readings, and eight used voluntary slide (prolongation) after the first readings. All sixth readings were control readings utilizing no technique for reduction of stuttering. These were used as controls to measure adaptation after the five previous readings of the passages.

In reading the four different passages, the subjects used their respective techniques: (1) on the same words stuttered in first readings, (2) on words just previous to those stuttered in first readings, (3) on randomly indicated words, and (4) not at all. The experimenters judged how many blocks occurred in all readings. Their ability was reported as "good," though not stated in figures.

Summary: None of the negative practice techniques reduced stuttering more than did simple adaptation through repeated reading of the passages. However, both bounce and slide reduced stuttering more quickly than did adaptation, and under the imitating condition, significantly (.01) more blocks occurred than under the other three conditions (bounce, slide and control).

In studying the point of application of negative practice, it was found that there was least improvement when imitation was applied to the word previous to the feared word, and most improvement when slide was applied to the word previous to the feared word. Other points of application made little difference.

Conclusions: Although no negative practice method was apparently better than adaptation in reducing stuttering, the following conclusions were drawn:

1. Slide on the word previous to the feared word may reduce stuttering, functioning as practice of an approach response.

2. Imitation of actual stuttering may increase stuttering, functioning as practice of a avoidance response.

TITLE

Meissner, J. H.: The Relationship Between Voluntary Non-Fluency and Stuttering, *Journal of Speech Disorders*, 11 (1946), 13-23.

Purpose: To determine the relationship between voluntary non-fluency and the frequency of stuttering during oral reading, and to evaluate the effect of certain grammatical factors on stuttering.

Experimental Design: Subjects were 24 stutterers (8 females, 16 males (ranging in age from 13-22. Each S read eight 500-word passages. Five were control passages, and in three the S was required to use the bounce technique on certain underlined words in the passage. The total number of words bounced on was varied for each of the three experimental passages: first reading, 50%; second 25%; third, 5%. Each experimental passage was preceded and followed by a control passage except for the third experimental reading which was followed by two control passages. S's were divided into three groups and the passages were presented in counter-balanced order.

Summary: It was found that when five per cent of the words were read non-fluently there was significantly more stuttering on the non-underlined words than when 25 and 50% of the words were bounced. Also, significantly less stuttering occurred in the 25 and 50% passages than in the control passage in which no non-fluency was asked for.

The expected adaptation effect was demonstrated from the first to the fifth control passages ignoring the experimental passages. It was found that the greatest adaptation occurred in the control passage following the 50% experimental passage.

Analysis of the stuttered words corroborated Brown's finding that the higher weighted the word (word length, grammatical function, position in sentence, initial sound) the more it was stuttered.

Conclusions: It was concluded that "the frequency of stuttering in the immediate context of the words which are spoken with voluntary non-fluency is significantly less in passages in which 50 or 25% of the words are spoken non-fluently than in passages in which 0 (control passage) or five per cent of the words are spoken non-fluently voluntarily."

TITLE

Shames, G. H.: A Utilization of Adaptation Phenomena in Theory for Stuttering, *Journal of Speech and Hearing Disorders,* 18 (1953), 256-257.

Purpose: To report the use of adaptation phenomena with negative practice as a therapy for stutterers.

Experimental Design: None.

Summary: When a stutterer employs the technique of negative practice, the author reports, he often discovers that his voluntary blocking becomes involuntary. This is called the contaminating effect in negative practice.

The author feels that one way to alleviate the contaminating effect is to employ adaptation in reading. The stutterer, he suggests, should read a passage until he is relatively free from involuntary blocks. Then using this same passage he employs negative practice. Following successful use of negative practice in reading to an individual therapist, a transition is then attempted from a reading medium to a conversational medium. The transition is engendered by increasing the size and kind of audience and by introducing the stutterer into situations resembling real life situations. In all these situations, he feels, the stutterer should be employing relatively uncontaminated negative practice by first having allowed adaptation to occur.

The author reports that this procedure was tried with a small number of stutterers and found to be very practical and successful. There was, however, no reliable measuring instrument used. For some stutterers, it was reported, this technique was not appropriate.

Conclusions: As above.

TITLE

Trotter, W. D.: The Severity of Stuttering During Successive Readings of the Same Material, *Journal of Speech and Hearing Disorders,* 20 (1955), 17-25.

Purpose: To find if anxiety is reduced with occurrence of adaptation as measured by the severity of the stuttering.

Experimental Design: Five successive readings of 500-word passages for each of 20 stutterers (12-35 years) were tape recorded. The 100 experimental records were arranged in random order and played back twice to two judges, who independently marked what they believed to be moments of stuttering. Intervals of two days separated first and second listening sessions. Any word marked at least twice out of a possible four times was regarded as a stuttered word. Severity was measured on a nine point scale. Raters were 11 advanced students in speech pathology. Ratings were made in six sessions of about two hours each.

Summary:

1. Mean severity was obtained by averaging across all raters, all words, and all stutterers. Means decreased from reading one through reading three and increased from reading three through reading five. Analysis of variance revealed significantly (.05) more severe stuttering on reading one than on any subsequent reading. Reversal in trend for reading three through five was not significant. (F-test)

2. Means, curves, etc., drawn for four categories (words stuttered five, four, three, two times). Four curves show downward trend. First three categories were significant at .05 on F-test. The *t*-test for difference between two means of words in category four revealed a significant difference between severity the first time and severity the succeeding times the same words were stuttered.

Conclusions: It was concluded on the basis of the data that a reduction in frequency of stuttering during successive readings of the same material is accompanied by a reduction in mean severity of stuttering on individual words stuttered. Those most persistent and severely stuttered words are apparently amenable to reduction under experimental conditions.

The experiment, it was felt also, demonstrated that reliable difference can be detected by trained listeners based only upon vocal attributes and without benefit of visual or kinaesthetic clues. Concomitant differences may be much more evident to the stutterer. Assuming that a stutterer can detect improvement, the procedure might be therapeutically beneficial in two ways:

1. The major goal of therapy is a gradual decrease in severity of stuttering and frequency and this could be demonstrated to him in a meaningful way.

2. It would give him some conception of what it feels like to stutter with reduced tension and would provide evidence that even the most severe blocks may be modified.

Results, it is felt, support modern therapy in whch emphasis is placed on reducing severity of stuttering by having the stutterer develop a pattern of stuttering that is easier and more simple than his usual pattern.

TITLE

Sheehan, J. G.: The Modification of Stuttering Through Non-Reinforcement, *Journal of Abnormal and Social Psychology*, 46 (1951), 51-63.

Purpose: To test the hypothesis that less reinforcement results from the stutterer's repeating a stuttered word until spoken fluently than from simply stuttering it and proceeding with speech.

Experimental Design: Since it was theorized that the block followed by fluent speech acts to reinforce the block as the predecessor of fluent speech, an experimental situation was designed in which this reinforcement of the block could not take place by its being followed directly by more speech. The situation was the simple demand that a stuttered word be repeated until spoken fluently; it was theorized that this insertion of fluency on the previously stuttered word between the block and further speech attempt would act as an agent of non-reinforcement on the stuttering behavior.

Fourteen subjects (six female) ranging in age from 18 to 25 read a 200-word passage six times in their characteristic ways; a seventh reading followed after 30 minutes, also in their characteristic speech patterns. On another day, they read another 200-word passage six times under the experimental (non-reinforcing) conditions, i.e., repeating each stuttered word until it was spoken fluently before further speech attempt. A seventh reading after 30 minutes was performed also under the experimental conditions. The sequence of the readings was randomized; adaptation was tabulated and statistical adjustments made; observer reliability was tabulated by Pearson product-moment correlations and was found to be from .93 to .98.

Summary: There was found to be less stuttering in the experimental condition than in the control condition in all cases, though the difference between them for the first reading was not statistically significant. By the third reading, the difference was significant at the .05 level; in the fourth at the .05 level, and thereafter at the .10 level. To measure the persistence of reduced stuttering (the reason for having the seventh readings after 30 minute interval) the last readings were compared with first ones. The significance of the reduction of stuttering in the control condition was .30; in the experimental condition, the significance of the difference was .01.

Conclusions: It was concluded that there may be more wisdom than folly in having a child repeat a stuttered word until he speaks it correctly. This may seem undesirable since it seems to operate as a penalty; but it was suggested that it may be desirable if the child is instructed to so repeat, since then this may act as a non-reinforcement agent by inserting fluency between stuttered words and further speech attempt. It was further concluded that:

1. Stuttering decreased more rapidly in such a non-reinforcement condition.

2. This decrease in stuttering was more lasting than that normally resulting from adaptation.

TITLE

Sheehan, J. G.: Theory and Treatment of Stuttering as an Approach-Avoidance Conflict, *Journal of Psychology*, 36 (1953), 27-49.

Purpose: To answer the following questions: (1) What makes the stutterer stop? and (2) What enables him to continue?

The central hypothesis for the author's theory is based on (1) *The Conflict Hypothesis:* The stutterer stops whenever the approach and avoidance tendencies reach an equilibrium, and (2) *The Fear-Reducing Hypothesis:* The occurrence of stuttering reduces the fear which elicited it, so that during the block there is sufficient reduction in fear-motivated avoidance to resolve the conflict, permitting release of the blocked word.

Experimental Design: None.

Summary: *Conflict Hypothesis:* Stuttering has previously been depicted as a simple approach-avoidance conflict; however, there are at times approach and avoidance tendencies toward the act of speaking as well as the act of not speaking.

Different levels at which conflict may occur, it is felt, are as follows: (1) word level-anticipation of the feared "Jonah" word; (2) situation level-speaking on the telephone, in classes; (3) emotional content level—as illustrated by an increase in the frequency of spasms while describing a traumatic experience, etc.; (4) relationsip level-stutterer and listener situation, role playing; and (5) ego-protective level—a defense mechanism toward dangerous competition.

Fear-Reduction Hypothesis: Once stuttering has begun to appear it can no longer be hidden. The block makes the stutterer face the situation, thus, reduction of fear occurs.

Stuttering, when it appears, is no longer anticipated. It has appeared. It is known. To the extent stuttering can be interpreted as an aggresive act against the listener (Fenichel) the stuttering relieves the aggression, hence, reduces the inhibition to aggression, then reducing the approach-avoidance conflict.

Successful treatment, it is suggested, involves the gaining of mastery over fear, finding expression of needs, feelings and tendencies that have been locked up in the symptom. The bounce and negative practice are recommended.

When the stutterer is caught in the vicious cycle of reinforcement, the author feels, he has no tools with which to break the cycle. It is important to give him these tools early in treatment. He should be paced and care should be taken not to place him in too traumatic a situation at first. He should be helped to view the effects of his handicap upon his aspirations. He should be asked specifically structured questions which are thought-provoking. He must undergo in many cases a change in self-concept. This should be gradual. All levels upon which conflict occur must be attacked.

Conclusions: As above.

TITLE

Sheehan, J. G.: An Integration of Psychotherapy and Speech Therapy Through a Conflict Theory of Stuttering, *Journal of Speech and Hearing Disorders*, 19 (1954), 474-482.

Purpose: Therapists who attempt to treat stuttering simultaneously as a habit and as a neurosis sometimes, it is felt, find themselves working at cross purposes. The central thesis of this article is that psychotherapy and speech therapy do not need to be in competition, but can have a common goal. This basic goal follows logically from the author's theory of stuttering as an approach-avoidance conflict.

Experimental Design: None.

Summary:

1. Why is Speech Therapy necessary? The author feels that the principal reasons for the inclusion of speech therapy in a program of psychotherapy for stuttering are as follows:

   a. In the symptom of stuttering the conflicts of the stutterer are externalized and given outward expression. Moreover, the stutterer's whole struggle to meet life and to conquer his fears and blocks is a necessary part of any therapy which respects the stutterer's own desires and feelings. It is better, then, to begin where the stuttering occurs and to work back through the unsatisfactory relationships producing the conflict. This facilitates it for the stutterer.

b. A large part of the stutterer's fear stems from the guilt the stutterer feels punishing others with his unpleasant and socially unacceptable speech. Through speech therapy we are able to create an attitude of extreme permissiveness toward the stuttering, even encouraging the expression of the symptom through "negative practice" techniques and faking or voluntary stuttering. Society has punished the stutterer for the stuttering, and, since speech is such an important tool of social adjustment, the secondary effects of stuttering are perhaps more important than those of any other neurosis.

c. Stutterers may undergo profound personality changes as a result of successful speech therapy, and the speech therapy itself is an important specialized form of psychotherapy.

d. Encouraging the stutterer to attack feared and difficult situations may support him strongly in something he has really wanted to do. Through speech therapy, with very little insight oriented psychotherapy, the stutterers have been freed from many of their conflicts and problems.

e. All stuttering, at least in secondary stages, involves some degree of learned behavior. For many adult cases the original causes may have ceased to operate, and the disorder becomes self-maintained or functionally autonomous.

f. If no direct speech therapy is used, then whenever the stutterer hits a low mood or a period of upset, this is going to be reflected inevitably in his speech, so that his social and vocational handicap may return at any time in full force. Through speech therapy it is possible to teach the stutterer a mode of handling his problem which may be relatively independent of the way he feels at the moment.

g. When the speech therapist supports a stutterer in facing his problem and helps him to face it, he removes the reinforcement inherent in its ego-protective functions.

2. *The Sequence of Treatment.* The speech therapy portion of treatment is emphasized first, with supportive and abreactive psychotherapy next, and finally deeper psychotherapy, should this become necessary.

3. *Feelings, Relationships and Goals.* The psychotherapeutic portion of the treatment in stuttering involves releasing and expressing feelings, developing more adequate interpersonal relationships, and freeing the individuals from unadaptive goals.

4. *The Fear of Fluency.* Finally, the ego-protective functions of the symptom and its secondary gains must be dealt with psychotherapeutically. At some point in the treatment of the stutterer, it is necessary to consider the effect of recovery from it, upon what the individual has planned to do with his life. Open-ended questions or partially structured sentence completion items may be especially revealing. Just as in the early stages of treatment, the stutterer needs to accept himself as a stutterer, so in the final stages he must learn to accept himself as a normal speaker. This second adjustment is sometimes bigger than the first. In accepting normality, the stutterer not only gives up the secondary gains which have helped to maintain the disorder, but acquires a radically different self-concept.

5. *Preparation for Recovery.* Although many stutterers are initally resistant to speech therapy, the really substantial resistance is likely to come following a certain amount of recovery. When the stutterer makes enough progress so that he is threatened with the loss of secondary gains, his resistances are likely to assert themselves.

Relapses are not necessarily to be avoided in the treatment of the stutterer, but may be utilized in these ways: (1) As a means of helping the stutterer understand his resistance, and the ego-protective functions of the disorder; (2) to teach the stutterer that relapse is not catastrophic, and that he can learn to come out of it by the same methods he has used to conquer the problem initially.

Finally, it is considered advisable to maintain therapy for some time following the attainment of fluency, and to plan therapy with this assumption.

Conclusions: As above.

TITLE

Johnson, W.: **The Indians Have No Word for It: I. Stuttering in Children, and, II. Stuttering in Adults,** *Quarterly Journal of Speech,* **30 (1944), 330-336, 456-465.**

Purpose: To suggest a practical approach in the treatment of stuttering in young children and adults.

Experimental Design: None.

Summary:

Part I. Little is actually said about Indians—merely that no stuttering is found among the North American Indians who are comparatively free from white man's influence. It was noted that the Indian semantic environment is far different from ours. The parents regard any speech effort of their young as normal— absolutely no stress is placed on the child to speak. This, it is felt, is suggestive of the probable reason for the absence of stuttering among the Indians.

It was pointed out that research on stuttering children has demonstrated that in almost every case the diagnosis had been made by a layman—usually the parents. What was diagnosed as stuttering, however, was largely the hesitations and repetitions normally found in the speech of young children. After having been diagnosed as stutterers, almost all the children did develop overt speech behavior sufficiently different to justify clinical attention. Their therapy, it was suggested, should consist of a re-evaluation of the children by the parents and teachers. A semantic environment should be created which is reasonably free of tensions and high standards. The child should be praised for acceptable although not perfect speech. An affectionate and friendly relationship between child and parents should be created.

Part II. The problem with the stuttering adult, it is felt, is that he cannot speak non-fluently—he hesitates to hesitate. The treatment of stuttering in adults should be directed first to the semantic environment—praise for handling non-fluency calmly and without tension rather than for fluent speech. Subject should be encouraged to speak more and to feel that he is a worthy individual. The difference between stuttering and normal non-fluency should be explained. Starting mechanisms should be eliminated through mirror practice and a streamlined pattern of non-fluency should be introduced. As tolerance is developed for hesitations they will diminish and the vicious circle of the stuttering mechanism is broken.

Conclusions: It was concluded generally that therapy for children should be directed toward the child's environment including his parents and teachers. For adults, the treatment would probably have to be varied for each individual; however, the principles outlined above were felt to be basic to any approach.

TITLE

Lemert, E. M.: **Some Indians Who Stutter,** *Journal of Speech and Hearing Disorders,* 18 (1953), 168-174.

Purpose: To report on stuttering found in a Northwestern Indian Group.

Experimental Design: Data gathered by interviews among the Indian groups, reports from school officials and written materials from Indian children.

Summary: Contrary to previous reports, the author found some Indians who do stutter and are regarded as stutterers among their groups; evidence of preacculturational existence of stuttering and other speech defects; and a well-defined concept of stuttering and stutterers. In three different schools and three Indian tribes there was a percentage of about 1.9, which "approximates the estimated incidence of stutterers for our own population."

Two case histories were presented in which the subjects definitely manifested secondary symptoms and regarded themselves and were regarded by their families and tribe as stutterers. Evidence that stuttering occurred before any contacts with White culture was of three sorts: (1) dates of birth and childhood development of known cases of stutterers, (2) the knowledge of aboriginal methods of treatment and "curing" stuttering, and (3) the linguistic recognition of the defect. Several cases of stuttering were known where the birthplace and child preceded 1865—date of contact with White culture. Primitive techniques of curing stuttering bear no sign of White influence or borrowing. Also, in every tribal language, there was a word for stuttering (and other speech defects).

The attitude toward stuttering among the tribes ranged from mild to serious disapproval. Stories written by the school children for the authors revealed "Horatio Alger-type stutterers who are socially rejected, become socially isolated, and then overcome their defect to go on and become famous." Hence, even among the children there was a sensitivity to speech inadequacy. Penalties and rejections were generally of an informal nature; i.e., the stutterer was not insulted publicly, but he could be compelled to take a back seat in tribal ceremonies. Usually such a decision was made by the family; but in some cases where a whole clan could lose status by a defect of one member, it became the concern of the group.

It was noted that children of the Northwestern Indian tribes were subject to rigorous educational practices as early as six or seven. They were subjected to fear-inducing experiences such as being kidnapped, swung over a fire, etc., for ceremonial purposes.

Conclusions: Although this contradicts the generalization that American Indians do not stutter, the author felt that it does not contradict Johnson's findings among the Plains Indian cultures, where stuttering is absent—where few demands are made on the child until adolescence, where participation in tribal ceremonies are permissive rather than compulsory for the child, and where family treatment of deviants was kind, helpful, sympathetic, and although protective, not overprotective. As a matter of fact, this research tends to "support rather than refute the generally socio-psychological hypotheses of stuttering proposed by Johnson, Snidecor, Van Riper and others."

TITLE

Villarreal, J.: Two Aspects of Stuttering Therapy, *Journal of Speech and Hearing Disorders*, 15 (1950), 215-220.

Purpose: To suggest a clinical device for facilitating a program of assistance by clarifying two aspects of stuttering therapy.

Experimental Design: None.

Summary: The device suggested is essentially a semantic exercise in which the stutterer, early in his clinical program, is led to distinguish between *stuttering as defect* and *stuttering as handicap*, and to recognize the implications of this distinction in the therapeutic program. If stuttering is treated as a defect, "the desired goal is speech free from blockings, repetitions, hesitations, muscular spasms, prolongations, etc." If, however, stuttering is treated as a handicap, "the desired goal is the possession of an adequate instrument of verbal communication, used without restraint, embarrassment, reluctance, or apprehension. These two goals constitute two distinct aspects of stuttering therapy, each establishing its own criteria for adequate performance and each requiring a distinctive mode of clinical attack."

Therapeutic goals are suggested as follows:

1. *Insight into the problem:* The stutterer must be led to sort secondary symptoms and become thoroughly familiar with his own particular pattern. He must also become familar with the warped pattern of social withdrawal and non-participation that has become an integral part of his way of avoiding an exhibition of his non-fluent speech.

2. *Achievement of unemotional acceptance:* The stutterer cannot expect to discontine his stuttering way of talking until he has

reached a point in his program of social readjustment where it makes little difference whether he discontinues his non-fluency or not, i.e., does not mind exhibiting non-fluency in a social situation.

3. *Sequence of parts of therapeutic program:* The desired order of therapy is the elimination of a speech defect as a prerequisite to the elimination of a speech handicap. Therapy should begin its attack upon the total problem in the area of social performance rather than the mechanics of vocalization. The two patterns of deviation, vocal and social, are of course intimately tied together; but the therapist must find the proper part of the knot to begin untying. The author suggests that the proper point of attack aims at the alleviation of the speech handicap of stuttering rather than the speech defect.

4. *Evaluation of progress:* The distinction beween stuttering defect and stuttering handicap is particularly useful here, the auther feels, because it permits the therapist to set up an orderly sequence of improvement that does not hinge upon the complete elimination of non-fluent speech. The stutterer may thus feel he is making progress even though he exhibits non-fluent speech.

Conclusions: As above.

TITLE

Rotter, J. B.: The Nature and Treatment of Stuttering: A Clinical Approach, *Journal of Abnormal and Social Psychology,* 39 (1944), 150-172.

Purpose: To present a treatment of stuttering based on a psychological interpretation of stuttering.

Experimental Design: A study of the case histories of eight adult stutterers (two females, six males), who were given the author's method of treatment, and an analysis of some experimental data was made to arrive at the hypothesis presented.

Summary: In order for a child to begin stuttering, the author feels, two simultaneous conditions must exist—the availability of stuttering and the need for it. Availability is referred to as contact with stuttering, not necessarily the label, in which a definite attitude is taken toward interruption in speech through the behavior of the people in the immediate situation. The need, it is felt, is not necessarily for stuttering but for a mechanism which will serve a definite purpose.

An effective and lasting therapy, it is suggested, must concentrate on the need, although it may be necessary in some cases to carry on parallel work in the mechanics of speech.

The following therapy described was the actual procedure used on five of the eight cases mentioned above. The first step was a gathering of information. The first several sessions were concerned with asking questions so that the stutterer could re-evaluate to some extent his own history, and rationalize concerning stuttering. Also he was asked to read orally one hour every day. The second phase of therapy was to discuss the stutterer's own theory of the nature of his stuttering and stuttering in general. Reading assignments of literature in the field of personality and stuttering were made and the readings discussed. The third phase was interpretation. A group therapy situation was introduced in which the first half was devoted to discussion of some abstract concept, e.g., pampering, style of life, etc.; the second half was taken over by one of the group who discussed his own speech history in relation to the preceding discussion. This was considered a valuable part of the therapy.

The entire therapy required about three months, and included three weekly individual sessions, and a group session once a week. During the last month, in addition to the continuation of the interpretation phase, time was devoted to the building of new constructive attitudes. As therapy progressed, general factors of adjustment were increasingly stressed.

At the conclusion of therapy two of the cases did not stutter at all, and follow up reports one and one-half years later showed no re-occurrence of stuttering. Two cases felt that they no longer needed the clinic services, and no longer regarded themselves as stutterers, although they still had occasional slight interruptions.

The last case, although his attitude was greatly improved, manifested no correlating improvement in speech.

Conclusions: It was concluded that this approach was helpful in that it provided a framework in which stutterers could be studied individually.

TITLE

Bryngelson, B.: **Stuttering and Personality Development,** *The Nervous Child,* 2 (1943), 162-166.

Purpose: To present some of the personality problems of the stutterer and suggest techniques which might help to prevent their occurrence.

Experimental Design: None.

Summary: Stuttering is conceived as a peripheral symptom of a deep seated disintegration of the central nervous system. The author points out that at first the stuttering is easy and tensionless. The so-called nervousness so often associated with stuttering is, according to the author, a later development, secondary to the stuttering when it occurs in the young child. By their objective attitude, the child will be encouraged to accept this way of speaking. In the familiar and sympathetic home situation, he can learn to accept himself, even to laugh at himself. Then when he enters the more complicated situation of school, he will be less vulnerable to the taunts of the children and the pressures of recitation which otherwise might have caused nervousness and unhappiness. The author feels that such a program of mental hygiene initiated by the parents and associates of the very young child would prepare him to achieve optimum benefit from therapy itself.

The author also sets up an outline for a clinical program as follows:

1. Teach voluntary repetition of initial sound (minimizes length of spasm and teaches acceptance).

2. Teach the stutterer to verbalize the fact of his stuttering on many different occasions.

3. Study symptoms before the mirror.

4. Teach him to describe what he is actually doing.

5. Social assignments: Participation in social activities, it is suggested, will test the emotional security of the stutterer, and help to show him that the listener will be more accepting if *he* is.

Conclusions: As above.

TITLE

Schultz, D. A.: **A Study of Nondirective Counseling as Applied to Adult Stutterers**, *Journal of Speech Disorders*, 12 (1947), 421-427.

Purpose: To compare the adjustmental problems of stutterers as revealed in a non-directive counseling situation to those of neurotics.

Experimental Design: Twenty adult stutterers (18 males, 2 females), with a mean I.Q. (Otis) of 135, who were enrolled in a university class for stutterers, were counseled and their interviews recorded. Before the counseling was begun, the stutterers were oriented as to what to expect in the therapeutic relationship (complete freedom of expression and no advice or censorship). Summaries were compiled on each case and the emotional needs expressed were classified under the following headings: (1) affectional security giving satisfactions, (2) self enlarging, ego-building. After the counseling sessions all stutterers were given the California Test of Personality. Case histories of 239 diagnosed neurotics were compared with the above on the basis of Stricher and Ebaugh's classification of common neurotic characteristics.

Summary: The results of the California Test of Personality found the stuttering group as a whole with a median percentile of 25, suggesting that they are surpassed by three-fourths of the standardization group. Comparing characteristics of stutterers and neurotics it was found that stutterers had many symptoms in common with neurotics. The following symptoms were common to both groups: (1) submissive, (2) hypersensitive and inhibited,

(3) report lack of affection in the home and dominant parents, and (4) introvertive tendencies.

The stutterers and neurotics were found to be different to a statistically significant degree with respect to anxiety, and the routine use of sedatives.

Anxiety was shown by this stuttering group more frequently than by the psychoneurotic group. Fifteen per cent of the psychoneurotics used sedatives while none of the stutterers reported their use.

The author does not include scores made on the California Test of Personality prior to therapy nor does he suggest that non-directive counseling is of value in treating stuttering.

Conclusions: It was concluded that stutterers and psychoneurotics have many common symptoms. Stutterers indicated many various social and self adjustment problems.

TITLE

Coriat, I.: Active Therapy in the Analysis of Stammering, *Psychoanalytic Review*, 17 (1930), 342-347.

Purpose: To describe active therapy (a phase of psychoanalytic therapy) in relationship to the treatment of stuttering.

Experimental Design: None.

Summary: Since stuttering, the author feels, is due to a persistence in narcissistic gratifications as a carry-over from infancy and is perpetuated through oral satisfactions, active therapy must be directed toward depriving the stutterer of all oral objects which serve to prolong the gratification or to reinforce it. He suggests that all forms of smoking should be prohibited—the pipe, for example, he feels produces a relaxed state resembling the after affects of nursing in an infant. Gum chewing with its prolonged oral and dental gratifications, and the eating of candy in any of its forms should not be allowed.

This active intervention tends to free the anchored libido from the mouth zone which, the author feels has become a "hiding place for the libido." The removal of this satisfaction is necessary in order to work through the speech resistance. The patients must be induced to talk without any external sustenance for oral gratification. Active therapy should not be employed in early stages of the analysis, but only after a certain degree of transference has developed. Then the external pleasures should be prohibited step by step. This type of therapy, the author suggests, educates the ego to tolerate the forbidden and at the same time the desired oral gratifications.

In addition to these factors, stutterers, he notes, are often observed putting the left hand to the mouth and pressing the lips or patting the cheek with rhythmical movements. This is interpreted as a pleasure function and a form of regression to an infantile nursing activity. When this activity, which represents a substitute for grasping of the mother's breast, is forbidden, along with the other gratifications, an improvement in speech follows.

As a rule, he says, there is willingness to cooperate with these various prohibitions even though they produce a feeling of conflict and resistence tension.

Conclusions: As above.

TITLE

Barber, V.: Studies in the Psychology of Stuttering: XVI. Rhythm as a Distraction in Stuttering, *Journal of Speech Disorders*, 5 (1940), 29-42.

Purpose: To investigate the effect of rhythm as a distraction in stuttering.

Experimental Design: Subjects were 18 stutterers (2 females, 16 males) ranging in age from 14 to 33 years. Each S read under 15 conditions using different reading selections including three control situations and 12 distraction situations which involved synchronizing the oral reading with: (1) bodily rhythms (walking, tapping the foot, arm swing, and hand-wrist swing), (2) speech rhythms (sing-song, inflection and accent on every third word), and (3) rhythmic sensory stimulation (visual, auditory, and tactile). To determine whether the effectiveness of distraction is affected by the presence of an audience, five of the S's in an auxiliary study read four 250 word passages before a class of university students using rhythm from an arm swing and a metronome.

Summary: All of the rhythmic distractions studied acted as effective distractions in reducing the frequency of stuttering.

Rhythmic sensory distractions were the most effective.

The speech rhythm involving an accent on every third word tended to be significantly less effective than any of the other distractions studied.

The stutterer appeared to speak most fluently when his performance was not easily differentiated from the total activity of the moment (group reading).

The presence of an audience did not significantly reduce the effectiveness of rhythm distractions.

Conclusions: It was concluded that stuttering is not basically a phonetic difficulty, and that imposed rhythms generally seem to serve as effective distraction devices.

The author feels also that a better understanding of what happens to a stutterer during distraction might lead to a better understanding of the phenomenon.

TITLE

Barber, V.: Studies in the Psychology of Stuttering: XV. Chorus Reading as a Distraction in Stuttering, *Journal of Speech Disorders*, 4 (1939), 371-383.

Purpose: To investigate the effects of distraction upon stuttering, and to contribute to the understanding of this phenomenon.

Experimental Design: Chorus reading was analyzed into the following factors: sound factor (pitch, quality, etc.) meaning, personal factor, and amount of support. The following 14 situations were used in the experiment: (1) Subject read alone with no distractions. (2) Two stutterers and one normal speaker read the same material together. (3) Two stutterers read the same material with the subject. (4) Normal speaker read the same material with the subject. (5) One stutterer read the same material with the subject. (6) Two stutterers read a different passage together with the subject. (7) A normal speaker read a different passage together with the subject. (8) One stutterer read a different passage together with the subject. (9) A normal subject read nonsense syllables while subject read meaningful material. (10) One stutterer read nonsense syllables while subject read meaningful material. (11) Normal speaker says "ah" while subject read a meaningful passage. (12) Phonograph record played the word "ah" while the subject read. (13) Mechanical noises were made while the subject read. (14) Subject read alone with no distraction operating.

Subjects were 18 stutterers (3 females, 15 males) ranging in age from 15 to 33. Fourteen different 500-word passages were used. The series was arranged to minimize the effects of adaptation. At one sitting the subject read the 14 passages under the 14 conditions described previously. Audience situation was held constant. At all readings the same normal speaker, two adult stutterers and the experimenter were present. During the readings the experimenter marked the words on which the subject stuttered. The normal speaker checked with the experimenter throughout all situations in which he was not serving as pacer. The reliability of the experimenter's ratings was found to be .95.

Summary:

1. All the distractions except (10) were effective in the reduction of frequency of stuttering.

2. All four of the situations involving the reading of the same material as the subject were significantly more effective than any other of the distraction situations (2, 3, 4, 5).

3. The distraction used in (6) was significantly more effective than those employed in (8) and (9).

4. A normal speaker reading nonsense material has significantly more distractive value than a stutterer doing the same thing.

5. Two stutterers and one normal speaker reading a passage with the subject is significantly more effective than is the cooperation of only the normal speaker.

6. The cooperation of two stutterer-pacers and a normal speaker tends to have greater distractive effect than the cooperation of one stutterer-pacer. (Signif: .02.)

7. Unpatterned mechanical noise is more effective as a distraction than a phonograph recording of the normal speaker phonating "ah."

Conclusions: It was concluded that the study offers conclusive evidence that stuttering is not a phonetic disturbance.

The factor of "support" (several people reading along with stutterer), it was felt, seemed to be the most effective device for reducing the amount of stuttering.

TITLE

Pattie, F. A., and Knight, B. B.: Why Does the Speech of Stutterers Improve in Chorus Reading? *Journal of Abnormal and Social Psychology*, 39 (1944), 362-367.

Purpose: To test the theory that stutterers' speech improves when they read in chorus with another person because such a situation relieves the subject of the responsibility of communication (J. M. Fletcher's theory, based upon his idea that stuttering is not a disorder of speech but of communication) or reduces the prominence or conspicuousness of the stutterer's performance (Virginia Barber's theory).

Experimental Design: Previous experiments had involved chorus reading without the responsibility of communicating to an audience. In some of the situations in this experiment chorus reading was to occur together with the burden of communicating.

Twelve stutterers were used as subjects, including five adults and seven between 12 and 17 years of age. The reading material was prepared by Eugene Hahn and consisted of four narratives of 550 words each; each one contained the same words as the others but in different arrangements and with different sentence structure. Each subject(s) read to a small audience in the following ways and in the order indicated: (1) Alone. (2) While the experimenter (E) read in unison with him. (3) While listening to the E reading in unison with him, the voices of S and E being conveyed by telephone to each other while they were in different rooms. (4) and (5) were the same as (2) and (3), respectively, except that different material was read by S and E. (6) Alone. The number of blocks in each situation was recorded.

Summary: The performance of all Ss improved greatly in situations (2) and (3). Improvement was definitely present but to a lesser extent in (4) and (5). Taking the mean number of blocks in situation (1) as 100 per cent, the percentages are: (2) 10.4, (3) 16.1, (4) 48.7, (5) 51.3, (6) 78.2. The corresponding percentages for the median numbers of blocks are: (2) 7.6, (3) 7.0, (4) 40.1, (5) 40.1, (6) 45.9. The median is perhaps the better measure, since it is not influenced by the extreme cases in the distributions, which had a very wide range (from 18 to 423 in (1) and 3 to 163 in (3)).

Conclusions: The results lend no support to the theory that speech is improved in chorus reading because the emotional tension resulting from the "burden of communication" or the salience of the subject's performance is reduced.

(Abstract by F. A. Pattie.)

TITLE

Van Dantzig, M.: Syllable-Tapping, A New Method for the Help of Stammerers, *Journal of Speech Disorders,* 5 (1940), 127-131.

Purpose: To describe a method of syllable-tapping to be used as a therapeutic technique in the treatment of stutterers.

Experimental Design: None.

Summary: *First Stage:* S is taught to accompany the pronunciation of successive syllables by noiseless taps of fingers of preferred hand as follows:

I'll	try	to	speak	in	this	man	— ner
(little f.)	(ring f.)	(mid. f.)	(index f.)	(thumb)	(lit. f.)	(ring f.)	(mid. f.)

Tapping with the fingers rather than the hand is suggested because it is less tiring, less time consuming, and aids fluency and quickness. The author prefers to start with the little finger and move toward the thumb. This he calls "one way traffic." It is preferred because it is easier for people with stiff fingers and because the insertion of the little finger in movement is easier than the insertion of the thumb.

Therapist is cautioned against permitting the S's speech to revert into an unnaturally scanned staccato. The speech should retain its natural, fluent, legato character. S must not look at fingers and T. must see that the tapping does not become unrhythmical thumping of the table without connection with the syllabic division of speech.

If S's speech is interrupted by an involuntary repetition of an initial sound, he must stop finger movement and lower the whole hand and forearm a little, and stretch down the fingers on the table. Then, keeping the top of the concerned finger on the table, the finger and hand are slowly lifted and the difficult sound is at the same time calmly pronounced—process then continues. *Sound lifting* has a prophylactic and thence a curing effect, too.

In cases where speech is interrupted by spasm (tonic block) the S is taught to *divert the spasm* by stretching down the finger and whole arm and forearm with the arm and hand strained as long as the spasm continues. Spasm will be shortened, however, by mentally imitating the spasm in the hand and arm. Upon the cessation of the spasm, the arm and hand are lifted. This, it is felt has the same effect as syllable lifting.

Second Stage: After syllable tapping, sound lifting, and diverting spasm have been taught and the S has applied them to reading, reciting, answering questions, spontaneous speech, etc., he is taught to make movements against book covers, palm of other hand, against elbow of other arm, on knee, on back, against wall or door, in coat pocket, etc.

Third Stage: S is taught to reduce force of movements until they become "impulse movements" which are later substituted for by mere mental ideo-motoric impulses.

Conclusions: The author feels that this method has the following advantages: (1) Can be applied in groups and classes. (2) Children can apply it in their regular school subjects when questions must be answered. (3) It is appropriate for all intelligence levels above eight years or as soon as "syllable" is understood. (4) Can be applied in difficult situations. (5) Application provides S with assurance that he can speak, and reduces anxiety.

TITLE

Kastein, S.: **The Chewing Method of Treating Stuttering,** *Journal of Speech Disorders,* 12 (1947), 195-198.

Purpose: To present Froeschels' method of treating stuttering.

Experimental Design: None.

Summary: One point of agreement among speech therapists, it was felt, is that the foremost task in the treatment of stuttering is the breaking-down of the misconception on the part of the stutterer that speech is "difficult." The therapist must prove to the stutterer that it is "easy," and that his speech organs function normally. The question still remains, "How to do this?" (i.e., what method to use).

Froeschels has introduced a method which the author believes to be effective. His method is based on the conception that speech emanates from chewing. Men in the "pre-civilization" era chewed with vocal emissions. These sounds were interpreted as implying pleasure or displeasure, and from them eventually speech developed.

Everyone can chew and talk at the same time, although the same muscles are involved in both functions. Therefore, chewing and talking are regarded as being identical. This postulation is the starting point of Froeschels' treatment. After it has been explained to the patient, he is asked to chew silently and to visualize the process of chewing a tough piece of meat. Next, he attempts to chew with a vocal emission. (The therapist should first demonstrate.) Conversation "savage fashion" is then attempted. The patient is instructed to "chew aloud" at home 40 or 50 times a day. After doing this, he returns to the therapist and is told to "chew English" instead of chewing "nonsense." The two of them should hold simple conversations. At first, he is instructed to hold his fingers against his cheeks while he is doing this; later, he is asked to merely "think of chewing." But this time (in many cases) the stuttering symptoms will have disappeared.

With younger children, it is necessary for the mother to supervise the chewing exercises.

There are some stutterers who cannot, the author feels, be helped by this method (particularly psychoneurotics). In using any type of therapy, the personality of the patient should be considered.

Conclusions: As above.

TITLE

Hollingsworth, H. L.: Chewing as a Technique of Relaxation, *Science*, 90 (1939), 385-387.

Purpose: To determine whether motor automatisms (chewing) actually serve as tension outlets.

Experimental Design: For 20 experimental days, 20 subjects doing controlled tasks were studied under three conditions: "(a) Normal—not chewing and having nothing in the mouth; (b) Chewing—the masticatory being ordinary confectioned chicle, sweetened and flavored; (c) Control—allowing a flavored candy wafer to melt in the mouth, as a control over such things as suggestion, sensory stimulation and like influences." Factors of practice, fatigue and individual differences were equalized.

Summary: The following results were observed:

1. *Tension as Nervous Restlessness:* (A restless movement is defined as any motor activity irrelevant to the task.) On the whole an average decrease of about 10% in restlessness was found during mastication.

2. *Tension as Feeling of Strain:* After each 45 minute work period the subjects rated their subjective feeling on a 20 point scale. Subjects reported feeling more relaxed while chewing. The average subjective reduction was 10-15%

3. *Tension as Fatigue:* Evidence shows that if there is a change in rate of fluctuation of reversible figures while chewing, it is an increase—this being the opposite of the effect of fatigue.

4. *Tension as Effort:* ". . . determination of energy costs of chewing, with a resting state as a base, can by no means be generalized to cover the situation when this motor automatism is added to a livelier initial activity level." Metabolism and pulse rate revealed chewing can be carried on with no cost to the organism because of "surplus due to reduced motor restlessness."

5. *Direct Muscle Tension:* Muscular tension was reduced about 5% while chewing.

6. *Tension as Interference:* "With the possible exception of work in which a wholly new performance is being learned, chewing while working does not interfere with output." Chewing positively facilitated some types of work such as number checking and typing.

7. *The Energy of Work:* When the task required a tempo and accuracy, more energy was put into the activities while chewing. The motor automatism reduces restlessness and contributes more energy for the main task. However, this increased output depends on the nature of the work.

Conclusions: It was concluded that chewing, as one of the motor automatisms, results in the reduction of muscular tension. These results, it was felt, suggest techniques that might be put to good used in a "relaxation" type of therapy.

TITLE

Froeschels, E.: A Technique for Stutterers—'Ventriloquism,' *Journal of Speech and Hearing Disorders*, 15 (1950), 336-337.

Purpose: To discuss a technique which assists in convincing the stutterer of the ease of speaking fluently.

Experimental Design: None.

Summary: Numerous papers, the author states, have been devoted to description of the so-called "chewing method." If stutterers stick to the idea that they chew air, instead of thinking of speaking, which to them offers difficulties, the trouble may be cured in a relatively short time. In cases which do not react favorably, the author has used another method, "ventriloquism." This technique, he reports, has been successful in numerous patients over a period of more than 10 years. The core of this method consists of inconspicuous articulation by using almost invisible movements of the articulatory parts of the mouth, especially the lips.

1. First, the patient is told that the modulation of the speaking voice is of great significance. The same word will transmit different meanings to the listener if pronounced with different modulations. The significance of the same words changes with the placing of stress upon one or another word. The modulation is called "speech melody."

2. Next, it is explained that articulation is not put upon the speech melody like sugar on the pie. Articulation *is* the speech melody modified by shaping the upper resonating cavities differently. The therapist manipulates the patient's lips to demonstrate this. If vocalization offers difficulties in vowels or in voiced consonants, the patient is told that voice and sighing are essentially the same function.

3. The patient is then asked to read aloud with opened mouth, but to move neither the lips nor the tongue. After a few minutes he should start moving lips and tongue slightly like a ventriloquist. The patient may be surprised at how understandable such ventriloquistic speech is.

4. After a while the therapist starts a conversation, both he and the patient ventriloquizing.

5. The patient is then told to use this method whenever possible, but certainly always at home. The patient's family should be trained in ventriloquism in order to remind him how to speak.

6. For some days, he is required to read several times a day alternating "singing the speech melody" with ventriloquizing.

7. Normal articulation is reached step by step, slowly or rapidly, according to the clinical picture.

Conclusions: As above.

TITLE

Honig, P.: The Stutterer Acts It Out, *Journal of Speech Disorders*, 12 (1947), 105-109.

Purpose: To report on psychodrama as a technique for treating stuttering.

Experimental Design: Twenty stutterers (17 males, 3 females), ranging in age from 16-35 years, met two hours a week in classes of four or five. Sixteen stutterers attended for 18 weeks and four for 36 weeks. A room and furniture in the speech clinic were used to improvise the stage settings.

Summary: Background—Drama is not only entertainment, but according to Aristotle, "a means of purifying the spectator by artistically exciting certain emotions which act as homeopathic relief from the individual's own selfish passions." The spectator has found a vent for his feelings and experiences a mental catharsis.

Psychodrama allows the actor, not the spectator, to experience catharsis. "It is a form of drama in which the situations and roles, whether real or symbolic—reflect the actual life problems of the persons acting . . ."

The author believes that stuttering is, in a large part, a social maladjustment resulting from emotional disturbance. Since favorable social impressions are made largely by speech, the stutterer is at a disadvantage and feels inferior. When meeting a new person, his habit is to be subjective and obsequious. During psychodrama, he is trained to become aggressive and objective.

Therapy—Each stutterer submitted an autobiography which included what he thought were his most difficult speech situations. In addition, he submitted a weekly diary relating specific difficulties encountered. During the course of the treatment, four conferences were held with each subject. Here an attempt was made to understand the individual's progress as well as his problems. In addition to this, the treatment was divided into three variations of psychodrama:

First three weeks—Warm up period which involved games of charades, pantomiming skits, song fests, etc.

Following six weeks—Students acted out miscellaneous everyday life situations.

During the third phase—Students acted out the highly emotional situations in their lives. The dramatizations were based upon information from the autobiographies, interviews, etc. At this time, the students proved to themselves that they could rid themselves of their emotional blocks.

The fourth phase consisted of relating insights gained to real life situations.

At the termination of the treatment, the author reports, there was a marked improvement in personality adjustment and an increased skill in handling situations outside the clinic. There was also, according to the testimonies of the subjects, a carry-over of security feelings to speech situations outside the clinic.

Conclusions: It was concluded that psychodrama proved to be an excellent medium for re-educating the stutterer and adjusting him to his environment.

TITLE

Lemert, E., and Van Riper, C.: The Use of Psychodrama in the Treatment of Speech Defects, *Sociometry*, 7 (1944), 190-195.

Purpose: To discuss psychodrama as a method of treatment for speech defects.

Experimental Design: None.

Summary: Psychodrama, it is felt, differs from other methods of psychotherapy in that it presents the subject with a much more extensive and complex opportunity for manipulation of "others" than is present in the usual inter-personal relationships of life.

Various techniques for utilizing psychodrama are considered:

Role reversal, alternating between one's own role and that of another, produces catharsis and insight.

Hand puppet manipulation for children, who might have trouble in verbalizing their feelings, is suggested as a non-verbal instrument of expression and catharsis.

Phonograph recordings of dramatized conflict situations so structured as to be similar to the subject's conflicts, present opportunity for identification in the roles depicted. Extensive interruption of the recording to have the subject play the role(s) "*ad lib*" is used to good advantage.

Having persons prepared to play certain roles in the real-life situation of the subject outside the clinic has proved useful.

Play composition and/or direction by the subject, as well as role-playing in such compositions, are often mediums of catharsis and achievement of insight.

Conclusions: Psychodrama, the authors conclude, has definite therapy uses in cases of speech defect. However, it is pointed out that there may be some danger in dealing with non-psychotics, in that the subject may suddenly achieve a shocking amount of insight into himself and react quite negatively. As a part of therapy, it was found that deliberate exaggeration of symptoms, upon direction of the therapist, almost always resulted in improvement, since such exaggeration acted as a rich emotional release.

TITLE

Moore, W. E.: Hypnosis in a System of Therapy for Stutterers, *Journal of Speech Disorders*, **11 (1946), 117-122.**

Purpose: The author briefly reports on his experiences with hypnosis as a supplementary method in a system of therapy for stutterers.

Experimental Design: Over a period of four years, 40 stutterers who had been examined and treated by the author personally, each receiving at least 18 hours of individual work supplemented by at least 20 hours of group therapy distributed throughout a period never shorter than seven weeks, had submitted to hypnosis by the method of inhibited writing. Of the 40, five did not respond to suggestion beyond the hypnoidal stare, and four fell into a hypnotic sleep but made no somnambulistic responses. Each of the other 31, however, was sufficiently responsive so that some type or degree of somnambulism could be induced.

Summary:

1. Hypnosis greatly facilitated deep relaxation.

2. The relaxation persisted during subsequent performances in complex speech situations, according to introspective reports of the subjects.

3. The method was of incalculable help in working with severe stutterers who had difficulty in mastering "more relaxed" patterns of stuttering such as the "bounce," "whispered bounce," "phrasal bounce," etc.

4. Both the hypnotic speech and the post-hypnotic speech aided greatly in training the subjects in extensional evaluations of both their speech and the complexity of situations, i.e., the 31 stutterers, following hypnosis, could enter what were apparently very complex situations and speak "easily" in a relaxed manner. Hence, the subjects learned that "complexity" is not inherent to a situation, but in the individual's evaluations of the situation.

5. In stutterers in whom the symptoms of hysteria were marked, hypnosis was of incalculable value in facilitating the necessary communication between subject and correctionist.

6. The author has discovered no other method by which highly successful speech experiences can be so quickly given to a stutterer as by means of hypnotic and post-hypnotic speech.

Conclusions: The author does not suggest that a miraculous "cure" for stuttering lies in hypnosis. In respect to the values enumerated above, however, he believes that hypnosis can be a valuable adjunct to any system of therapy for stutterers.

TITLE

Stuttering Cured by Hypnotism, *Scientific American,* 151 (1934), 311.

Purpose: This article is a very brief journalistic notice of a reported use of hypnosis for stuttering treatment.

Experimental Design: None.

Summary: The article states that doctors at the Marine Hospital in San Francisco, connected with the U.S. Public Health Service, announced that "hypnotism has been successfully used . . . in curing patients of stuttering." The announcement was made by Dr. Victor H. Vogel of the U.S.P.H.S.

The methodology involved "revelation and aeration of the cause" and suggestion, under hypnosis, that since the cause is known the patient can desist stuttering. It was reported that this type of treatment was especially helpful in cases of "psychic cause," such as trauma, early in the patient's childhood. Success was "not so marked" if the cause(s) was not revealed to the patient.

One case of a cure was noted; the patient was "cured" in three sessions, though he reported that he still "stammered a bit" in times of excitement.

Conclusions: None.

TITLE

Carhart, R.: Two-Room Technique in the Treatment of Stuttering, *Journal of Speech Disorders,* 3 (1938), 105-112.

Purpose: To present a technique in the treatment of stuttering. (Technique is based on Scripture's principle of Encreasing Embarrassment.)

Experimental Design: None.

Summary: Many treatments start from a situation in which the stutterer experiences no difficulty and then progressively complicate the situation, transferring speech fluency to situations which, for the stutterer, are more difficult. The two-room technique is of this variety. In it, the complexity of the speech situation is progressively increased by working from a stage where the stutterer is isolated, through one where auditors placed in a second room hear him, to a stage where the stutterer practices in the same room with auditors.

Two sound-proof rooms are used which are connected by means of a window and recording equipment. The procedure consists of:

1. S is alone in one room and E is in the other room busily engaged in his own work and ignoring S. The recording equipment is turned off. S may read or alternate it with spontaneous conversation.

2. Same as Step 1 except that S is told that E will listen to him via the recording system for brief intervals during the session, and S will not know when these intervals will occur.

3. Same as before except that S is told that E will listen all the time.

4. S speaks spontaneously or reads while observers (O) watch him from the other room. Recording equipment is turned off.

5. Same as Step 4 except that S is told that O will listen on occasions, and S will not know when these occasions take place.

6. Same as Step 4 except that S is told that O will listen all the time.

Up to this point there has been a certain artificiality in the whole method. The next step is to reproduce more closely ordinary speaking situations. In doing this the steps already listed above are repeated again, but this time E *moves into the same room* with S. The final stage is reached when a small group is brought into the room where the stutterer is practicing.

The total process requires a considerable period of time. Each step is taken only when progress so indicates.

Conclusions: The author feels that in cases where building up confidence is the goal, this method can often be employed to advantage. With some it has proved gratifyingly successful while with others it has been less effective. However, even in successful instances, he suggests that it should not be used as the only attack upon the speech difficulty. Rather, it should be used in connection with other remedial techniques.

TITLE

Cypreansen, L.: Group Therapy for Adult Stutterers, *Journal of Speech and Hearing Disorders*, 13 (1948), 313-319.

Purpose: To describe and subjectively evaluate a program of group therapy for adult stutterers.

Experimental Design: The subjects were 14 male college students of above average intelligence ranging in age from 18 to 23 and in classification from freshman to senior. They had various patterns of stuttering with varying degrees of severity.

Summary: The following is a step by step outline of the therapy as it was followed in the weekly hour and a half sessions.

1st Week: Get acquainted, establish rapport, work for objective attitude.

2nd   Take individual case histories and assign writing of autobiographies.

3rd   Read and discuss autobiographies.

4th   Take personality test (California, Adult Form A).

5th   Analyze test results as a group, assign readings (articles on stuttering).

6th   Reports on reading.

7th   Reports on reading (continued).

8th   Auditory analysis of patterns.

9th   Assignment of individual plans for the changing of bad habits of speech.

10th   Practice of various techniques such as negative practice, distractions, etc. with assignments to continue them at home, using what seemed helpful and discarding the others.

11th	Speak alone and listen as a group to the recordings.
12th	Modified psychodrama.
13th	Oral reading of material practiced on wire recorder with a partner.
14th	Record made of oral reading to be played for friends.
15th	Group meeting with psychiatrist.

On the California Test of Personality, Form B, which was given some months after the completion of this course of therapy, general changes for the better were noted. The individuals seemed to have a more objective attitude and were more willing to accept their stuttering. In the group itself, the speech seemed improved; among the members there was more social activity such as dating, and a reduction in secondary symptoms.

Conclusions: The author concluded that although there was nothing new in this so called "method" of working with stutterers, it seems to be a sensible course and appeared to be getting results.

TITLE

Hahn, E. F.: A Study of the Effect of Remedial Treatment on the Frequency of Stuttering in Oral Reading, *Journal of Speech Disorders*, 6 (1941), 29-38.

Purpose: To report the effects of certain remedial measures on the speech of stutterers.

Experimental Design: Twenty-two adult stutterers using matched selections were tested in four oral reading situations: (a) reading alone, (b) reading to a concealed listener known to be present, (c) reading to one person, and (d) reading before a small group. After a three month period of remedial treatment, the group was retested in the same situations.

Summary: The remedial techniques used are as follows:

1. Attainment of bodily relaxation—progressive relaxation method used.

2. Establishment of sound on the outgoing breath.

3. Use of silent recall. Subjects were asked to produce vowel sounds with the eyes closed and then to recall the sensation of that production of the vowel on the "out-pouring" breath. Silent recall was used for autosuggestion in building up confidence that a sound could be repeated.

4. Establishment of words and phrases on the out-going breath.

5. Use of passive and loose mouth action.

6. Establishment of pauses in speech.

7. Prolongation of vowel sounds in speaking.

8. Technique of merging speech situations from the simple to the complex.

9. Use of the multiple-room technique.

10. Establishment of the use of patterns in situations outside the clinic.

11. Establishment of personal contact between student and instructor.

12. Presentation of short lectures on mental hygiene.

Conclusions: On the basis of comparisons between the results of the initial test situations and those of the retest situations it was concluded that stuttering frequently can be significantly reduced by proper remedial treatment. The remedial procedures thought to be responsible for this reduction are bodily relaxation, physical control, emotional control, disruption of old habit patterns in speaking and the substitution of a new speech pattern, positive suggestion, and change of attitudes.

TITLE

Carhart, R.: **An Experimental Evaluation of Suggestion Relaxation,** *Speech Monographs,* **10** (1943), 29-40.

Purpose: To investigate the influence of suggestion relaxation upon general bodily tension as revealed by palmar resistance measures.

Experimental Design: Ninety students (thirty males) were divided into the following three groups:

1. Control group-(C)-no instructions to relax.
   a. CN—no speech instructions
   b. CT—instructions to speak
2. Relax group-(R)-simple command to relax without being told how.
   a. RN—no speech instructions
   b. RT—instructions to speak
3. Suggestion group-(S)-detailed instructions on how to relax.
   a. SN—no speech instructions
   b. ST—instructions to speak

Each S reclined on a couch during the entire experiment. He was not told the purpose of the experiment; however, the apparatus was explained. (Palmar PGSR.) Readings were taken initially to determine that each S's skin resistance would be normal. During the experimental situation readings were taken each minute for a period of ten minutes. The suggestion relaxation instructions, given via phonograph recordings, included statements like, "Imagine a numbness moving into your fingers."

Summary: It was found that during the rest period the groups were not different as far as skin resistance was concerned. During situation 2 it was found that the different instructions did produce different affects in the skin resistance. Differences between Groups S and R was significant past the .01 level and between Groups S and C at the .05 level. The difference between Groups C and R was not significant. It was concluded, therefore, that simple directions to relax had about the same affect as no instructions at all. The mean skin resistance for the S group was the highest of the three groups and was interpreted as meaning that suggestion relaxation instructions produced more tension than the other types of instructions. A possible explanation of this, it was felt, was that the suggestion method held the subject's attention, and, thus, inhibited full relaxation.

In relationship to the affect of suggestion relaxation on tension level during subsequent speech, it was found that all the subjects who were requested to speak showed an immediate and marked tension increase in their PGSR readings. Within each group the differences were significant; however, the differences between groups was not. The data indicated a tendency for tension to increase as speech continued.

Conclusion: It was concluded on the basis of the data that tension increased when suggestion relaxation is used—even to a greater degree than when the simple instructions to relax is given. There also appeared to be little differential carry-over following suggestion relaxation.

It was felt that although this study seemed to refute the suggestion relaxation method it might be related to the particular type of suggestion used in the experiment, and that other types might be more effective. More research was suggested. The possibility that palmar PGSR might not be a valid measure of bodily tension was mentioned.

TITLE

Greene, J.: **Treatment of the Stutterer-Type Personality in a Medical-Social Clinic,** *Journal of the American Medical Association,* 104 (1935), 2239-2242.

Purpose: A description of a method of unconditioning the stutterer.

Experimental Design: None.

Summary: Medical-social clinic therapy has undergone many modifications and extensions. It is best described as a composite therapy of a medical, psychologic, re-educational and social nature, the essential feature of which is the group approach. The aim is to treat the stutterer's whole personality. "The group psychology has proved practical because, beyond a certain point, the individual problems of the stutterer-type become the problems of all."

The basic procedures mentioned by the author are as follows:

1. First, an initial interview is of far-reaching importance since stutterers often "carry chips on their shoulders" and may view the situation with suspicion.

2. Next, the stutterer is given a physical examination and everything is done to improve his physical status.

3. Thirdly, he is given a speech test and the session is recorded. The recording provides a sample of pre-treatment speech and it may also be compared with subsequent recordings to demonstrate improvement.

4. Next, he is examined by a psychologist. This provides a measure of the stutterer's mental capacities, and of the degree of control and intensity of the individual's emotions.

5. In viewing stuttering as an emotional and personality disorder, re-educational speech work *per se* is not enough. Instead, therapy should focus on the whole personality.

    a. The physiology of breathing is explained to the stutterer. This permits the stutterer to view his problem more objectively.

    b. Alternating group and individual reading is an excellent means of gaining confidence. Emotions are tranquilized.

    c. Muscular relaxation and coordination exercises to music are important group activities.

    d. The greatest problem, it is felt, is to change the personality and develop emotional control. A specially created atmosphere of informality, encouragement and sympathy holds sway. A special procedure of "open-door" psychiatry is used. The patient consults with the doctor in a large room, the door remaining open. The open-door method permits the doctor to call in other patients who happen to pass and utilize them in various ways, such as serving as listeners or participating in the discussion. An occasional closed door interview may be necessary so that unconscious difficulties which have been evaded are gotten under control.

6. Since stutterers are afraid to go places, social therapy brings society to the stutterers by providing different types of activities such as clubs, dinners, dances, etc.

7. Once a week the entire clinic holds a meeting which takes the form of a business meeting. Topics are assigned or chosen, and speeches are short and all voluntary. It takes courage to volunteer; consequently, as a therapeutic procedure, it is of great value.

Conclusions: The author feels that "the most practical agency for unconditioning the stutterer is one of encompassing medical, psychologic, psychiatric, re-educational and social therapies" such as have been developed in the medical-social clinic.

TITLE

Maraist, J. A., and Hutton, C.: Effects of Auditory Masking Upon the Speech of Stutterers. *Journal of Speech and Hearing Disorders,* **22 (1957), 385-389.**

Purpose: To investigate the effect of various levels of auditory masking on the speech output of stutterers.

Experimental Design: S's were 15 adult stutterers (14 males and 1 female) with a mean age of 20 years. The stimulus material was a set of five 75 word passages to be read aloud by the subjects under five levels of masking noise, the five passages being used to minimize adaptation. Twenty-five different combinations of masking levels were used.

Summary: Results of the readings show that the mean number of errors is seen to decrease in approximately equal amounts as the masking level increases. The data also show decreases in reading time of the passages as the masking level is increased.

It was noted that the 50 db masking level produced sizable decreases in the several measures of severity of stuttering. At this level, the number of errors was decreased by 31%, the duration by 41%, and the rate, proportionally. That such a masking level apparently had substantial effect on speech was considered to have important theoretical implications. It was suggested that a noise of this magnitude could easily be built into a small portable amplifier which could be used in a clinical situation.

The difference between errors, words, duration, and rate for the various passages were relatively constant, indicating that the passages were of approximately equal difficulty.

Adaption was evidenced during the reading of the five passages, with its effect modified by the use of two reading sessions.

The major results of the investigation showed:

"(1) The number of errors and the duration of passages decreased as masking level increased from 0 db to 90 db.

(2) With the number of words remaining approximately constant, the rate in words per minute increased as the masking level increased. The subjects' mean rate of 144 words per minute under 90 db masking noise approximated normalcy.

(3) Since the relatively low masking level of 50 db produced sizable decreases in the severity of stuttering, this method of limiting stuttering would seem to be clinically feasible."

Conclusion: It was concluded that the hearing mechanism may be a factor in the cause of stuttering.

THERAPY

Additional Reading References

Adamo, C.: Stammering or Stuttering: Its Elimination, *Eye, Ear, Nose and Throat Monthly*, 11 (1933), 478-480.

Ainsworth, S.: Present Trends in the Treatment of Stuttering, *Journal of Exceptional Children*, 16 (1949), 41-43.

Appelt, A.: *Stammering and Its Permanent Cure*, Methuen, London, 1929.

Bender, J. F.: The Prophylaxis of Stuttering, *Nervous Child*, 2 (1943), 181-198.

Blanton, S., and Blanton, M.: *For Stutterers*, D. Appleton-Century, New York, 1936.

Boome, E. J., and Richardson, M. A.: *The Nature and Treatment of Stuttering*, Dutton, New York, 1932.

Brown, F. W.: The Permanent Cure of Stuttering, *Mental Hygiene*, 17 (1933), 266-277.

Brown, S. F.: Advising Parents of Early Stutterers, *Journal of Pediatrics*, 4 (1949), 170-176.

Browning, W.: *Etiology of Stammering and Methods for its Treatment,* A. T. Huntington, Brooklyn, 1915.

Bryngelson, B.: Treatment of Stuttering, *Journal of Expression,* 5 (1931), 19-26.

———, Chapman, M., and Hansen, O.: *Know Yourself: A Workbook for Those Who Stutter,* Burgess Publishing Company, Minneapolis, 1944.

Bullwinkle B. A.: Methods and Outcome of Treatment of Stutterers in a Child Guidance Clinic, *Smith College Student Social Work,* 1933, 101.

Case, H. W.: Therapeutic Methods in the Treatment of Stuttering, *Psychological Bulletin,* 37 (1940), 586.

Claiborne, J. H.: Stuttering Relieved by Reversal of Manual Dexterity with Remarks on the Subject of Symbol Amblyopia, *New York Medical Journal,* 105 (1917), 577.

Clark, R.: Supplementary Techniques to Use with Secondary Stutterers, *Journal of Speech and Hearing Disorders,* 13 (1948), 131-134.

Clark, L. P.: Mental Treatment of Stammering, *Psychiatric Quarterly,* 8 (1934), 306-318.

Coriat, I. H.: Active Therapy in the Analysis of Stammering, *Psychoanalytic Review,* 17 (1930).

———: Nature and Analytical Treatment of Stammering, *Yearbook American Speech Correction Association,* College Typing Company, Madison, 1930.

Curtis, J.: A Study of the Effect of Muscular Exercises Upon Stuttering, *Speech Monographs,* 9 (1942), 61-74.

Despert, J. L.: A Therapeutic Approach to the Problem of Stuttering in Children, *Nervous Child,* 2 (1943), 134-147.

Dow, C. W.: Stuttering: A Tentative Outline of an Hypothesis and Therapy, *Journal of Speech Disorders,* 6 (1941), 40-45.

Eder, M. D.: Stammering as a Psychoneurosis and its Treatment by Psychoanalysis, Tr. XVII International Medical Congress: Psychiatry Section.

Fagan, L. B.: A Clinico-Experimental Approach to the Reeducation of the Speech of Stutterers, *Psychological Monographs,* 43 (1932), 53-66.

Froeschels, E.: Pathology and Therapy of Stuttering, *Nervous Child,* 2 (1942), 148-161.

Geniesse, H.: Stuttering: Improvement Noted When the Stutterer Spoke While Walking on All Fours, *Science,* 82 (1935), 518.

Gifford, M. F.: *Free Speech: The Stammerers Right,* Thomson Printing and Publishing Service, San Francisco, 1937.

———: *How to Overcome Stammering,* Prentice-Hall, New York, 1940.

———: The Mental and Emotional Re-Education of the Stammerer, *Better Health,* March, 1929.

Glauber, P.: The Treatment of Stuttering, *Journal of Social Casework*, 34 (1953), 162-167.

Harle, M.: Dynamic Interpretation and Treatment of Acute Stuttering in a Young Child, *American Journal of Orthopsychiatry*, 15 (1946), 156-162.

Hebenstreit, M. B.: The Effect of Negative Instruction on the Motor Control of Stutterers, *Stuttering in Children and Adults*, University of Minnesota Press, Minneapolis, 1955.

Higgins, W. H.: We Overcame Stammering, *Parents Magazine*, 9 (1934), 28.

Jameson, A. M.: Stammering in Children—Some Factors in Prognosis, *Speech*, 19 (1955), 60-67.

Johnson, W.: Aiding the Stuttering Pupil, *School Executives Magazine*, 53 (1934), 314-315.

————: Helping the Stuttering Child, *Hygeia*, 12 (1934), 790.

————: An Open Letter to the Mother of a Stuttering Child, *You and Your Child*, Reprinted in *Journal of Speech and Hearing Disorders*, 14 (1949), 3-8.

————: The Rehabilitation of the Stutterer, *Illinois Medical Journal*, 98 (1950), December.

————: Stuttering, *High School Teacher*, 8 (1935), 3-5.

————: Stuttering: Research Findings and their Therapeutic Implications, *Journal of the Iowa Medical Society*, 26 (1936), 464-469.

————: The Treatment of Stuttering, Journal of Speech Disorders, 4 (1939), 170-172.

Kemble, R. P.: Constructive Use of the Ending of Treatment, *American Journal of Orthopsychiatry*, 11 (1941), 684-591.

Knudson, T. A.: What the Classroom Teacher Can Do For Stutterers, *Quarterly Journal of Speech*, 26 (1940), 207-212.

Kopp, G. A.: Treatment of Stuttering, *Journal of Speech Disorders*, 4 (1939), 166-168.

Kosh, Z. H.: Integrated Course for Stutterers and Voice Defectives, *Quarterly Journal of Speech*, 27 (1941), 97-104.

Lane, R. R.: Suggestions for Handling Young Stutterers, *Elementary School Journal*, 44 (1944), 416-419.

Levbarg, J. J.: Hypnosis-Treatment Used on a Stammerer with Marked Mental Disturbance, *Eye, Ear, Nose and Throat Monthly*, 20 (1941) 55-56; 60.

Lewis, D., and Sherman, D.: Measuring the Severity of Stuttering, *Journal of Speech and Hearing Disorders*, 16 (1951), 320-326.

Livingood, F. G.: Hypnosis as an Aid to Adjustment, *Journal of Psychology*, 12 (1941), 203-207.

Love, W. R.: The Effect of Pentobarbital Sodium (Nembutal) and Amphetamine Sulphate (Benzedrine) on the Severity of Stuttering, *Stuttering in Children and Adults,* University of Minnesota Press, Minneapolis, 1955.

————: Stuttering: The Problem and the Physician's Responsibility, *Canadian Medical Association Journal,* 57 (1947), 4-9.

Lynch, E. M.: Bibliotherapy for Stutterers, *Stuttering in Children and Adults,* University of Minnesota Press, Minneapoliss, 1955.

McCord, H.: Hypnotherapy and Stuttering, *Journal of Clinical and Experimental Hypnosis,* 3 (1955), 210-214.

Malhant, M.: Pathogenesis and Therapy of Stammering: Clinical and Physiopathologic Study, *Mental Hygiene,* 29 (1934), 101-118.

Naylor, R. V.: A Comparative Study of Methods of Estimating the Severity of Stuttering, *Journal of Speech and Hearing Disorders,* 18 (1953), 30-37.

Obermann, C. E.: Steps in Overcoming Stuttering, *The Nation's School,* 39 (1942), 37-39.

Peters, C. A.: Public Speaking: A Therapeutic Procedure in the Re-Training of Stutterers, *Quarterly Journal of Speech,* 19 (1933), 64-70.

Robbins, S. D.: Distraction in Stuttering, *Proceedings of the American Speech Correction Association,* 2 (1932), 103-110.

————: The Role of Rhythm in the Correction of Stammering, *Quarterly Journal of Speech,* 21 (1935), 331-343.

————: Stammering and its Treatment, *Boston Stammerers' Institute,* Boston, 1926, 121.

Rotter, J. B.: A Working Hypothesis as to the Nature and Treatment of Stuttering, *Journal of Speech Disorders,* 7 (1942), 263-288.

Schaef, R., and Matthew, J.: A First Step in the Evaluation of Stuttering Therapy, *Journal of Speech and Hearing Disorders,* 19 (1954), 459-556.

Schuell, H.: Working with Parents of Stuttering Children, *Journal of Speech and Hearing Disorders,* 14 (1949), 251-254.

Shames, G.: An Investigation of Prognosis and Evaluation in Speech Therapy, *Journal of Speech and Hearing Disorders,* 17 (1952), 386-392.

Sherman, D.: Reliability and Utility of Individual Ratings of Severity of Audible Characteristics of Stuttering, *Journal of Speech and Hearing Disorders,* 20 (1955), 11-16

————: Clinical and Experimental Use of the Iowa Scale of Severity of Stuttering, *Journal of Speech and Hearing Disorders,* 17 (1952), 316-320.

————, and McDermott, R.: Individual Ratings of Severity of Moments of Stuttering," *Journal of Speech and Hearing Research,* 1 (1958), 61-67.

Shumak, I. C.: A Speech Situation Rating Sheet for Stutterers, *Stuttering in Children and Adults,* University of Minnesota Press, Minneapolis, 1955.

Solomon, J. A.: Stammering, Stuttering, Pediatrician's Responsibility," *American Journal of Diseases of Children,* 45 (1933), 1079-1086.

Stoddard, C. B.: A Public School Approach to Treatment of Stuttering, *Journal of Speech Disorders,* 4 (1939), 219-222.

Travis, L. E.: Diagnosis and Treatment of Stuttering, *Mind and Body,* 39 (1932), 14-15.

Trotter, W. D., and Brown, L.: Speaking Time Behavior of the Stutterer Before and After Speech Therapy, *Journal of Speech and Hearing Research,* 1 (1958), 48-51.

Van Riper, C.: Methods of Tearing Down the Adult Stutterer's Spasm Pattern, *Proceedings of American Speech Correction Association,* 8 (1938), 63-65.

——: The Systematic Treatment of Stuttering, *Ibid.,* 6 (1936), 110-120.

Voelker, C. H.: A New Therapy for Spasmophemia on Gestalt Principles, *Archives of Pediatrics,* 69 (1942), 657-662.

——: The Visualization Treatment of Spasmophemia, *Medical Record,* 142 (1935), 272.

Wedberg, C. F.: *The Stutterer Speaks,* Valley Fine Arts Press, Redlands, California, 1937.

Whitten, I. E.: Therapies for Stuttering: A Report of the Author's Own Case, *Quarterly Journal of Speech,* 24 (1938), 227-233.

Williams, D. E.: Intensive Clinical Case Studies of Stuttering Therapy, *Stuttering in Children and Adults,* University of Minnesota Press, Minneapolis, 1955.

——: A Point of View About Stuttering, *Journal of Speech and Hearing Disorders,* 22 (1957), 390-397.

GENERAL

Additional Reading References

Ainsworth, S.: Integrating Theories of Stuttering, *Journal of Speech Disorders,* 10 (1945), 205-210.

Anderson, V.: *Improving the Child's Speech,* Oxford University Press, New York, 1953.

Belgum, D.: Stuttering, *Hygeia,* 22 (1944), 346-347; 391.

Berry, M., and Eisenson, J.: *The Defective in Speech,* F. S. Crofts, New York, 1942.

Blanton, M., and Blanton, S.: What is the Problem of Stuttering? *Quarterly Journal of Speech,* 5 (1919), 38-53.

Bluemel, C. S.: *Stammering and Allied Disorders,* Macmillan, New York, 1935.

Boome, E. J.: Stammering, *Mental Welfare,* 15 (1934), 91-109.

Brigance, W. N.: Why Children Stutter, *Ladies Home Journal,* 52 (1935), 132-133.

Brown, F. W.: Child Who Stutters, *Hygeia,* 12 (1934), 212.

———: Problem of Stuttering, *Yearbook American Speech Correction Association,* College Typing Company, Madison, 1930.

———: Viewpoints on Stuttering, *American Journal of Orthopsychiatry,* 2 (1932), 1-24.

Bryngelson, B., and Brown, S.: Season of Birth of Speech Defectives in Minnesota, *Journal of Speech Disorders,* 4 (1940), 319-321.

Chittenden, G. E.: A Stutterer is What You Make Him, *Hygeia,* 21 (1943), 68-69.

Cobb, S., and Cole, E. N.: Stuttering, *Physiological Review,* 19 (1939), 49-62.

Dennison, W. D.: *The Correction of Stammering,* W. D. Dennison, 543 Jarvis Street, Toronto, 1932.

Fletcher, J. M.: *The Problem of Stuttering,* Longmans, Green, New York, 1928.

Fogerty, E.: *Stammering,* Dutton, New York, 1930.

Gottlober, A. B.: *Understanding Stuttering,* Grune and Stratton, New York, 1953.

Greene, J. S.: Stuttering: What About It? *Proceedings of the American Speech Correction Association,* 1 (1931), 165-176.

———: Good News for Everyone Who Stutters, *Literary Digest,* December 22, 1934, 118.

———, and Wells, E. J.: *The Cause and Cure of Speech Disorders,* Macmillan, New York, 1927.

Guns, P.: Etiology of Stammering, *Scalpel,* 86 (1933), 1273-1275.

Hahn, E. F.: Compendium of Some Theories and Therapies of Stuttering, *Quarterly Journal of Speech,* 23 (1937), 318, 396.

————: *Stuttering: Significant Theories and Therapies,* Stanford University Press, Stanford University, 1943.

Heltman, H. J.: *First Aids for Stutterers,* Expression Company, Boston, 1943.

Johnson, W.: *Because I Stutter,* Appleton, New York, 1930.

————: Eighteen Years of Stuttering, *Hygeia,* 7 (1929), 907-909.

————: For the Stutterer, a Sympathetic Ear, *New York Times Magazine,* February 13, 1955.

————: An Interpretation of Stuttering, *Quarterly Journal of Speech,* 19 (1933), 70-76.

————: A Million Forgotten Children, *Hygeia,* 15 (1937), 336-337.

————: (Editor) *Speech Handicapped School Children,* Harper and Brothers, New York, 1948.

————: *Speech Problems of Children,* Grune and Stratton, New York, 1950.

————: Stuttering: Its Cause and Treatment, *Parents' Magazine,* 7 (1932), 24-26.

————: The Time, the Place, and the Problem, *Stuttering in Children and Adults,* Minnesota University Press, Minneapolis, 1955.

————: Stuttering: An Interpretation of Research Finds, *Journal of the South Africa Logopedic Society,* 1954.

————: Tongues that Learn to Stumble, *Hygeia,* 19 (1941), 416-420.

————: Darley, F. L., and Spriestersbach, D. C.: *Diagnostic Manual in Speech Correction,* Harper and Brothers, New York, 1952.

Koepp-Baker, H.: *Handbook of Clinical Speech,* Edwards Brothers, Ann Arbor, 1936.

Makuen, H. H.: A Study of 1,000 Cases of Stammering, *Therapeutic Gazette,* 38, 1914), 385-390.

Parker, W.: *Pathology of Speech,* Prentice-Hall, New York, 1951.

Scripture, E. W.: *Stuttering, Lisping and Correction of the Deaf,* Macmillan, New York, 1923.

Solomon, M.: Stuttering, Nature and Mechanism, *Illinois Medical Journal,* 65 (1934), 329-335.

Tanberg, M. C.: Clinical Significance of the Symptomatology and Etiology of Stuttering, *Quarterly Journal of Speech,* 23 (1937), 654-659.

Travis, L. E.: My Present View on Stuttering, *Western Speech,* 10 (1946), 3-5.

————: *Speech Pathology,* Appleton-Century, New York, 1931.

Van Riper, C.: *Speech Correction Principles and Methods,* Prentice-Hall, New York, 1954.

——: *Speech Therapy: A Book of Readings,* Prentice-Hall, New York, 1953.

——: *Stuttering,* National Society for Crippled Children and Adults, 11 South La Salle Street, Chicago, 1948.

Wallin, J. E.: Theories of Stuttering, *Journal of Applied Psychology,* 1 (1917), 349-367.

West, R. (Editor): A Symposium on Stuttering, *Proceedings of the American Society for the Study of the Disorders of Speech,* 1 (1931), 37.

——, Kennedy, L., and Carr, A.: *The Rehabilitation of Speech,* Harper and Brothers, New York, 1947.

Representative Foreign Language References

DeParrel, G., and Hoffer, H.: Stammering in Children, *Clinique,* Paris, 30 (1935), 254-259.

Demaney, P.: Conditioned Reflex in Pathogenesis of Stammering, *Revue Francaise de Phoniatrie,* 3 (1935), 25-38.

Freund, H.: Stuttering, *LIJECNICKI vjesnik,* 55 (1933), 566-572.

——: Studies in the Interrelationship between Stuttering and Cluttering, *Folia phoniatrica,* 4 (1952), 146-168.

——: Über Inneres Stottern, *Zeitschrift für die gesamte Neurologie und Psychiatrie,* 151 (1934), 591-598.

Friedmann, A.: Individual Psychologic Studies of Stutterers, *Monatschrift für Ohrenheilkunde,* 69 (1935), 608-611.

Froeschels, E.: Zur Frage der Geschwisterzahl, *Wiener Klinische Wochenschrift,* 46 (1933), 1291-1292.

——: Symptomatology of Stammering, *Monatschrift für Ohrenheilkunde,* 68 (1934), 814-832.

——: The Significance of Symptomatology for the Understanding of the Essence of Stuttering, *Folia phoniatrica,* 4 (1952), 217-230.

——: Stuttering and Nystagmus, *Monatschrift für Ohrenheilkunde,* 49 (1915), 161-167.

——: Beiträge zur Symptomatologie des Stotterns, *Ibid.,* 55 (1921).

——: Über des Wesen des Stotterns, *Wiener Medizinische Wochenschrift,* 64 (1914), 1067-1078.

——: Zur Diagnose des Nachahmungsstotterns, *Ibid.,* 78 (1928), 955-956.

——: The Care of Stuttering, *Acta Otolaryngologica,* 45 (1955), 115-119.

Fuchs, E.: Psychoanalytical Study of Stuttering, *Internationale Zeitschrift für Psychoanalyse,* 20 (1934), 375-389.

Galant, J. S.: Development of Stuttering in Post-Pubertal Period, *Münchener Medizinische Wochenschrift,* 81 (1934), 1578-1579.

Kistler, K.: Linkshändigkeit und Sprachstörungen, *Schweizerische Medizinische Wochenschrift,* 60 (1930), 32.

Lambeck, A.: Errors Due to Stammering in Stuttering School Children, *Zeitschrift für Kinderforschung,* 41 (1933), 429-438.

Moscisher, E.: Pathogenesis of Nostril Symptom in Stutterers, *Monatschrift für Ohrenheilkunde,* 69 (1935), 106-110.

Mussafia, M.: Stuttering, its Development and Treatment according to the School of Fröschels in Vienna, *Scalpel,* Brussels (1934), 87-510.

Patzay-Libermann, L.: Movements of Stammerers, *Zeitschrift für Kinderforschung,* 42 (1933), 365-368.

————: Bewegungstherapie bei Stotten, *Ibid.,* 46 (1937), 337-345.

Roese, J.: Deafness in Relation to Stammering, *Internationales Zentralblatt für Ohrenheilkunde,* 39 (1934), 257-281.

Schulmann, A.: Constitutional Analysis of Stuttering, *Budapesti orvosi ujsag,* 33 (1935), 49-51.

Seeman, M.: Somatic Findings in Stutterers, *Monatschrift für Ohrenheilkunde,* 68 (1934), 895-912.

Sorat, M.: Vegetative Nervous System in Stutterers, *Monatschrift für Ohrenheilkunde,* 69 (1935), 666-680.

Stein, L.: Stammering as a Psychosomatic Disorder, *Folio phoniatrica,* 5 (1953), 12-46.

Viela, A.: Respiratory Cure of Stuttering Case, *Révue Francaise de Phoniatrie,* 2 (1934), 96-101.

Von Sarbo, A.: Nature of Stuttering, *Monatschrift für Kinderforschung,* 44 (1935), 119-133.

Von Stochert, F. C.: Psychogenesis of Stuttering, *Monatschrift für Ohrenheilkunde,* 68 (1934), 913-919.

INDEX OF AUTHORS

INDEX OF SOURCES

INDEX OF SUBJECTS

SETON HALL UNIVERSITY
McLAUGHLIN LIBRARY
SO. ORANGE, N. J.